CHILLERS
for CHRISTMAS

CHILLERS

for CHRISTMAS

Edited by Richard Dalby

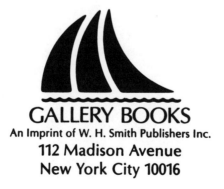

GALLERY BOOKS
An Imprint of W. H. Smith Publishers Inc.
112 Madison Avenue
New York City 10016

First published in the United States
in 1990 by Gallery Books, an imprint of
W.H. Smith Publishers, Inc., 112 Madison Avenue,
New York, New York 10016 by arrangement with
Michael O'Mara Books, London

Gallery Books are available for bulk purchase for sales
promotions and premium use. For details write or
telephone the Manager of Special Sales, W.H. Smith
Publishers, Inc., 112 Madison Avenue, New York,
New York 10016. (212) 532-6600

ISBN 0-8317-1274-0

Manufactured in the United States

CONTENTS

FOREWORD

Christmas has always been associated with ghosts and chilling tales. The winter solstice — the darkest time of year — produced a legacy of folklore and superstitions from early pagan times. Shadows flickering in the firelight and old timbers creaking in the howling winds, the traditional background of chilly winter evenings, always encouraged the impression of strange uncanny presences close at hand. In mediaeval times, ghosts and goblins were said to be appeased with gifts of food and hospitality.

The art of the Christmas story was immortalised during the nine-teenth century by such great writers as Charles Dickens, William Makepeace Thackeray, and Washington Irving. In his essay on 'Old Christmas', Irving described how he found wonderful British Yuletide hospitality at Bracebridge Hall: plentiful food and drink, the whimsical humorist and solid eater of solid fare, snow, games, and tales of ghosts.

Like the companion volume *Ghosts For Christmas*, published last year, this anthology is devoted mainly to seasonal tales of the super-natural, ranging over more than a hundred years, from Frank Cowper's superb atmospheric piece, 'Christmas Eve on a Haunted Hulk', to several new examples. Six stories were specially written for the present volume by some of the best modern 'masters of the macabre'. Two others achieved first and second place in a ghost story competition which I judged last Christmas.

The subject matter is further extended this time to include a selection of classic non-supernatural chillers and thrillers by Kipling, Conan Doyle, Amelia Edwards, 'Sarban', and John Collier.

I hope the stories in this collection will not only entertain the reader, but also stimulate and revive the old traditional art of story-telling around the Christmas hearth.

R.D.

THE STRANGE
RIDE OF
MORROWBIE JUKES

by Rudyard Kipling

Rudyard Kipling (1865–1936) was only nineteen
when he wrote this memorable and powerful story
shortly before Christmas in 1885, and it was soon
reprinted in his early collection *The Phantom
Rickshaw & other eerie tales*. In his biography
entitled *The Strange Ride of Rudyard Kipling*, Angus
Wilson wrote in homage of this tale: 'It remains
one of the most powerful nightmares of the
precariousness of a ruling group, in this case
haunted by memories of the Mutiny not yet
twenty years old.'

Alive or dead—there is no other way.
—*Native Proverb.*

T here is, as the conjurors say, no deception about this tale.
Jukes by accident stumbled upon a village that is well known to
exist, though he is the only Englishman who has been there.
A somewhat similar institution used to flourish on the outskirts of
Calcutta, and there is a story that if you go into the heart of Bikanir,
which is in the heart of the Great Indian Desert, you shall come across
not a village but a town where the Dead who did not die but may not
live, have established their headquarters. And, since it is perfectly
true that in the same Desert is a wonderful city where all the rich
money-lenders retreat after they have made their fortunes (fortunes so

vast that the owners cannot trust even the strong hand of the Government to protect them, but take refuge in the waterless sands), and drive sumptuous Cee-spring barouches, and buy beautiful girls and decorate their palaces with gold and ivory and Minton tiles and mother-o'-pearl, I do not see why Jukes's tale should not be true. He is a Civil Engineer, with a head for plans and distances and things of that kind, and he certainly would not take the trouble to invent imaginary traps. He could earn more by doing his legitimate work. He never varies the tale in the telling, and grows very hot and indignant when he thinks of the disrespectful treatment he received. He wrote this quite straightforwardly at first, but he has since touched it up in places and introduced moral reflections, thus: —

In the beginning it all arose from a slight attack of fever. My work necessitated my being in camp for some months between Pakpattan and Mubarakpur—a desolate sandy stretch of country, as everyone who has had the misfortune to go there may know. My coolies were neither more nor less exasperating than other gangs, and my work demanded sufficient attention to keep me from moping, had I been inclined to so unmanly a weakness.

On the 23rd December, 1884, I felt a little feverish. There was a full moon at the time, and, in consequence, every dog near my tent was baying it. The brutes assembled in twos and threes and drove me frantic. A few days previously I had shot one loud mouthed singer and suspended his carcass *in terrorem* about fifty yards from my tent-door. But his friends fell upon, fought for, and ultimately devoured, the body; and, as it seemed to me, sang their hymns of thanksgiving afterwards with renewed energy.

The light-headedness which accompanies fever acts differently on different men. My irritation gave way, after a short time, to a fixed determination to slaughter one huge black and white beast who had been foremost in song and first in flight throughout the evening. Thanks to a shaking hand and a giddy head I had already missed him twice with both barrels of my shot-gun, when it struck me that my best plan would be to ride him down in the open and finish him off with a hog-spear. This, of course, was merely the semi-delirious notion of a fever-patient; but I remember that it struck me at the time as being eminently practical and feasible.

I therefore ordered my groom to saddle Pornic and bring him round quietly to the rear of my tent. When the pony was ready, I stood at his head prepared to mount and dash out as soon as the dog should again lift up his voice. Pornic, by the way, had not been out of his pickets for a couple of days; the night air was crisp and chilly and I was armed with a specially long and sharp pair of persuaders with which I had been rousing a sluggish cob that afternoon. You will easily believe, then, that when he was let go he went quickly. In one moment, for the brute bolted as straight as a die, the tent was left far behind, and we were flying over the smooth sandy soil at racing speed. In another we had passed the wretched dog, and I had almost forgotten why it was that I had taken horse and hog-spear.

The delirium of fever and the excitement of rapid motion through the air must have taken away the remnant of my senses. I have a faint recollection of standing upright in my stirrups and of brandishing my hog-spear at the great white Moon that looked down so calmly on my mad gallop; and of shouting challenges to the camel-thorn bushes as they whizzed past. Once or twice, I believe, I swayed forward on Pornic's neck and literally hung on by my spurs—as the marks next morning showed.

The wretched beast went forward like a thing possessed, over what seemed to be a limitless expanse of moonlit sand. Next, I remember, the ground rose suddenly in front of us, and as we topped the ascent I saw the waters of the Sutlej shining like a silver bar below. Then Pornic blundered heavily on his nose, and we rolled together down some unseen slope.

I must have lost consciousness, for when I recovered I was lying on my stomach in a heap of soft white sand, and the dawn was beginning to break dimly over the edge of the slope down which I had fallen. As the light grew stronger I saw that I was at the bottom of a horse-shoe shaped crater of sand, opening on one side directly on to the shoals of the Sutlej. My fever had altogether left me, and, with the exception of a slight dizziness in the head, I felt no bad effects from the fall overnight.

Pornic who was standing a few yards away was naturally a good deal exhausted, but had not hurt himself in the least. His saddle, a favourite polo one, was much knocked about, and had been twisted under his belly. It took me some time to put him to rights, and in the meantime I had ample opportunities of observing the spot into which I had so foolishly dropped.

At the risk of being considered tedious, I must describe it at length; inasmuch as an accurate mental picture of its peculiarities will be of material assistance in enabling the reader to understand what follows.

Imagine then, as I have said before, a horse-shoe shaped crater of sand with steeply graded sand walls about thirty-five feet high. (The slope, I fancy, must have been about 65°.) This crater enclosed a level piece of ground about fifty yards long by thirty at its broadest part, with a rude well in the centre. Round the bottom of the crater, about three feet from the level of the ground proper, ran a series of eighty-three semi-circular, ovoid, square and multilateral holes, all about three feet at the mouth. Each hole on inspection showed that it was carefully shored internally with drift-wood and bamboos, and over the mouth a wooden dripboard projected, like the peak of a jockey's cap, for two feet. No sign of life was visible in these tunnels, but a most sickening stench pervaded the entire amphitheatre—a stench fouler than any which my wanderings in Indian villages have introduced me to.

Having remounted Pornic, who was as anxious as I to get back to camp, I rode round the base of the horse-shoe to find some place whence an exit would be practicable. The inhabitants, whoever they might be, had not thought fit to put in an appearance, so I was left to my own devices. My first attempt to 'rush' Pornic up the steep sand-banks showed me that I had fallen into a trap exactly on the same model as that which the ant-lion sets for its prey. At each step the shifting sand poured down from above in tons, and rattled on the drip-boards of the holes like small shot. A couple of ineffectual charges sent us both rolling down to the bottom, half choked with the torrents of sand; and I was constrained to turn my attention to the river-bank.

Here everything seemed easy enough. The sand-hills ran down to the river edge, it is true, but there were plenty of shoals and shallows across which I could gallop Pornic and find my way back to firm ground by turning sharply to the right or the left. As I led Pornic over the sands I was startled by the faint pop of a rifle across the river; and at the same moment a bullet dropped with a sharp 'whit' close to Pornic's head.

There was no mistaking the nature of the missile—a regulation Martini-Henri 'picket'. About five hundred yards away a country-boat was anchored in midstream; and a jet of smoke drifting away from its bows in the still morning air showed me whence the delicate attention had come. Was ever a respectable gentleman in such an *impasse*? The treacherous sand slope allowed no escape from a spot which I had visited most involuntarily, and a promenade on the river frontage was the signal for a bombardment from some insane native in a boat. I'm afraid that I lost my temper very much indeed.

Another bullet reminded me that I had better save my breath to cool my porridge; and I retreated hastily up the sands and back to the horse-shoe, where I saw that the noise of the rifle had drawn sixty-five human beings from the badger-holes which I had up till that point supposed to be untenanted. I found myself in the midst of a crowd of spectators—about forty men, twenty women, and one child who could not have been more than five years old. They were all scantily clothed in that salmon-coloured cloth which one associates with Hindu mendicants, and at first sight gave me the impression of a band of loathsome *fakirs*. The filth and repulsiveness of the assembly were beyond all description, and I shuddered to think what their life in the badger-holes must be.

Even in these days, when local self-government has destroyed the greater part of a native's respect for a Sahib, I have been accustomed to a certain amount of civility from my inferiors, and on approaching the crowd naturally expected that there would be some recognition of my presence. As a matter of fact there was; but it was by no means what I had looked for.

The ragged crew actually laughed at me—such laughter I hope I may never hear again. They cackled, yelled, whistled, and howled as I walked into their midst; some of them literally throwing themselves down on the ground in convulsions of unholy mirth. In a moment I had let go Pornic's head, and, irritated beyond expression at the morning's adventure, commenced cuffing those nearest to me with all the force I could. The wretches dropped under my blows like nine-pins, and the laughter gave place to wails for mercy; while those yet untouched clasped me round the knees, imploring me in all sorts of uncouth tongues to spare them.

In the tumult, and just when I was feeling very much ashamed of myself for having thus easily given way to my temper, a thin, high voice murmured in English from behind my shoulder: 'Sahib! Sahib! Do you not know me? *Sahib*, it is Gunga Dass, the telegraph-master.'

I spun round quickly and faced the speaker.

Gunga Dass (I have, of course, no hesitation in mentioning the man's real name) I had known four years before as a Deccanee Brahmin lent by the Punjab Government to one of the Khalsia States. He was in charge of a branch telegraph-office there, and when I had last met him was a jovial, full-stomached, portly Government servant with a marvellous capacity for making bad puns in English—a peculiarity which made me remember him long after I had forgotten

[5]

his services to me in his official capacity. It is seldom that a Hindu makes English puns.

Now, however, the man was changed beyond all recognition. Caste-mark, stomach, slate-coloured continuations, and unctuous speech were all gone. I looked at a withered skeleton, turbanless and almost naked, with long, matted hair and deep-set codfish-eyes. But for a crescent-shaped scar on the left cheek, I should never have known him. But it was indubitably Gunga Dass, and—for this I was thankful—an English-speaking native who might at least tell me the meaning of all that I had gone through that day.

The crowd retreated to some distance as I turned towards the miserable figure, and ordered him to show me some method of escaping from the crater. He held a freshly-plucked crow in his hand, and in reply to my question climbed slowly on a platform of sand which ran in front of the holes, and commenced lighting a fire there in silence. Dried bents, sand-poppies and driftwood burn quickly; and I derived much consolation from the fact that he lit them with an ordinary sulphur-match. When they were in a bright glow, and the crow was neatly spitted in front thereof, Gunga Dass began without a word of preamble:

'There are only two kinds of men, Sar. The alive and the dead. When you are dead you are dead, but when you are alive you live.' (Here the crow demanded his attention for an instant as it twirled before the fire in danger of being burnt to a cinder.) 'If you die at home and do not die when you come to the ghât to be burnt, you come here.'

The nature of the reeking village was made plain now, and all that I had known or read of the grotesque and the horrible paled before the fact just communicated by the ex-Brahmin. Sixteen years ago, when I first landed in Bombay, I had been told by a wandering Armenian of the existence, somewhere in India of a place to which such Hindus as had the misfortune to recover from trance or catalepsy were conveyed and kept; and I recollect laughing heartily at what I was then pleased to consider a traveller's tale. Sitting at the bottom of the sand-trap, the memory of Watson's Hotel with its swinging punkhas, white-robed attendants and the swallow-faced Armenian, rose up in my mind as vividly as a photograph, and I burst into a loud fit of laughter. The contrast was too absurd!

Gunga Dass, as he bent over the unclean bird, watched me curiously. Hindus seldom laugh, and his surroundings were not such as to move Gunga Dass to any undue excess of hilarity. He removed the crow solemnly from the wooden spit and as solemnly devoured it. Then he continued his story, which I give in his own words: —

'In epidemics of the cholera you are carried to be burnt almost before you are dead. When you come to the riverside the cold air, perhaps, makes you alive, and then, if you are only little alive, mud is put on your nose and mouth and you die conclusively. If you are rather more alive, more mud is put; but if you are too lively they let you go and take you away. I was too lively, and made protestation with anger against the indignities that they endeavoured to press upon me. In those days I was Brahmin and proud man. Now I am dead man and eat'—here he eyed the well-gnawed breast bone with the first sign of emotion that I had seen in him since we met—'crows, and—other things. They took me from my sheets when they saw that I was too lively and gave me medicines for one week, and I survived successfully. Then they sent me by rail from my place to Okara Station, with a man to take care of me; and at Okara Station we met two other men, and they conducted we three on camels, in the night, from Okara Station to this place, and they propelled me from the top to the bottom, and the other two succeeded, and I have been here ever since two and a half years. Once I was Brahmin and proud man; and now I eat crows.'

'There is no way of getting out?'

'None of what kind at all. When I first came I made experiments frequently and all the others also, but we have always succumbed to the sand which is precipitated upon our heads.'

'But surely,' I broke in at this point, 'the river-front is open, and it is worth while dodging the bullets; while at night—'

I had already matured a rough plan of escape which a natural instinct of selfishness forbade me sharing with Gunga Dass. He, however, divined my unspoken thought almost as soon as it was formed; and, to my intense astonishment, gave vent to a long low chuckle of derision—the laughter, be it understood, of a superior or at least of an equal.

'You will not'—he had dropped the Sir completely after his opening sentence—'make any escape that way. But you can try. I have tried. Once only.'

The sensation of nameless terror and abject fear which I had in vain attempted to strive against overmastered me completely. My long fast—it was now close upon ten o'clock, and I had eaten nothing since tiffin on the previous day, combined with violent and unnatural agitation of the ride had exhausted me, and I verily believe that, for a few minutes, I acted as one mad. I hurled myself against the pitiless sand-slope. I ran round the base of the crater, blaspheming and praying by turns. I crawled out among the sedges of the river-front, only to be driven back each time in an agony of nervous dread by the rifle bullets which cut up the sand round me—for I dared not face the death of a mad dog among that hideous crowd—and finally fell, spent and raving, at the kerb of the well. No one had taken the slightest notice of an exhibition which makes me blush hotly even when I think of it now.

Two or three men trod on my panting body as they drew water, but they were evidently used to this sort of thing, and had no time to waste upon me. The situation was humiliating, Gunga Dass, indeed, when he had banked the embers of his fire with sand, was at some pains to throw half a cupful of fetid water over my head, an attention for which I could have fallen on my knees and thanked him, but he was laughing all the while in the same mirthless, wheezy key that greeted me on my first attempt to force the shoals. And so, in a semi-comatose condition, I lay till noon. Then being only a man after all, I felt hungry, and intimated as much to Gunga Dass whom I had begun to regard as my natural protector. Following the impulse of the outer world when dealing with natives, I put my hand into my pocket and drew out four annas. The absurdity of the gift struck me at once, and I was about to replace the money.

Gunga Dass, however, was of a different opinion. 'Give me the money,' said he; 'all you have, or I will get help, and we will kill you!' All this as if it were the most natural thing in the world.

A Briton's first impulse, I believe, is to guard the contents of his pockets; but a moment's reflection convinced me of the futility of differing with the one man who had it in his power to make me comfortable; and with whose help it was possible that I might eventually escape from the crater. I gave him all the money in my possession, Rs. 9–8–5—nine rupees, eight annas and five pie—for I always keep small change as *backshish* when I am in camp. Gunga Dass clutched the coins, and hid them at once in his ragged loin-cloth, his expression changing to something diabolical as he looked round to assure himself that no one had observed us.

'Now I will give you something to eat,' said he.

What pleasure the possession of my money could have afforded him I am unable to say; but inasmuch as it did give him evident delight I was not sorry that I had parted with it so readily, for I had no doubt that he would have had me killed if I had refused. One does not protest against the vagaries of a den of wild beasts; and my companions were lower than any beasts. While I devoured what Gunga Dass had provided—a coarse cake and a cupful of the foul well-water, the people showed not the faintest sign of curiosity—that curiosity which is so rampant, as a rule, in an Indian village.

I could even fancy that they despised me. At all events they treated me with the most chilling indifference, and Gunga Dass was nearly as bad. I plied him with questions about the terrible village, and received extremely unsatisfactory answers. So far as I could gather, it had been in existence from time immemorial—whence I concluded that it was at least a century old—and during that time no one had ever been known to escape from it. [I had to control myself here with both hands, lest the blind terror should lay hold of me a second time and drive me raving round the crater.] Gunga Dass took a malicious pleasure in emphasising this point and in watching me wince. Nothing that I could do would induce him to tell me who the mysterious 'They' were.

'It is so ordered,' he would reply, 'and I do not yet know anyone who has disobeyed the orders.'

'Only wait till my servants find that I am missing,' I retorted, 'and I promise you that this place shall be cleared off the face of the earth, and I'll give you a lesson in civility, too, my friend.'

'Your servants would be torn in pieces before they came near this place; and, besides, you are dead, my dear friend. It is not your fault, of course, but, none the less, you are dead *and* buried.'

At irregular intervals, supplies of food, I was told, were dropped down from the land side into the amphitheatre, and the inhabitants fought for them like wild beasts. When a man felt his death coming on he retreated to his lair and died there. The body was sometimes dragged out of the hole and thrown on to the sand, or allowed to rot where it lay.

The phrase 'thrown on to the sand' caught my attention, and I asked Gunga Dass whether this sort of thing was not likely to breed a pestilence.

'That,' said he, with another of his wheezy chuckles, 'you may see for yourself subsequently. You will have much time to make observations.'

Whereat, to his great delight, I winced once more and hastily continued the conversation:—'And how do you live here from day to day? What do you do?' The question elicited exactly the same answer as before—coupled with the information that 'this place is like your European Heaven; there is neither marrying nor giving in marriage'.

Gunga Dass had been educated at a Mission School, and, as he himself admitted, had he only changed his religion 'like a wise man,' might have avoided the living grave which was now his portion. But as long as I was with him I fancy he was happy.

Here was a Sahib, a representative of the dominant race, helpless as a child and completely at the mercy of his native neighbours. In a deliberate lazy way he set himself to torture me as a school-boy would devote a rapturous half-hour to watching the agonies of an impaled beetle, or as a ferret in a blind burrow might glue himself comfortably to the neck of a rabbit. The burden of his conversation was that there was no escape 'of no kind whatever,' and that I should stay here till I died and was 'thrown on to the sand.' If it were possible to forejudge the conversation of the Damned on the advent of a new soul in their abode, I should say that they would speak as Gunga Dass did to me throughout that long afternoon. I was powerless to protest or answer; all my energies being devoted to a struggle against the inexplicable terror that threatened to overwhelm me again and again. I can compare the feeling to nothing except the struggles of a man against the overpowering nausea of the Channel passage—only my agony was of the spirit, and infinitely more terrible.

As the day wore on the inhabitants began to appear in full strength to catch the rays of the afternoon sun, which were now sloping in at the mouth of the crater. They assembled in little knots, and talked among themselves without even throwing a glance in my direction.

About four o'clock, as far as I could judge, Gunga Dass rose and dived into his lair for a moment, emerging with a live crow in his hands. The wretched bird was in a most draggled and deplorable condition, but seemed to be in no way afraid of its master. Advancing cautiously to the river-front, Gunga Dass stepped from tussock to tussock until he had reached a smooth patch of sand directly in the line of the boat's fire. The occupants of the boat took no notice. Here he stopped, and with a couple of dexterous turns of the wrist, pegged the bird on its back with outstretched wings. As was only natural, the crow began to shriek at once and beat the air with its claws. In a few seconds the clamour had attracted the attention of a bevy of wild crows on a shoal a few hundred yards away, where they were discussing something that looked like a corpse. Half-a-dozen crows flew over at once to see what was going on, and also, as it proved, to attack the pinioned bird. Gunga Dass, who had lain down on a tussock, motioned to me to be quiet, though I fancy this was a needless precaution. In a moment, and before I could see how it happened, a wild crow who had grappled with the shrieking and helpless bird, was entangled in the latter's claws, swiftly disengaged by Gunga Dass, and pegged down beside its companion in adversity. Curiosity, it seemed, overpowered the rest of the flock, and almost before Gunga Dass and I had time to withdraw to the tussock, two more captives were struggling in the up-turned claws of the decoys. So the sport—if I can give it so dignified a name—continued until Gunga Dass had captured seven crows. Five of them he throttled at once, reserving two for further operations another day. I was a good deal impressed by this, to me, novel method of securing food, and complimented Gunga Dass on his skill.

'It is nothing to do,' said he. 'To-morrow you must do it for me. You are stronger than I am.'

This calm assumption of superiority upset me not a little, and I answered peremptorily: 'Indeed, you old ruffian! What do you think I have given you money for?'

'Very well,' was the unmoved reply. 'Perhaps not tomorrow, nor the day after, nor subsequently; but in the end, and for many years, you will catch crows and eat crows, and you will thank your European God that you have crows to catch and eat.'

I could have cheerfully strangled him for this; but judged it best under the circumstances to smother my resentment. An hour later I was eating one of the crows; and, as Gunga Dass had said, thanking my God, that I had a crow to eat. Never as long as I live shall I forget that Christmas evening meal. The whole population were squatting on the hard sand platform opposite their dens, huddling over tiny fires of refuse and dried rushes. Death having once laid his hand upon these men and forborne to strike, seemed to stand aloof from them now; for most of our company were old men, bent and worn and twisted with years, and women aged to all appearance as the Fates themselves. They sat together in knots and talked—God only knows what they found to discuss—in low equable tones, curiously in contrast to the strident babble with which natives are accustomed to make day hideous. Now and then an access of that sudden fury which had possessed me in the morning would lay hold on a man or woman; and with yells and imprecations the sufferer would attack the steep slope

[11]

until, baffled and bleeding, he fell back on the platform incapable of moving a limb. The others would never even raise their eyes when this happened, as men too well aware of the futility of their fellows' attempts, and wearied with their useless repetition. I saw four such outbursts in the course of that evening.

Gunga Dass took an eminently business-like view of my situation, and while we were dining—I can afford to laugh at the recollection now, but it was painful enough at the time—propounded the terms on which he would consent to 'do' for me. My nine rupees eight annas, he argued, at the rate of three annas a day, would provide me with food for fifty-one days, or about seven weeks; that is to say, he would be willing to cater for me for that length of time. At the end of it I was to look after myself. For a further consideration—my boots—he would be willing to allow me to occupy the den next to his own, and would supply me with as much dried grass for bedding as he could spare.

'Very well, Gunga Dass,' I replied; 'to the first terms I cheerfully agree, but, as there is nothing on earth to prevent my killing you as you sit here and taking everything that you have' (I thought of the two invaluable crows at the time), 'I flatly refuse to give you my boots, and shall take whichever den I please!'

The stroke was a bold one, and I was glad when I saw that it had succeeded. Gunga Dass changed his tone immediately, and disavowed all intention of asking for my boots. At the time it did not strike me as at all strange that I, a Civil Engineer, a man of thirteen years' standing in the Service, and, I trust, an average Englishman, should thus calmly threaten murder and violence against the man who had, for a consideration it is true, taken me under his wing. I had left the world, it seemed, for centuries. I was as certain then as I am now of my own existence, that in the accursed settlement there was no law save that of the strongest; that the living dead men had thrown behind them every canon of the world which had cast them out; and that I had to depend for my own life on my strength and vigilance alone. The crew of the ill-fated *Mignonette* are the only men who would understand my frame of mind. 'At present,' I argued to myself, 'I am strong and a match for six of these wretches. It is imperatively necessary that I should, for my own sake, keep both health and strength until the hour of my release comes—if it ever does.'

Fortified with these resolutions, I ate and drank as much as I could, and made Gunga Dass understand that I intended to be his master, and that the least sign of insubordination on his part would be visited with the only punishment I had it in my power to inflict—sudden and violent death. Shortly after this I went to bed. That is to say, Gunga Dass gave me a double-armful of dried bents which I thrust down the mouth of the lair to the right of his, and followed myself, feet foremost; the hole running about nine feet into the sand with a slight downward inclination, and being neatly shored with timbers. From my den, which faced the river-front, I was able to watch the waters of the Sutlej flowing past under the light of a young moon and compose myself to sleep as best I might.

The horrors of that night I shall never forget. My den was nearly as narrow as a coffin, and the sides had been worn smooth and greasy by the contact of innumerable naked bodies; it smelt abominably. Sleep was altogether out of question to one in my excited frame of mind. As the night wore on, it seemed that the entire amphitheatre was filled with legions of unclean devils that, trooping up from the shoals below, mocked the unfortunates in their lairs.

Personally I am not of an imaginative temperament—very few Engineers are—but on that occasion I was as completely prostrated with nervous terror as any woman. After half an hour or so, however, I was able once more to calmly review my chances of escape. Any exit by the steep sand walls was, of course, impracticable. I had been thoroughly convinced of this some time before. It was possible, just possible, that I might, in the uncertain moonlight, safely run the gauntlet of the rifle shots. The place was so full of terror for me that I was prepared to undergo any risk in leaving it. Imagine my delight, then, when after creeping stealthily to the river-front I found that the infernal boat was not there. My freedom lay before me in the next few steps!

By walking out of the first shallow pool that lay at the foot of the projecting left horn of the horse-shoe, I could wade across, turn the flank of the crater, and make my way inland. Without a moment's hesitation I marched briskly past the tussocks where Gunga Dass had snared the crows, and out in the direction of the smooth white sand beyond. My first step from the tufts of dried grass showed me how utterly futile was any hope of escape; for, as I put my foot down, I felt an indescribable drawing, sucking motion of the sand below. Another moment and my leg was swallowed up nearly to the knee. In the moonlight the whole surface of the sand seemed to be shaken with devilish delight at my disappointment. I struggled clear, sweating with terror and exertion, back to the tussocks behind me and fell on my face.

[13]

My only means of escape from the semi-circle was protected with a quicksand!

How long I lay I have not the faintest idea; but I was roused at last by the malevolent chuckle of Gunga Dass at my ear. 'I would advise you, Protector of the Poor,'—the ruffian was speaking English—'to return to your house. It is unhealthy to lie down here. Moreover, when the boat returns, you will most certainly be rifled at.' He stood over me in the dim light of the dawn, chuckling and laughing to himself. Suppressing my first impulse to catch the man by the neck and throw him on to the quicksand, I rose suddenly and followed him to the platform below the burrows.

Suddenly, and futilely as I thought while I spoke, I asked: 'Gunga Dass, what is the good of the boat if I can't get out anyhow?' I recollect that even in my deepest trouble I had been speculating vaguely on the waste of ammunition in guarding an already well protected foreshore.

Gunga Dass laughed again and made answer: 'They have the boat only in day-time. It is for the reason that *there is a way*. I hope we shall have the pleasure of your company for much longer time. It is a pleasant spot when you have been here some years and eaten roast crow long enough.'

I staggered, numbed and helpless towards the fetid burrow allotted to me and fell asleep. An hour or so later I was awakened by a piercing scream—the shrill, high-pitched scream of a horse in pain. Those who have once heard that will never forget the sound. I found some little difficulty in scrambling out of the burrow. When I was in the open, I saw Pornic, my poor old Pornic, lying dead on the sandy soil. How they had killed him I cannot guess. Gunga Dass explained that horse was better than crow, and 'greatest good of greatest number is political maxim. We are now Republic, Mister Jukes, and you are entitled to a fair share of the beast. If you like, we will pass a vote of thanks. Shall I propose?'

Yes, we were a Republic indeed! A Republic of wild beasts penned at the bottom of a pit, to eat and fight and sleep till we died. I attempted no protest of any kind, but sat down and stared at the hideous sight in front of me. In less time almost than it takes me to write this, Pornic's body was divided, in some unclean way or other; the men and women had dragged the fragments on to the platform and were preparing their morning meal. Gunga Dass cooked mine. The almost irresistible impulse to fly at the sand walls until I was wearied laid hold of me afresh, and I had to struggle against it with all my might. Gunga Dass was offensively jocular till I told him that if he addressed another remark of any kind whatever to me I should strangle him where he sat. This silenced him till silence became insupportable, and I bade him say something.

'You will live here till you die like the other Feringhi,' he said coolly, watching me over the fragment of gristle that he was gnawing.

'What other *Sahib*, you swine? Speak at once, and don't stop to tell me a lie.'

'He is over there,' answered Gunga Dass, pointing to a burrow-mouth about four doors to the left of my own, 'You can see for yourself. He died in the burrow as you will die, and I will die, and as all these men and women and the one child will also die.'

'For pity's sake tell me all you know about him. Who was he? When did he come, and when did he die?'

This appeal was a weak step on my part. Gunga Dass only leered and replied: 'I will not—unless you give me something first'.

Then I recollected where I was, and struck the man between the eyes, partially stunning him. He stepped down from the platform at once, and, cringing and fawning and weeping, and attempting to embrace my feet, led me round to the burrow which he had indicated.

'I know nothing whatever about the gentleman. Your God be my witness that I do not. He fell in here to this place. He was as anxious to escape as you were, and he was shot from the boat, though we all did all things to prevent him from attempting. He was shot here.' Gunga Dass laid his hand on his lean stomach and bowed to the earth.

'Well, and what then? Go on!'

'And then—and then, Your Honour, we carried him into his house and gave him water, and put wet clothes on the wound, and he laid down in his house and gave up the ghost.'

'In how long? In how long?'

'About half an hour after he received his wound. I call Vishnu to witness,' yelled the wretched man, 'that I did everything for him. Everything which was possible that I did!'

He threw himself down on the ground and clasped my ankles. But I had my doubts about Gunga Dass's benevolence, and kicked him off as he lay protesting.

'I believe you robbed him of everything he had. But I can find out in a minute or two. How long was the *Sahib* here?

'Nearly a year and a half. I think he must have gone mad. But hear me swear, Protector of the Poor! Won't Your Honour hear me swear that I never touched an article that belonged to him? What is Your Worship going to do?'

I had taken Gunga Dass by the wrist and had hauled him on to the platform opposite the deserted burrow. As I did so I thought of my wretched fellow-prisoner's unspeakable misery among all these horrors for eighteen months, and the final agony of dying like a rat in a hole with a bullet-wound in the stomach. Gunga Dass fancied I was going to kill him and howled pitifully. The rest of the population, in the plethora that follows a full flesh-meal, watched us without stirring.

'Go inside, Gunga Dass,' said I, 'and fetch it out.'

I was feeling sick and faint with horror now. Gunga Dass nearly rolled off the platform and howled aloud.

'But I am Brahmin, *Sahib*—a high-caste Brahmin. By your soul, by your father's soul, do not make me do this thing!'

'Brahmin or no Brahmin, by my soul and my father's soul, in you go!' I said, and seizing him by the shoulders I crammed his head into the mouth of the burrow, kicked the rest of him in, and, sitting down, covered my face with my hands.

At the end of a few minutes I heard a rustle and a creak; then Gunga Dass in a sobbing, choking whisper speaking to himself; then a soft thud—and I uncovered my eyes.

The dry sand had turned the corpse entrusted to its keeping into a yellow-brown mummy. I told Gunga Dass to stand off while I examined it. The body—clad in an olive-green shooting-suit much stained and worn, with leather pads on the shoulders—was that of a man between thirty and forty, above middle height, with light, sandy hair, long moustache, and a rough unkempt beard. The left canine of the upper jaw was missing, and a portion of the lobe of the right ear was gone. On the second finger of the left hand was a ring—a shield-shaped blood-stone set in gold, with a monogram that might have been either 'B.K.' or 'B.L.'. On the third finger of the right hand, was a silver ring in the shape of a coiled cobra, much worn and tarnished. Gunga Dass deposited a handful of trifles he had picked out of the burrow at my feet, and, covering the face of the body with my handkerchief, I turned to examine these. I give the full list in the hope that it may lead to the identification of the unfortunate man:—

1. Bowl of a briarwood pipe, serrated at the edge; much worn and blackened; bound with string at the screw.
2. Two patent-lever keys: both broken.

3. Tortoise-shell handled penknife, silver or nickle name-plate, marked with monogram 'B.K.'.

4. Envelope, post-mark undecipherable, bearing a Victorian stamp, addressed to 'Miss Mon—' (rest illegible)—'ham'—'nt'.

5. Imitation crocodile-skin note-book with pencil. First forty-five pages blank; four and a half illegible; fifteen others filled with private memoranda relating chiefly to three persons—a Mrs. L. Singleton, abbreviated several times to 'Lot Single' or 'Mrs. S. May' and 'Garmison,' referred to in places as 'Jerry' or 'Jack'.

6. Handle of small-sized hunting-knife. Blade snapped short. Buck's horn, diamond cut, with swivel and ring on the butt; fragment of cotton cord attached.

It must not be supposed that I inventoried all these things on the spot as fully as I have here written them down. The note-book first attracted my attention, and I put it in my pocket with a view to studying it later on. The rest of the articles I conveyed to my burrow for safety's sake, and there, being a methodical man, I inventoried them. I then returned to the corpse and ordered Gunga Dass to help me to carry it out to the river-front. While we were engaged in this, the exploded shell of an old brown cartridge dropped out of one of the pockets and rolled at my feet. Gunga Dass had not seen it; and I fell to thinking that a man does not carry exploded cartridge-cases, especially 'browns' which will not bear loading twice, about with him when shooting. In other words, that cartridge-case had been fired inside the crater. Consequently, there must be a gun somewhere. I was on the verge of asking Gunga Dass, but checked myself, knowing that he would lie. We laid the body down on the edge of the quicksand by the tussocks. It was my intention to push it out and let it be swallowed up—the only possible mode of burial that I could think of. I ordered Gunga Dass to go away.

Then I gingerly put the corpse out on the quicksand. In doing so, it was lying face downward, I tore the frail and rotten shooting-coat open, disclosing a hideous cavity in the back. I have already told you that the dry sand had, as it were, mummified the body. A moment's glance showed that the gaping hole had been caused by a gun-shot wound: the gun must have been fired with the muzzle almost touching the back. The shooting coat, being intact, had been drawn over the body after death which must have been instantaneous. The secret of the poor wretch's death was plain to me in a flash. Some one of the

[17]

crater, presumably Gunga Dass, must have shot him with his own gun—the gun that fitted the brown cartridges. He had never attempted to escape in the face of the rifle fire from the boat.

I pushed the corpse out hastily, and saw it sink from sight literally in a few seconds. I shuddered as I watched. In a dazed, half-conscious way I turned to peruse the note-book. A stained and discoloured slip of paper had been inserted between the binding and the back, and dropped out as I opened the pages. This is what it contained: — '*Four out from crow-clump; three left; nine out; two right; three back; two left; fourteen out; two left; seven out; one left; nine back; two right; six back; four right; seven back*'. The paper had been burnt and charred at the edges. What it meant I could not understand. I sat down on the dried bents turning it over and over between my fingers, until I was aware of Gunga Dass standing immediately behind me with glowing eyes and outstretched hands.

'Have you got it?' he panted. 'Will you not let me look at it also? I swear that I will return it.'

'Got what? Return what?' I asked.

'That which you have in your hands. It will help us both.' He stretched out his long, bird-like talons, trembling with eagerness.

'I could never find it,' he continued. 'He had secreted it about his person. Therefore I shot him, but nevertheless I was unable to obtain it.'

Gunga Dass had quite forgotten his little fiction about the rifle-bullet. I received the information perfectly calmly. Morality is blunted by consorting with the Dead who are alive.

'What on earth are you raving about? What is it you want me to give you?'

'The piece of paper in the note-book. It will help us both. Oh, you fool! You fool! Can you not see what it will do for us? We shall escape!'

His voice rose almost to a scream, and he danced with excitement before me. I own I was moved at the chance of getting away.

'Don't skip! Explain yourself. Do you mean to say that this slip of paper will help us? What does it mean?'

'Read it aloud! Read it aloud! I beg and I pray to you to read it aloud.'

I did so. Gunga Dass listened delightedly, and drew an irregular line in the sand with his fingers.

'See now! It was the length of his gun-barrels without the stock. I have those barrels. Four gun-barrels out from the place where I caught crows. Straight out; do you follow me? Then three left—Ah! I remember when that man worked it out night after night. Then nine out, and so on. Out is always straight before you across the quicksand. He told me so before I killed him.'

'But if you knew all this why didn't you get out before?'

'I did *not* know it. He told me that he was working it out a year and-a-half ago, and how he was working it out night after night when the boat had gone away, and he could get out near the quicksand safely. Then he said that we would get away together. But I was afraid that he would leave me behind one night when he had worked it all out, and so I shot him. Besides, it is not advisable that the men who once get in here should escape. Only I, and *I* am a Brahmin.'

The prospect of escape had brought Gunga Dass's caste back to him. He stood up, walked about and gesticulated violently. Eventually I managed to make him talk soberly, and he told me how this Englishman had spent six months night after night, in exploring, inch by inch, the passage across the quicksand; how he had declared it to be simplicity itself up to within about twenty yards of the river bank after turning the flank of the left horn of the horse-shoe.

In my frenzy of delight at the possibilities of escape I recollect shaking hands effusively with Gunga Dass, after we had decided that we were to make an attempt to get away that very night. It was weary work waiting throughout the afternoon.

About ten o'clock, as far as I could judge, when the Moon had just risen above the lip of the crater, Gunga Dass made a move for his burrow to bring out the gun-barrels whereby to measure our path. All the other wretched inhabitants had retired to their lairs long ago. The guardian boat had drifted downstream some hours before, and we were utterly alone by the crow-clump. Gunga Dass, while carrying the gun-barrels, let slip the piece of paper which was to be our guide. I stooped down hastily to recover it, and as I did so, I was aware that he was aiming a violent blow at the back of my head with the gun-barrels. It was too late to turn round. I must have received the blow somewhere on the nape of my neck. A hundred thousand fiery stars danced before my eyes, and I fell forward senseless at the edge of the quicksand.

When I recovered consciousness, the Moon was going down, and I was sensible of intolerable pain in the back of my head. Gunga Dass had disappeared and my mouth was full of blood. I lay down again and prayed that I might die without more ado. Then the unreasoning fury which I have before mentioned laid hold upon me, and I staggered inland towards the walls of the crater. It seemed that someone was calling to me in a whisper, 'Sahib! Sahib! Sahib!' exactly as my bearer used to call me in the morning. I fancied that I was delirious until a handful of sand fell at my feet. Then I looked up and saw a head peering down into the amphitheatre—the head of Dunnoo, my dog-boy, who attended to my collies. As soon as he had attracted my attention, he held up his hand and showed a rope. I motioned, staggering to and fro the while, that he should throw it down. It was a couple of leather punkah-ropes knotted together, with a loop at one end. I slipped the loop over my head and under my arms; heard Dunnoo urge something forward; was conscious that I was being dragged, face downward, up the steep sand slope, and the next instant found myself choked and half fainting on the sand hills overlooking the crater. Dunnoo, with his face ashy grey in the moonlight, implored me not to stay but to get back to my tent at once.

It seems that he had tracked Pornic's hooves fourteen miles across the sands to the crater; had returned and told my servants, who flatly refused to meddle with any one, white or black, once fallen into the hideous Village of the Dead; whereupon Dunnoo had taken one of my ponies and a couple of punkah ropes, returned to the crater, and hauled me out as I have described.

CHRISTMAS EVE
ON A
HAUNTED HULK

by Frank Cowper

Frank Cowper (1849–1930) was a renowned
yachtsman who compiled five volumes of *Sailing
Tours*, and wrote an invaluable guide on *Yachting
and Cruising for Amateurs*. His popular collection,
Cruising Sails and Yachting Tales (1921), was
reprinted several times. Cowper's atmospheric
horror tale 'Christmas Eve on a Haunted Hulk' is
one of the best in the genre, but has been largely
ignored by anthologists. It originally appeared in
the January 1889 issue of *Blackwood's Magazine*.

I shall never forget that night as long as I live.
It was during the Christmas vacation 187–. I was staying with
an old college friend who had lately been appointed the curate of
a country parish, and had asked me to come and cheer him up, since
he could not get away at that time.

As we drove along the straight country lane from the little wayside
station, it forcibly struck me that a life in such a place must be dreary
indeed. I have always been much influenced by local colour; above all
things, I am depressed by a dead level, and here was monotony with
a vengeance. On each side of the low hedges, lichen-covered and
wind-cropped, stretched bare fields, the absolute level of the horizon
being only broken at intervals by some mournful tree that pointed like
a decrepit finger-post towards the east, for all its western growth was

nipped and blasted by the roaring south-west winds. An occasional black spot, dotted against the grey distance, marked a hay-rick or labourer's cottage, while some two miles ahead of us the stunted spire of my friend's church stood out against the wintry sky, amid the withered branches of a few ragged trees. On our right hand stretched dreary wastes of mud, interspersed here and there with firmer patches of land, but desolate and forlorn, cut off from all communication with the mainland by acres of mud and thin streaks of brown water.

A few sea-birds were piping over the waste, and this was the only sound, except the grit of our own wheels and the steady step of the horse, which broke the silence.

'Not lively is it?' said Jones; and I couldn't say it was. As we drove 'up street', as the inhabitants fondly called the small array of low houses which bordered the highroad, I noticed the lack-lustre expression of the few children and untidy women who were loitering about the doors of their houses.

There was an old tumbledown inn, with a dilapidated sign-board, scarcely held up by its rickety ironwork. A daub of yellow and red paint, with a dingy streak of blue, was supposed to represent the Duke's head, although what exalted member of the aristocracy was thus distinguished it would be hard to say. Jones inclined to think it was the Duke of Wellington; but I upheld the theory that it was the Duke of Marlborough, chiefly basing my arguments on the fact that no artist who desired to convey a striking likeness would fail to show the Great Duke in profile, whereas this personage was evidently depicted full face, and wearing a three-cornered hat.

At the end of the village was the church, standing in an untidy churchyard, and opposite it was a neat little house, quite new, and of that utilitarian order of architecture which will stamp the Victorian age as one of the least imaginative of eras. Two windows flanked the front door, and three narrow windows looked out overhead from under a slate roof; variety and distinction being given to the façade by the brilliant blending of the yellow bricks with red, so bright as to suggest the idea of their having been painted. A scrupulously clean stone at the front door, together with the bright green of the little palings and woodwork, told me what sort of landlady to expect, and I was not disappointed. A kindly featured woman, thin, cheery, and active, received us, speaking in that encouraging tone of half-compassionate, half-proprietary patronage, which I have observed so many women adopt towards lone beings of the opposite sex.

'You will find it precious dull, old man,' said Jones, as we were eating our frugal dinner. 'There's nothing for you to do, unless you care to try a shot at the duck over the mud-flats. I shall be busy on and off nearly all tomorrow.'

As we talked, I could not help admiring the cheerful pluck with which Jones endured the terrible monotony of his life in this dreary place. His rector was said to be delicate, and in order to prolong a life, which no doubt he considered valuable to the Church, he lived with his family either at Torquay or Cannes in elegant idleness, quite unable to do any duty, but fully equal to enjoying the pleasant society of those charming places, and quite satisfied that he had done his duty when he sacrificed a tenth of his income to provide for the spiritual needs of his parish. There was no squire in the place; no 'gentlefolk', as the rustics called them, lived nearer than five miles; and there was not a single being of his own class with whom poor Jones could associate. And yet he made no complaint. The nearest approach to one being the remark that the worst of it was, it was so difficult, if not impossible, to be really understood. 'The poor being so suspicious and ignorant, they look at everything from such a low standpoint, enthusiasm and freshness sink so easily into formalism and listlessness.'

The next day, finding that I really could be of no use, and feeling awkward and bored, as a man always is when another is actively doing his duty, I went off to the marshes with a gun to see if I could get any sport.

I took some sandwiches and a flask with me, not intending to return until dinner. After wandering about for some time, crossing dyke after dyke by treacherous rails more or less rotten, I found myself on the edge of a wide mere. I could see some duck out in the middle, and standing far out in the shallow water was a heron. They were all out of shot, and I saw I should do no good without a duck-punt.

I sat down on an old pile left on the top of the sea-wall, which had been lately repaired. The duck looked very tempting; but I doubted if I should do much good in broad daylight, even if I had a duck-punt, without a duck-gun. After sitting disconsolately for some time, I got up and wandered on.

The dreariness of the scene was most depressing: everything was brown and grey. Nothing broke the monotony of the wide-stretching mere; the whole scene gave me the impression of a straight line of interminable length, with a speck in the centre of it. That speck was myself.

[23]

At last, as I turned an angle in the sea-wall, I saw something lying above high-water mark, which looked like a boat.

Rejoiced to see any signs of humanity, I quickened my pace. It was a boat, and, better still, a duck-punt. As I came nearer I could see that she was old and very likely leaky; but here was a prospect of adventure, and I was not going to be readily daunted. On examination, the old craft seemed more watertight than I expected. At least she held water very well, and if she kept it in, she must equally well keep it out. I turned her over to run the water out, and then dragging the crazy old boat over the line of seaweed, launched her. But now a real difficulty met me. The paddles were nowhere to be seen. They had doubtless been taken away by the owner, and it would be little use searching for them. But a stout stick would do to punt her over the shallow water; and after some little search, I found an old stake which would answer well.

This was real luck. I had now some hope of bagging a few duck; at any rate, I was afloat, and could explore the little islets, which barely rose above the brown water. I might at least find some rabbits on them. I cautiously poled myself towards the black dots; but before I came within range, up rose first one, then another and another, like a string of beads, and the whole flight went, with outstretched necks and rapidly beating wings, away to my right, and seemed to pitch again beyond a low island some half-mile away. The heron had long ago taken himself off; so there was nothing to be done but pole across the mud in pursuit of the duck. I had not gone many yards when I found that I was going much faster than I expected, and soon saw the cause. The tide was falling, and I was being carried along with it. This would bring me nearer to my ducks, and I lazily guided the punt with the stake.

On rounding the island I found a new source of interest. The mere opened out to a much larger extent, and away towards my right I could see a break in the low land, as if a wide ditch had been cut through; while in this opening ever and anon dark objects rose up and disappeared again in a way I could not account for. The water seemed to be running off the mud-flats, and I saw that if I did not wish to be left high, but not dry, on the long slimy wastes, I must be careful to keep in the little channels or 'lakes' which acted as natural drains to the acres of greasy mud.

A conspicuous object attracted my attention some mile or more towards the opening in the land. It was a vessel lying high up on the mud, and looking as if she was abandoned.

The ducks had pitched a hundred yards or so beyond the island, and I approached as cautiously as I could; but just as I was putting down the stake to take up my gun, there was a swift sound of beating wings and splashing water, and away my birds flew, low over the mud, towards the old hulk.

Here was a chance, I thought. If I could get on board and remain hidden, I might, by patiently waiting, get a shot. I looked at my watch; there was still plenty of daylight left, and the tide was only just beginning to leave the mud. I punted away, therefore, with renewed hope, and was not long in getting up to the old ship.

There was just sufficient water over the mud to allow me to approach within ten or twelve feet, but farther I could not push the punt. This was disappointing; however, I noticed a deep lake ran round the other side, and determined to try my luck there. So with a slosh and a heave I got the flat afloat again, and made for the deeper water. It turned out quite successful, and I was enabled to get right under the square overhanging counter, while a little lane of water led alongside her starboard quarter. I pushed the nose of the punt into this, and was not long in clambering on board by the rusty irons of her fore-chains.

The old vessel lay nearly upright in the soft mud, and a glance soon told she would never be used again. Her gear and rigging were all rotten, and everything valuable had been removed. She was a brig of some two hundred tons, and had been a fine vessel, no doubt. To me there is always a world of romance in a deserted ship. The places she has been to, the scenes she has witnessed, the possibilities of crime, of adventure—all these thoughts crowd upon me when I see an old hulk lying deserted and forgotten, left to rot upon the mud of some lonely creek.

In order to keep my punt afloat as long as possible, I towed her round and moored her under the stern, and then looked over the bulwarks for the duck. There they were, swimming not more than a hundred and fifty yards away and they were coming towards me. I remained perfectly concealed under the high bulwark, and could see them paddling and feeding in the greasy weed. Their approach was slow, but I could afford to wait. Nearer and nearer they came; another minute, and they would be well within shot. I was already congratulating myself upon the success of my adventure, and thinking of the joy of Jones at this large accession to his larder, when suddenly there was a heavy splash, and with a wild spluttering rush the whole pack rose out of the water, and went skimming over the mud towards the distant sea. I let off both barrels after them, and tried to console myself by thinking that I saw the feathers fly from one; but not a bird dropped, and I was left alone in my chagrin.

What could have caused the splash, I wondered. There was surely no one else on board the ship, and certainly no one could get out here without mud-pattens or a boat. I looked round. All was perfectly still. Nothing broke the monotony of the grey scene—sodden and damp and lifeless. A chill breeze came up from the south-west, bringing with it a raw mist, which was blotting out the dark distance, and fast limiting my horizon. The day was drawing in, and I must be thinking of going home. As I turned round, my attention was arrested by seeing a duck-punt glide past me in the now rapidly falling water, which was swirling by the mud-bank on which the vessel lay. But there was no one in her. A dreadful thought struck me. It must be my boat, and how shall I get home? I ran to the stern and looked over. The duck-punt was gone.

The frayed and stranded end of the painter told me how it had happened. I had not allowed for the fall of the tide, and the strain of the punt, as the water fell away, had snapped the line, old and rotten as it was.

I ran to the bows and, jumping on to the bitts, saw my punt peacefully drifting away, some quarter of a mile off. It was perfectly evident I could not hope to get her again.

It was beginning to rain steadily. I could see that I was in for dirty weather, and became a little anxious about how I was to get back, especially as it was now rapidly growing dark. So thick was it that I could not see the low land anywhere, and could only judge of its position by remembering that the stern of the vessel pointed that way.

The conviction grew upon me that I could not possibly get away from this doleful old hulk without assistance; and how to get it, I could not for the life of me see. I had not seen a sign of a human being the whole day. It was not likely any more would be about at night. However, I shouted as loud as I could, and then waited to hear if there were any response. There was not a sound, only the wind moaned slightly through the stumps of the masts, and something creaked in the cabin.

Well, I thought, at least it might be worse. I shall have shelter for the night; while had I been left on one of these islands, I should have had to spend the night exposed to the pelting rain. Go below before it gets too dark, and see what sort of a berth can be got, if the worst comes to the worst. So thinking, I went to the booby-hatch, and found as I expected that it was half broken open, and anyone could go below who liked.

As I stepped down the rotting companion, the air smelt foul and dank. I went below very cautiously, for I was not at all sure that the boards would bear me. It was fortunate I did so, for as I stepped off the lowest step the floor gave way under my foot, and had I not been holding on to the stair-rail, I should have fallen through. Before going any farther, I took a look round.

The prospect was not inviting. The light was dim; I could scarcely make out objects near me, all else was obscurity. I could see that the whole of the inside of the vessel was completely gutted. What little light there was came through the stern ports. A small round speck of light looked at me out of the darkness ahead, and I could see that the flooring had either given way or been taken out of her. At my feet a gleam of water showed me what to expect if I should slip through the floor-joists. Altogether, a more desolate, gloomy, ghostly place it would be difficult to find.

I could not see any bunk or locker where I could sit down, and everything moveable had been taken out of the hulk. Groping my way with increasing caution, I stepped across the joists, and felt along the side of the cabin. I soon came to a bulkhead. Continuing to grope, I came to an opening. If the cabin was dim, here was blackness itself. I felt it would be useless to attempt to go farther, especially as a very damp foul odour came up from the bilge-water in her hold. As I stood looking into the darkness, a cold chilly shudder passed over me, and with a shiver I turned round to look at the cabin. My eyes had now become used to the gloom. A deeper patch of darkness on my right suggested the possibility of a berth, and groping my way over to it, I found the lower bunk was still entire. Here at least I could rest, if I found it impossible to get to shore. Having some wax vestas in my pocket, I struck a light and examined the bunk. It was better than I expected. If I could only find something to burn, I should be comparatively cheerful.

Before reconciling myself to my uncomfortable position, I resolved to see whether I could not get to the shore, and went up the rickety stairs again. It was raining hard, and the wind had got up. Nothing could be more dismal. I looked over the side and lowered myself down from the main-chains, to see if it were possible to walk over the mud.

I found I could not reach the mud at all; and fearful of being unable to climb back if I let go, I clambered up the side again and got on board.

It was quite clear I must pass the night here. Before going below I once more shouted at the top of my voice, more to keep up my own spirits than with any hope of being heard, and then paused to listen. Not a sound of any sort replied. I now prepared to make myself as comfortable as I could.

It was a dreary prospect. I would rather have spent the night on deck than down below in that foul cabin; but the drenching driving rain, as well as the cold, drove me to seek shelter below. It seemed so absurd to be in the position of a shipwrecked sailor, within two or three miles of a prosy country hamlet, and in a landlocked harbour while actually on land, if the slimy deep mud could be called land. I had not many matches left, but I had my gun and cartridges. The idea occurred to me to fire off minute-guns. 'That's what I ought to do, of course. The red flash will be seen in this dark night', for it was dark now and no mistake. Getting up on to the highest part of the vessel, I blazed away. The noise sounded to me deafening; surely the whole countryside would be aroused. After firing off a dozen cartridges, I waited. But the silence only seemed the more oppressive, and the blackness all the darker. 'It's no good; I'll turn in,' I thought dejectedly.

With great difficulty I groped my way to the top of the companion-ladder, and bumped dismally down the steps. If only I had a light I should be fairly comfortable, I thought. 'Happy thought, make a "spit-devil!" ' as we used when boys to call a little cone of damp gunpowder.

I got out my last two cartridges, and emptying the power carefully into my hand, I moistened it and worked it up to a paste. I then placed it on the smooth end of the rail, and lighted it. This was brilliant: at least so it seemed by contrast with the absolute blackness around me. By its light I was able to find my way to the bunk, and it lasted just long enough for me to arrange myself fairly comfortably for the night. By contriving a succession of matches, I was enabled to have enough light to see to eat my frugal supper; for I had kept a little sherry and a few sandwiches to meet emergencies, and it was a fortunate thing I had. The light and the food made me feel more cheery, and by the time the last match had gone out, I felt worse might have happened to me by a long way.

As I lay still, waiting for sleep to come, the absurdity of the situation forced itself upon me. Here was I, to all intents and purposes as much cut off from all communication with the rest of the world as if I were cast away upon a desert island. The chances were that I should make someone see or hear me the next day. Jones would be certain to have the country searched, and at the longest I should only endure the discomfort of one night, and get well laughed at for my pains; but meanwhile I was absolutely severed from human contact, and was as isolated as Robinson Crusoe, only 'more so', for I had no other living thing whatever to share my solitude. The silence of the place was perfect; and if silence can woo sleep, sleep ought very soon to have come. But when one is hungry and wet, and in a strange uncanny kind of place, besides being in one's clothes, it is a very difficult thing to go to sleep. First, my head was too low; then, after resting it on my arms, I got cramp in them. My back seemed all over bumps; when I turned on my side, I appeared to have got a rather serious enlargement of the hip-joint; and I found my damp clothes' smell very musty. After sighing and groaning for some time, I sat up for change of position, and nearly fractured my skull in so doing, against the remains of what had once been a berth above me. I didn't dare to move in the inky blackness, for I had seen sufficient to know that I might very easily break my leg or my neck in the floorless cabin.

There was nothing for it but to sit still, or lie down and wait for daylight. I had no means of telling the time. When I had last looked at my watch, before the last match had gone out, it was not more than six o'clock; it might be now about eight, or perhaps not so late. Fancy twelve long hours spent in that doleful black place, with nothing in the world to do to pass away the time! I *must* go to sleep; and so, full of this resolve, I lay down again.

I suppose I went to sleep. All I can recollect, after lying down, is keeping my mind resolutely turned inwards, as it were, and fixed upon the arduous business of counting an imaginary and interminable flock of sheep pass one by one through an ideal gate. This meritorious method of compelling sleep had, no doubt, been rewarded; but I have no means of knowing how long I slept. All I know is that the next thing I can remember after getting my five-hundredth sheep through the gate is that I heard two most horrible yells ring through the darkness. I sat bolt-upright; and as a proof that my senses were 'all there', I did not bring my head this time against the berth overhead, remembering to bend it outwards so as to clear it.

There was not another sound. The silence was as absolute as the darkness. 'I must have been dreaming,' I thought; but the sounds were ringing in my ears, and my heart was beating with excitement. There must have been some reason for this. I never was 'taken this way' before. I could not make it out, and felt very uncomfortable. I sat there listening for some time. No other sound breaking the deathly stillness, and becoming tired of sitting, I lay down again. Once more I set myself to get my interminable flocks through that gate, but I could not help myself listening.

There seemed to me a sound growing in the darkness, a something gathering in the particles of the air, as if molecules of the atmosphere were rustling together, and with stilly movement were whispering something. The wind had died down, and I would have gone on deck if I could move; but it was hazardous enough moving about in the light: it would have been madness to attempt to move in that blackness. And so I lay still and tried to sleep.

But now there was a sound, indistinct, but no mere fancy; a muffled sound, as of some movement in the forepart of the ship.

I listened intently and gazed into the darkness.

What was the sound? It did not seem like rats. It was a dull, shuffling kind of noise, very indistinct, and conveying no clue whatever as to its cause. It lasted for only a short time. But now the cold damp air seemed to have become more piercingly chilly. The raw iciness seemed to strike into the very marrow of my bones, and my teeth chattered. At the same time a new sense seemed to be assailed: the foul odour which I had noticed arising from the stagnant water in the bilge appeared to rise into more objectionable prominence, as if it had been stirred.

'I cannot stand this,' I muttered, shivering in horrible aversion at the disgusting odour. 'I will go on deck at all hazards.'

Rising to put this resolve in execution, I was arrested by the noise beginning again. I listened. This time I distinctly distinguished two separate sounds: one, like a heavy soft weight being dragged along with difficulty; the other like the hard sound of boots on boards. Could there be others on board after all? If so, why had they made no sound when I clambered on deck, or afterwards, when I shouted and fired my gun?

Clearly, if there were people, they wished to remain concealed, and my presence was inconvenient to them. But how absolutely still and quiet they had kept! It appeared incredible that there should be anyone. I listened intently. The sound had ceased again, and once more the most absolute stillness reigned around. A gentle swishing, wobbling, lapping noise seemed to form itself in the darkness. It increased, until I recognised the chattering and bubbling of water. 'It must be the tide which is rising,' I thought. 'It has reached the rudder, and is eddying round the stern-post.' This also accounted, in my mind, for the other noises, because, as the tide surrounded the vessel, and she thus became water-borne, all kinds of sounds might be produced in the old hulk as she resumed her upright position.

However, I could not get rid of the chilly horrid feeling those two screams had produced, combined with the disgusting smell, which was getting more and more obtrusive. It was foul, horrible, revolting, like some carrion, putrid and noxious. I prepared to take my chances of damage, and rose up to grope my way to the companion-ladder.

It was a more difficult job than I had any idea of. I had my gun, it was true, and with it I could feel for the joists; but when once I let go of the edge of the bunk I had nothing to steady me, and nearly went headlong at the first step. Fortunately I reached back in time to prevent my fall; but this attempt convinced me that I had better endure the strange horrors of the unknown, than the certain miseries of a broken leg or neck.

I sat down, therefore, on the bunk.

Now that my own movements had ceased, I became aware that the shuffling noise was going on all the time. 'Well,' thought I, 'they may shuffle. They won't hurt me, and I shall go to sleep again.' So reflecting, I lay down, holding my gun, ready to use as a club if necessary.

Now it is all very well to laugh at superstitious terrors. Nothing is easier than to obtain a cheap reputation for brilliancy, independence of thought, and courage, by deriding the fear of the supernatural when comfortably seated in a drawing-room well lighted, and with company. But put those scoffers in a like situation with mine, and I don't believe they would have been any more free from a feeling the reverse of bold, mocking, and comfortable, than I was.

I had read that most powerful ghost-story, 'The Haunted and the Haunters', by the late Lord Lytton, and the vividness of that weird tale had always impressed me greatly. Was I actually now to experience in my own person, and with no possibility of escape, the trying ordeal that bold ghost-hunter went through, under much more favourable circumstances? He at least had his servant with him. He had fuel and a light, and above all, he could get away when he wanted to. I felt I could face any number of spiritual manifestations, if only I had warmth and light. But the icy coldness of the air was eating into my bones, and I shivered until my teeth chattered.

I could not get to sleep. I could not prevent myself listening, and at last I gave up the contest, and let myself listen. But there seemed now nothing to listen to. All the time I had been refusing to let my ears do their office, by putting my handkerchief over one ear, and lying on my arm with the other, a confused noise appeared to reach me, but the moment I turned round and lay on my back, everything seemed quiet. 'It's only my fancy after all; the result of cold and want of a good dinner. I will go to sleep.' But in spite of this I lay still, listening a little longer. There was the sound of trickling water against the broad bilge of the old hulk, and I knew the tide was rising fast; my thoughts turned to the lost canoe, and to reproaching myself with my stupidity in not allowing enough rope, or looking at it more carefully. Suddenly I became all attention again. An entirely different sound now arrested me. It was distinctly a low groan, and followed almost immediately by heavy blows—blows which fell on a soft substance, and then more groans, and again those sickening blows.

'There must be men here. Where are they, and what is it?' I sat up, and strained my eyes towards where the sound came from. The sounds had ceased again. Should I call out, and let the man or men know that I was here? What puzzled me was the absolute darkness. How could anyone see to hit an object, or do anything else in this dense obscurity? It appalled me. Anything might pass at an inch's distance, and I could not tell who or what it was. But how could anything human find its way about, any more than I could? Perhaps there was a solid bulkhead dividing the forecastle from me. But it would have to be very sound, and with no chink whatever, to prevent a gleam or ray of light finding its way out somewhere. I could not help feeling convinced that the whole hull was open from one end to the other. Was I really dreaming after all? To convince myself that I was wide awake, I felt in my pockets for my note-book, and pulling out my pencil, I opened the book, and holding it in my left hand, wrote as well as I could, by feel alone: 'I am wide awake; it is about midnight— Christmas eve, 187—.' I found I had got to the bottom of the page, so I shut the book up, resolving to look at it the next morning. I felt curious to see what the writing looked like by daylight.

But all further speculation was cut short by the shuffling and dragging noise beginning again. There was no doubt the sounds were louder, and were coming my way.

[32]

I never in all my life felt so uncomfortable—I may as well at once confess it—so frightened. There in that empty hull, over that boardless floor, over these rotting joists, somebody or something was dragging some heavy weight. What, I could form no conjecture; only the shrieks, the blows, the groans, the dull thumping sounds, compelled me to suspect the worst—to feel convinced that I was actually within some few feet of a horrible murder then being committed. I could form no idea of who the victim was, or who was the assassin. That I actually heard the sounds I had no doubt; that they were growing louder and more distinct I felt painfully aware. The horror of the situation was intense. If only I could strike a light, and see what was passing close there—but I had no matches. I could hear a sound as of someone breathing slowly, stertorously, then a dull groan. And once more the cruel sodden blows fell again, followed by a drip, drip, and heavy drop in the dank water below, from which the sickening smell rose, pungent, reeking, horrible.

The dragging shuffling noise now began again. It came quite close to me, so close that I felt I had only to put out my hand to touch the thing. Good heavens! was it coming to my bunk? The thing passed, and all the time the dull drip, as of some heavy drops, fell into the water below. It was awful. All this time I was sitting up, and holding my gun by its barrel, ready to use it if I were attacked. As the sound passed me at the closest, I put out the gun involuntarily; but it touched nothing, and I shuddered at the thought that *there was no floor over which the weight could be drawn.*

I must be dreaming some terribly vivid dream. It could not be real. I pinched myself. I felt I was pinching myself. It was no dream. The sweat poured off my brow, my teeth chattered with the cold. It was terrific in its dreadful mystery.

And now the sounds altered. The noises had reached the companion-ladder. Something was climbing them with difficulty. The old stairs creaked. Bump, thump, the thing was dragged up the steps with many pauses, and at last it seemed to have reached the deck. A long pause now followed. The silence grew dense around. I dreaded the stillness—the silence that made itself be heard almost more than the sounds. What new horror would that awful quiet bring forth?

The absolute silence was broken by a dull drip from the stairs, and then the dragging began again. Distant and less distinct, but the steps were louder. They came nearer—over my head—the old boards creaked, and the weight was dragged right over me. I could hear it above my head;

for the steps stopped, and two distinct raps, followed by a third heavier one, sounded so clearly above me that it seemed almost as if it was something striking the rotten woodwork of the berth over my head. The sounds were horribly suggestive of the elbows and head of a body being dropped on the deck.

And now, as if the horrors had not been enough, a fresh ghastliness was added. So close were the raps above me that I involuntarily moved, as if I had been struck by what caused them. As I did so, I felt something drop on to my head and slowly trickle over my forehead. I sprang up in my disgust, and with a wild cry I stepped forward, and instantly fell between the joists into the rank water below.

The shock was acute. Had I been asleep and dreaming before, this must inevitably have roused me up. I found myself completely immersed in water, and, for a moment, was absolutely incapable of thinking. As it was pitch-dark and my head had gone under, I could not tell whether I was above water or not, as I felt the bottom and struggled and splashed on to my legs. It was only by degrees I knew I must be standing with my head out of the foul mixture, because I was able to breathe easily, although the wet running down from my hair dribbled into my mouth as I stood shivering and gasping.

It was astonishing how a physical discomfort overcame a mental terror. Nothing could be more miserable than my present position, and my efforts were at once directed to getting out of this dreadful place. But let anyone who has ever had the ill-luck to fall out of bed in his boyhood try and recollect his sensations. The bewildering realisation that he is not in bed, that he does not know where he is, which way to go, or what to do to get back again; everything he touches seems strange, and one piece of furniture much the same as any other.

If, then, one is so utterly at fault in a room every inch of which one knows intimately, how much more hopeless was my position at the bottom of this old vessel, half immersed in water, and totally without any clue which could help me to get out! I had not the least idea which was the ship's stern or which her stem, and every movement I made with my feet only served to unsteady me, as the bottom was covered with slime, and uneven with the great timbers of the vessel.

My first thought on recovering my wits was to stretch my arms up over my head, and I was relieved to find that I could easily reach the joists above me. I was always fairly good at gymnastics, and I had not much difficulty in drawing myself up and sitting on the joist, although the weight of my wet clothes added to my exertions considerably. Having so far succeeded, I sat and drained, as it were, into the water below. The smell was abominable. I never disliked myself so much, and I shivered with cold.

As I could not get any wetter, I determined to go on deck somehow, but where was the companion-ladder? I had nothing to guide me. Strange to say, the reality of my struggles had almost made me forget the mysterious phenomena I had been listening to. But now, as I looked round, my attention was caught by a luminous patch which quivered and flickered on my right, at what distance from me I could not tell. It was like the light from a glow-worm, only larger and changing in shape; sometimes elongated like a lambent oval, and then it would sway one way or another, as if caught in a draught of air. While I was looking at it and wondering what could cause it, I heard the steps over my head; they passed above me, and then seemed to grow louder on my left. A creeping dread again came over me. If only I could get out of this horrible place—but where were the stairs? I listened. The footfall seemed to be coming down some steps; then the companion-ladder must be on my left. But if I moved that way I should meet the thing, whatever it was, that was coming down. I shuddered at the thought. However, I made up my mind. Stretching out my hand very carefully, I felt for the next joist, reached it, and crawled across. I stopped to listen. The steps were coming nearer. My hearing had now become acute; I could almost tell the exact place of each footfall. It came closer—closer—quite close, surely—on the very joist on which I was sitting. I thought I could feel the joist quiver, and involuntarily moved my hand to prevent the heavy tread falling on it. The steps passed on, grew fainter, and ceased, as they drew near the pale lambent light. One thing I noticed with curious horror, and that was that although the thing must have passed between me and the light, yet it was never for a moment obscured, which it must have been had any body or substance passed between, and yet I was certain that the steps went directly from me to it.

It was all horribly mysterious; and what had become of the other sound—the thing that was being dragged? An irresistible shudder passed over me; but I determined to pursue my way until I came to something. It would never do to sit still and shiver there.

After many narrow escapes of falling again, I reached a bulkhead, and cautiously feeling along it, I came to an opening. It was the companion-ladder. By this time my hands, by feeling over the joists, had become dry again. I felt along the step to be quite sure that it was the stairs, and in so doing I touched something wet, sticky, clammy. Oh, horror! what was it? A cold shiver shook me nearly off the joist, and I felt an unutterable sense of repulsion to going on. However, the fresher air which came down the companion revived me, and, conquering my dread, I clambered on to the step. It did not take long to get upstairs and stand on the deck again.

I think I never in all my life experienced such a sense of joy as I did on being out of that disgusting hole. It was true I was soaking wet, and the night wind cut through me like a knife; but these were things I could understand, and were matter of common experience. What I had gone through might only be a question of nerves, and had no tangible or visible terror; but it was none the less very dreadful, and I would not go through such an experience again for worlds. As I stood cowering under the lee of the bulwark, I looked round at the sky. There was a pale light as if of daybreak, and it seemed as if all my troubles would be over with the dawn. It was bitterly cold. The wind had got round to the north, and I could faintly make out the low shore astern.

While I stood shivering there, a cry came down the wind. At first I thought it was a sea-bird, but it sounded again. I felt sure it was a human voice. I sprang up on to the taffrail, and shouted at the top of my lungs, then paused. The cry came down clearer and distinct. It was Jones's voice—had he heard me? I waved my draggled pocket-handkerchief and shouted again. In the silence which followed, I caught the words 'We are coming'. What joyful words! Never did shipwrecked mariner on a lonely isle feel greater delight. My misery would soon be over.

Unfortunately the tide was low, and was still falling. Nothing but a boat could reach me, I thought, and to get a boat would take some time. I therefore stamped up and down the deck to get warm; but I had an instinctive aversion for the companion-ladder, and the deep shadows of the forepart of the vessel.

As I turned round in my walk, I thought I saw something moving over the mud. I stopped. It was undoubtedly a figure coming towards me. A voice hailed me in gruff accents—

'Lily, ahoy! Be anyone aboard?'

What an absurd question! and here I had been shouting myself hoarse. However, I quickly reassured him, and then understood why my rescuer did not sink in the soft mud. He had mud-pattens on. Coming up as close as he could, he shouted to me to keep clear, and then threw first one, then the other, clattering wooden board on to the deck. I found them, and under the instructions of my friend, I did not take long in putting them on. The man was giving me directions as to how to manage; but I did not care how much wetter I got, and dropped over the side into the slime. Sliding and straddling, I managed to get up to my friend, and then together we skated, as it were, to the shore—although skating very little represents the awkward splashes and slips I made on my way to land. I found quite a little crowd awaiting me on the bank; but Jones, with ready consideration, hurried me off to a cart he had in a lane nearby, and drove me home.

I told him the chief points of the adventure on our way; but did not say anything of the curious noises. It is odd how shy a man feels at telling what he knows people will never believe. It was not until the evening of the next day that I began to tell him, and then only after I was fortified by an excellent dinner, and some very good claret. Jones listened attentively. He was far too kindly and well-bred to laugh at me; but I could see he did not believe one word as to the reality of the occurrence. 'Very strange!' 'How remarkable!' 'Quite extraordinary!' he kept saying, with evident interest. But I was sure he put it all down to my fatigue and disordered imagination. And so, to do him justice, has everybody else to whom I have told the tale since.

The fact is, we cannot, in this prosaic age, believe in anything the least approaching the supernatural. Nor do I. But nevertheless I am as certain as I am that I am writing these words, that the thing did really happen, and will happen again, may happen every night for all I know. I have a theory which of course will be laughed at, and as I am not in the least scientific, I cannot bolster it up by scientific arguments. It is this. As Mr Edison has now discovered that by certain simple processes human sounds can be reproduced at any future date, so accidentally, and owing to the combination of most curious coincidences, it might happen that the agonised cries of some suffering being, or the sounds made by one at a time when all other emotions are as nothing compared to the supreme sensations of one committing some awful crime, could be impressed on the atmosphere or surface of an enclosed building, which could be reproduced by a current of air passing into that building under the same atmospheric conditions. This is the vague explanation I have given to myself.

However, be the explanation what it may, the facts are as I have stated them. Let those laugh who did not experience them. To return to the end of the story. There were two things I pointed out to Jones as conclusive that I was not dreaming. One was my pocket-book. I showed it him, and the words were quite clear—only, of course, very straggling. This is a facsimile of the writing, but I cannot account for the date being 1837—

I am under a wake it is about midnight Christmas Eve 1837

The other point was the foul-smelling dark chocolate stains on my hair, hands, and clothes. Jones said, of course, this was from the rust off the mouldering ironwork, some of which no doubt had trickled down, owing to the heavy rain, through the defective caulking of the deck. The fact is, there is nothing that an ingenious mind cannot explain; but the question is, is the explanation the right one?

I could easily account for the phosphorescent light. The water was foul and stagnant, and it was no doubt caused by the same gases which produce the well-known *ignisfatuus* or Will-o'-the-wisp.

We visited the ship, and I recovered my gun. There were the same stains on the deck as there were on my clothes; and curiously enough they went in a nearly straight line over the place where I lay from the top of the companion to the starboard bulwark. We carefully examined the fore-part of the ship; it was as completely gutted as the rest of her. Jones was glad to get on deck again, as the atmosphere was very unpleasant, and I had no wish to stay.

At my request Jones made every inquiry he could about the old hulk. Not much was elicited. It bore an evil name, and no one would go on board who could help it. So far it looked as if it were credited with being haunted. The owner, who had been the captain of her, had died about three years before. He bore an ill reputation; but as he had left his money to the most influential farmer in the district, the country-people were unwilling to talk against him.

I went with Jones to call on the farmer, and asked him point-blank if he had ever heard whether a murder had been committed on board the *Lily*. He stared at me, and then laughed. 'Not as I know of' was all his answer—and I never got any nearer than that.

I feel that this is all very unsatisfactory. I wish I could give some thrilling and sensational explanation. I am sorry I cannot. My imagination suggests many, as no doubt it will to each of my readers who possesses that faculty; but I have written this only to tell the facts, not to add to our super-abundant fiction.

If ever I come across any details bearing upon the subject, I will not fail to communicate them at once.

The vessel I found was the *Lily* of Goole, owned by one Master Gad Earwaker, and built in 1801.

THE PHANTOM RIDERS

by Ernest R. Suffling

A contemporary of Frank Cowper, the antiquary
Ernest Richard Suffling
was also a keen boating enthusiast who
produced some fine horror tales during the late
Victorian era. In addition to a series of books and
articles on the Norfolk Broads, Suffling wrote
extensively on church architecture, brasses and
stained glass. His ghost stories were related by
various clients of a hypnotist in two entertaining
collections: *The Decameron of a Hypnotist* (1898)
and *The Story Hunter, or Tales of the Weird and Wild*
(1896). 'The Phantom Riders' is taken from the
latter volume.

'Once upon a time' might fittingly be the initial words of this
story, for the terrible events of which it is a narration took
place long, long years ago; in fact, at the end of the
seventeenth century.

To be precise, the day on which the stirring narrative commences
was December 23, 1695, two hundred years ago this very Christmas,
but heaven protect us from such a dreadful Christmastide as that.

The old Manor House at Minehead, in Somersetshire, no longer
exists, for the legends attached to it were of such a terrifying nature,
that no one dare rent it after the death of John Simmonds in 1696, so
that being uncared for, the old house lingered and decayed till it
looked an ideal picture of 'desolation'.

Haunted or no, there was something so uncanny in the appearance of the old gables, fast tottering to ruin, that even in the crepuscular light of early evening, persons would hurry by it with a shudder, while later at night, many would go a long way round rather than pass its weather-worn walls. The very air that blew past the ruin seemed to gather a deathly fragrance, which was doubtless due to the fast-rotting timbers of the floors and ceilings.

Be that as it may, the evil repute of the old house grew so great, and such dreadful stories were current concerning its sights and sounds, that it was some years ago pulled down, the ground ploughed up, and crops now flourish where, for generations, owls and bats held their habitation undisturbed.

Minehead Manor House was an Elizabethan red-brick structure, with tall twisted chimneys, curved gables, and dormer windows peeping out from the red clay tiles. Its grounds were extensive, its gardens prim, and its fish-pond well stocked with carp, eel, and pike; for John Simmonds, the owner, was fond of wandering about and improving his domain. His gardens and fish-pond were his hobbies, and so fully occupied his entire time that he was seldom seen in the village, where he was greatly respected and admired for his kindness to the poor, while his grand old English appearance had all the stateliness of a typical country squire.

He had an only daughter, Julia, an accomplished young lady as accomplishments went in those days. She could sing and accompany herself upon the spinet, could embroider beautifully, spin, and generally comport herself as a young lady of twenty-three should, who has a whole household on her shoulders.

Of lady friends she had few, and her gentlemen friends were even still more scarce. One young gentleman, Wynne Clarge (a distant relative), who lived near, assumed, probably because of the non-existence of any rival, that he should some day claim her for his wife, but he was very apathetic in the matter. There was little real *love* between them; they were passable friends, and that was all; he looked upon Julia as he did upon his horse—they were both nice in their way, and ministered to his wants; for the rest he took everything as a matter of course, simply because he had no rival.

Things were running in their usual groove, when one day, early in December, a gentleman was announced, who had called to pay his respects to Mr Simmonds.

[41]

It was soon explained that he was Charles Benwell, the son of Mr Simmonds' sister, who had for many years resided in Virginia.

The cousins (for Charles was invited to stay at the Manor House for a few weeks) fell in love with each other at first sight, and the love was so sincere and intense, that ere three weeks had passed, Mr Simmonds was solicited for Julia's hand.

'Quick work, my boy,' quoth the genial old man. 'Why, you have scarcely had time to know each other yet. It puts me in mind of Julius Caesar, does this visit of yours, "He came, he saw, he conquered," and so have you, apparently. Well, well, we shall see. But you must not expect a fat dowry with her, for she can sing, "My face is my fortune," like the maid in the song; but still she will not be penniless—no, no! I will see that she has a suitable maintenance.'

'As to that, Mr Simmonds, you know I am over here for the purpose of selling the property which my poor mother—your sister—has left me. There are three estates of considerable size, amounting in the aggregate to something like twelve hundred acres, besides several houses, the documents appertaining to which I have left at the solicitor's at Dulverton.

'Now, Mr Simmonds, tell me, have you any objection to my looking upon your daughter as my affianced bride?'

Mr Simmonds had no objection, but being a very cautious, business man, would like just a glance at the documents empowering Charles to sell his late mother's estates, simply as a matter of precaution, and to ascertain if there were a flaw anywhere that might cause any delay in the disposal of the property.

'As to that,' rapturously vociferated Benwell, 'the papers shall be in your hands by this time tomorrow, so that you may search them through, and then on glorious Christmas Eve give your sanction and blessing to our engagement.'

'Only fancy being engaged on Christmas Eve, Julia!' exclaimed Charles. 'How romantic! It is like the beginning of a story-book.'

*   *   *   *   *

From the day of Benwell's arrival, Wynne Clarge had roamed about the house and grounds, snarling at every one and everything. He had treated Julia very rudely, and one day suddenly asked her—

'What is that fellow dangling about after you for? I will not have it, Julia.'

'But, Wynne,' his fair cousin replied, 'it can surely be no business of yours if he wishes to pay me attention; he is my cousin, and who knows but he may make me a proposal before he leaves Minehead?'

All this was said coquettishly, but looking up at Wynne she was frightened at the look of hatred she perceived on his face.

'A proposal he *may* make, but your husband he shall never be while I wear this by my side,' and he touched the hilt of his rapier significantly, as he strode off down the garden path.

From that day he sought to quarrel with young Benwell, and his relations with Mr Simmonds became so strained, that the old gentleman grew alarmed at his manner, and quietly but firmly forbade him the house.

'It is not your house or lands I want,' exclaimed the irate Wynne; 'but hark ye, old man, Julia shall be my wife and no other's; willy-nilly she *shall* be mine. I have waited for years, and will not be baulked by this sallow-faced American loon! Let him have his holiday, and go as he came, and leave Julia in my hands, or—I will know the reason why!'

*   *   *   *   *

It was Christmas Eve, and Squire Simmonds had invited a few of the neighbouring gentry to spend the evening sociably together under his roof. Wynne had been invited with the rest, for at Christmastide the squire could not be at variance with any man; but in the evening no Wynne appeared. This gave rise to some little comments among the guests, who good-naturedly twitted pretty Julia with having two strings to her bow.

She blushed and bore it, only looking anxiously now and again at the face of the old clock at the end of the dining-room, for it was past the hour when Charley had promised he would return; for he had gone over to Dulverton in the morning to fetch the required documents. He had promised to be back by six o'clock, and it was now eight, and both Julia and her father began to exchange glances of alarm.

At nine o'clock the guests also became anxious and Mr Simmonds tried to persuade both himself and those present that all was right.

'You see, it is fifteen miles from here to Dulverton,' said Mr Simmonds. 'Possibly he did not start till six o'clock; then he had to make a *détour*, so as to call at Stoke Pero and deliver a message to one of Julia's friends, and that would make his homeward journey eighteen or twenty miles, and thirty-five miles there and back is a longish ride. Besides, his horse, Old Maggie, is none too good for a long trot over this hilly country. Fill up, my friends! Here's to our future squire, Charles Benwell!'

He raised the goblet to his lips, but had not commenced to quaff, when looking towards the door, he saw the absent Charley advancing toward the table, looking extremely pale. All in the room rose in greeting, but he turned from them, and unbuckling the clasp of his riding-cloak, walked to an alcove, formerly an immense fire-place, but now used as a closet for hanging outdoor coats, wraps, and accoutrements, a curtain being drawn across it.

To their surprise, every one present noticed, as he turned, that his deep white collar (which was the fashion of those days) was saturated with blood, and as they noted this, and had the words on their lips to speak to him about it, he disappeared into the alcove by walking, as it seemed, *right through the curtain*, and not drawing it aside in the usual way!

The assembled guests stood aghast.

What could it mean?

For a long time not a man stirred. But at length the spell was broken by a young fellow named William Rayner advancing to the curtain sword in hand: he snatched it suddenly aside.

The recess was empty!

Charles Benwell had apparently vanished through the solid wall!

The curtain fell from Rayner's grasp as he stood immovable with amazement. Then came another long pause; a consultation; a replenishment of glasses; and finally the conclusion was arrived at that it was the apparition of Julia's lover they had seen.

Fear now settled on them all, and as they sat, talking in hushed tones and glancing nervously about, the curtain guarding the alcove was seen to move.

It bulged out slightly as if caught by a draught of air, and then again its long, sombre folds trailed upon the floor and were still again.

No one moved from the spot where he happened to be sitting or standing, but all eyes were fixed in horror on the agitated tapestry.

Again it swayed.

This time the bold Will Rayner rose, and drawing his sword, was joined by some of the others, also sword in hand. Rapidly they advanced across the intervening space, and Rayner, plucking hold of the fabric with his left hand, drew it aside with a quick jerk.

Wonder of wonders, in place of the white-faced Benwell there stood his scowling rival, Wynne Clarge.

[44]

His right wrist was bared, and his sword point, which was advanced towards the spectators, was seen to be covered with blood.

As they looked with startled eyes, the blood slowly dripped to the floor, drip—drip—drip!

'How now, Master Clarge, think you to frighten us with such tom-foolery?' exclaimed Will Rayner. 'Get thee gone with thy mummery, or my sword shall teach thee a lesson not to make fools of thy betters.'

Then, rushing forward, he attempted to beat the sword out of Wynne's hand with his own, but to his amazement no clang of steel sounded as their weapons met.

'Here's at thee, Wynne,' cried the now enraged man; and suiting the action to the word, he made a deadly thrust at his opponent's breast: the blade pierced the figure without any resistance, and struck the wall so violently that it was knocked out of his hand and rolled clattering on the floor.

At the attack and thrust Wynne looked straight at his assailant, smiled sardonically, and—*slowly melted away.*

* * * * *

The guests stayed all night, sleeping where they best could, at least those whose eyelids had the power to close; while the more nervous scarce dare move from the room for fear of encountering one or other of their ghostly visitors.

It was useless trying to search the wild country between Minehead and Dulverton while it was yet dark, but with the first grey light of a dull morning—Christmas Day—a party of eight gentlemen rode off in search of the missing Charles Benwell.

Through Selworthy they silently rode, and turning to the left entered the lovely woods of Korner. Hills rose to a great height on either side of the valley up which they travelled; hills that seemed to touch—aye, and really did touch—the low-lying dun-coloured snow-clouds. There was a rough kind of path, which ran beside the brook— now swollen to a mountain torrent—but at best it was a mere cattle track, and was now fast becoming obliterated by the silently falling snow.

The men rode on, scarcely speaking a word; the only sound that was heard was the roar of the turbulent torrent as it tore through its rocky bed on its way to the sea at Porlock.

Presently they heard a horse neigh, and making at once towards the sound, quickly found poor Old Maggie grazing at the foot of Dunkery Beacon near the village of Stoke Pero.

The snow was now falling so fast that not the sharpest eye could perceive the summit of the Beacon, which towered sixteen hundred feet above them.

'Coup! coup! Maggie,' coaxingly cried Will Rayner, and the mare, whinnying, trotted to him. She was still saddled, and they found, as they feared to find, both upon the saddle and back, stains of blood.

'Follow up, friends,' said Will, 'as rapidly as possible, for if I mistake not, our poor friend lies not far away, and if we make not the best of our way, the snow may hide from us that which we seek.'

They accordingly travelled on much quicker, and as they turned to cross the rustic bridge, at the foot of the hill from which Stoke Pero looks dreamily down, they found poor Benwell, lying on his face, dead, frozen stark and stiff, and partly covered with snow as with a winding-sheet.

They dismounted, and examined the murdered man, discovering to their amazement and horror that he had been run through the base of the neck from *behind*, by some cowardly hand.

The body was laid over the back of a horse, and four of the gentlemen returned with it to the Manor House, while Will and the other three friends prosecuted their search for Wynne Clarge.

This search, however, was in vain; no signs of him could be found, and after wandering about in the snow for a long time they returned to Minehead.

It was indeed a sad Christmas Day for the good folks of the Manor House, which instead of being a place of rejoicing was now a house of the deepest sorrow.

Poor Julia was inconsolable.

No papers relating to the property were found on the body, and this gave some clue to Wynne's reason for waylaying the poor young fellow.

Benwell was buried in the churchyard which lies high upon the hill, a churchyard surrounded by walls that look out over the quiet town like the ramparts of a fortress dominating a city.

A week later, a great commotion was caused by the news being brought, that Wynne's body had been discovered in the trout pool, which lies nearly hidden under the great hill near Stoke Pero.

True it was, and for him too—murderer as well as murdered—a resting-place was found in the quiet hill-top churchyard.

*   *   *   *   *

The missing papers could not be discovered, although the woods had been searched in all directions, and as the unusually cold winter gave place to the genial early spring, people began to look upon the tragedy as a thing of the past, and talked no more of it.

Poor Julia drooped and faded; but with the advent of the lovely warm May days she revived, and, by and by, became her own sweet self again; not quite so tuneful in her songs as of yore, but still her father's own little warbling bird, for he delighted in music and in singing, particularly the songs his daughter sang to him of an evening.

Summer came with its flowers, and autumn with its grain and fruit, and then—then came cold dreary winter once more.

Christmas approached, but this year, instead of the usual jovial party at the Manor House, Julia and her father accepted an invitation to spend a few days with the sporting rector of Stoke Pero. They arrived at the Rectory on the 22nd of December (a Monday), and were invited to stay over Christmas Day, which was on the Thursday.

Julia was not at all in good spirits, and was evidently thinking of the dreadful Christmas a year ago and her lost love. She brooded so that, as Christmas Eve approached, she was positively unable to hide her state of intense nervousness and melancholy, and at noon on the 24th she felt herself so unwell that she implored her father to take her home.

Mr Simmonds and the worthy parson took counsel together, and as Julia appeared in a high state of nervous excitement bordering on fever, they gave her a sleeping draught, placing her in the chimney corner in the Rector's great arm-chair. There she slept for three hours, but when she awoke, again implored her father to take her home, as she felt so ill and did not wish to give her kind hosts trouble.

There was no resisting this second appeal, so after a little delay in getting ready, they mounted their horses, and with a boy riding a pony and carrying a lantern in advance, they set off on their journey homeward.

The snow lay thick on hill and tree, and they made but slow progress. The lantern gave but little light; it bobbed about hither and thither like an *ignis fatuus*, and finally the boy's pony stumbled, and boy, pony, and lantern were buried in a deep snow-drift. The boy scrambled out quickly, but by the squire's orders did not light his lantern again. They crossed the bridge and picked their uncertain way along the snow-covered path by the torrent's brink.

Suddenly the squire drew rein as a man rode quickly and silently past them, over the snow, going in the same direction as themselves.

'How like Old Maggie,' said the squire half aloud; 'and if I did not know to the contrary, I could have sworn that the rider was poor Benwell!'

The squire supported Julia with his left arm as she rode by his side, cheering her as best he could.

'Who was that, father?' she asked. 'How strange he did not speak as he passed us by.'

'It was indeed, my dear,' he rejoined; 'but probably he was a stranger, and unaccustomed to our hearty West Country greetings. But see, he has stopped and dismounted.'

They beheld him in the moonlight standing by his horse's side, but for some reason the squire's horse and his daughter's both stopped of their own accord, while the boy's pony wheeled round and dashed back towards Stoke.

The strange horseman patted his steed's neck, tightened the saddle-girth, and was about to remount, when another man suddenly bounded forward, with a drawn sword, and making a lunge at the unfortunate traveller, thrust him, from behind, right through the neck.

Then the murderer searched the dying man, taking a large bundle of papers from the saddle-bags, and transferring them to his own pockets.

Turning once more to his victim, who was not dead, but feebly struggling in the snow to regain his feet, he again stabbed him, this time clean through the heart. Then, with a malignant smile he turned away, strode to his own horse, which was tethered to a tree hard by, mounted, and in a trice galloped close past the spell-bound onlookers.

As he galloped silently by, the squire beheld, to his astonishment the features of Wynne Clarge!

Thus was re-enacted, in phantom-vision, the murder of Charles Benwell, as it took place twelve months before.

Trembling in every limb Mr Simmonds turned to his daughter. But Julia was no more, *his arm encircled her lifeless clay.*

*　　*　　*　　*　　*

An old man and feeble was John Simmonds, when, two months after the above events, he left his bed, slowly recovering from brain-fever; but although he was able occasionally to wander listlessly in his garden in the warm days of the summer, he lingered only till the first days of autumn tinged the foliage with gold and red, then drooped like the flowers, and like the flowers he died.

By his daughter's side, upon that hillside in the west, the old man sleeps, and to this day their tombs are pointed out; the one known as 'the Good Squire's Tomb,' and the other is called 'Julia's Grave.'

*　　*　　*　　*　　*

When the next Christmas Eve came round, bold Will Rayner organized a little party to watch the spot where the murder took place. They did not keep their dread vigil in vain, for a little after darkness set in they all saw the phantom horseman ride up, dismount to tighten his saddle-girth, and pat his tired horse on the neck. They saw the dastardly rush of his rival: they saw the deed enacted before their eyes, as Mr Simmonds and Julia had seen it in an identical manner, and Will had difficulty in restraining his comrades from rushing upon the murderous Wynne, although they knew him to be but the phantasm of a man.

Their purpose, however, in watching was to *follow* the ghost, and as it mounted its shadowy horse they all gave chase.

It was a wild sight to see these young men following the apparition, who pursued his course through the wild woods apparently unconscious that he was being followed.

For three miles he rode, and then drew rein by a low cliff which overhung the stream. He dismounted, took the bundle of papers from under his cloak, and hid them beneath the stump of a tree, whose roots flung themselves in fantastic shapes from the side of the cliff. Then he mounted his horse again, with a smile of triumph on his ghastly face, rode up the precipitous bank, and had nearly gained the brink, when his horse missed its footing, rolled over backwards with its rider, and both disappeared into the turbid water below.

The ghostly horse quickly emerged and galloped away, but the shade of Wynne Clarge, its rider, rose no more.

A search was made in the low cliff for the missing documents relating to the Benwell estate, and they were easily found; but having lain in a damp cavity impregnated with lime for two years, they fell to pieces as Rayner grasped them, and all that remained in his hand was an undecipherable pulp.

THE GUARD-SHIP
AT THE AIRE

by Amelia B. Edwards

Amelia B. Edwards (1831–1892) is still
remembered for her excellent travel books
Untrodden Peaks and Unfrequented Valleys (1873)
and *A Thousand Miles Up the Nile* (1877), and
for her invaluable work in creating the Egypt
Exploration Fund. She was also a gifted novelist,
and wrote several classic ghost stories (notably
'The Phantom Coach', reprinted many times) and
a large number of other horror, mystery and crime
stories. 'The Guard-Ship of the Aire' originally
appeared in her collection *Miss Carew*.

'A t Christmas time,' said the stranger in the chimney corner, 'folks seem to think themselves privileged to ask other folks to tell stories; but then it is not every man's vocation to tell stories. It comes especially hard on a plain man, who makes no pretence of knowing more than his neighbours. I am a plain man, and it comes hard upon me. I never wrote a page in a magazine, or a paragraph in a newspaper, in my life. How, then, can I be expected to tell a story?'

Having said which, the stranger relapsed into silence, and stared moodily at the fire.

On this particular evening, being Christmas Eve, and rather stormy, with a strong wind and mist blowing up from the sea, our gathering at the 'Tintagel Arms' was somewhat smaller than usual. The stranger had dropped in about two hours before, stabled his horse,

[50]

engaged his bed, and installed himself in the chimney-corner as comfortably as if he had been an old inhabitant of the place, and one of ourselves. Up to this moment, however, he had scarcely opened his lips, or taken his eyes from off the logs that blazed upon the hearth. We looked at each other, and no one seemed prepared with a reply.

'Besides,' added the stranger, as if it were an afterthought, and wholly unanswerable, 'the days of "Arabian Nights" are over. We want facts in these times—facts, gentlemen—facts.'

'And surely there are facts in the life of every individual,' observed the schoolmaster, 'which, if truthfully related, could not fail to impart both instruction and amusement. We prefer facts, sir; when we can get them. Indeed, I dare affirm that within the four walls of this parlour, many a poor seaman has, with his rude narrative of travel and peril, given us more genuine pleasure than could the best author of the best fiction that ever was written.'

(The schoolmaster, I should observe, is the orator of our little society. He has seen better days, is a classical scholar, and has, at times, quite a parliamentary style. We are proud of him up at the 'Tintagel Arms;' and he knows it.)

'Then do you mean to tell me,' said the stranger testily, 'that you impose this tax on every traveller who happens to put up at the house?'

'By no means, sir,' replied the schoolmaster. 'We only desire that every traveller who joins the society in this parlour should conform to the rules by which this society is governed. There is the coffee-room for whoever may prefer it.'

'And those rules?'

'And those rules are, that each person present shall tell a story, sing a song, or read aloud for the amusement of the rest.'

'Perhaps,' suggested the landlord, 'the gentleman would prefer to sing a song?'

'I can't sing,' growled the traveller.

'Some visitors prefer to read a scene from Shakespeare,' hinted the parish clerk.

'Might as well ask me to dance on the tight-rope,' retorted the traveller, fiercely.

A dead silence ensued, in the midst of which the landlady brought in our customary bowl of punch, and the schoolmaster filled the glasses. The stranger tasted his punch, gave a nod of approval, drank the rest at a draught, and coughed uneasily.

'I can't sing,' said he, after several minutes, during which no one had spoken; 'and I can't read plays; and I can't tell stories. But if plain facts will do, I don't mind telling the company about an—an adventure, I suppose I may call it, that happened to myself one Christmas Eve, some two-and-thirty years ago.'

'Sir,' said the schoolmaster, 'we shall be delighted.'

'That's more than I was,' retorted the traveller; 'for it was just the most disagreeable affair that I ever went through in my life.'

With this, he sent up his glass to be refilled; and, continuing to stare steadily into the fire, as if he was reading every word of his narrative from the pictures in the embers, thus began:—

'I am a commercial traveller, and have been on the road these last five-and-thirty years; that is to say, ever since I was twenty years of age. Mine is the Manchester line of business, and I have travelled in most parts of England and Wales, as well as in some parts of France and Germany, in my time. At the period of which I am about to speak, I was in the employment of Warren, Gray, and Company (then a famous Manchester firm of half a century's standing), and my beat lay through the north of France, all about those parts which lie between Calais, Paris, and Cherbourg—a wide district, in the form of a great irregular angle, as you may see by the map.

'Well, as I have said, it was two-and-thirty years ago; or, if you like it better, Anno Domini 1830. William IV had just become King of England, and Louis Philippe had just become King of the French. It was an exciting time. The Continent was all over in a restless, revolutionary state; and France, divided between Orleanists and Bourbons, Napoleonists and Republicans, was in a worse condition of fever and ferment than any of her neighbours.

'I hate politics, gentlemen. I am no politician now, and I was no politician then; but being a young fellow at that time, and better acquainted with the Continent than most Englishmen of my age and station (for people didn't travel abroad then as they do now), I gave myself great airs of superiority, and fancied I knew a vast deal about everything. When I was at home, I bragged about foreign life and manners; gave myself out as a wonderful judge of French wines; and loudly despised our homely English cookery. When I was abroad, on the contrary, I became violently national, boasted of British liberties, British arms, and British commerce, and never failed to avail myself, if possible, of a chance allusion to Wellington, or Nelson, or Waterloo. In short, as I said before, I loved to assume airs of superiority, and that

[52]

disposition by no means helped to make me popular. I was a fool for my pains, of course: and I suffered for it afterwards . . . but I must not run in advance of my story.

'Having been in Paris (which, you will remember, was the farthest point inland of my district) all July and August, I began travelling northwards again in September, according to the commands of my employers. There was no Northern of France Railway at that time, and the traveller who was unprovided with his own vehicle had no choice between the lumbering diligence and the scarcely less lumbering *calèche*. I, however, had my own gig, which I had brought over from England, and a capital brown horse bought at Compiègne; and I well remember how I used to dash past the diligences, clatter into the towns, and endeavour to eclipse all the *commis voyageurs* whom I encountered on the road.

'Having left Paris in September, I calculated on getting through the whole work of my northern district in about ten weeks, and hoped to arrive in England in time for Christmas-day. The change of government, however, had given an unusual impetus to international trade, and I found business accumulating on my hands day by day, to such an extent, that I soon gave up all hope of reaching home before the latter end of January. As Christmas approached, and I continued travelling slowly in a north and north-westerly direction, I began to wonder where my Christmas-day would be spent after all. At one time I thought it would be at Lisieux; at another at Caen; and at last I made sure it would be at Bayeux. I was mistaken, however, in all my conjectures, as you will hear presently.

'On the night of the 23rd of December, I slept at a populous little market town called Crépigny, which lies about eighteen miles inland, and about midway between Caen and Bayeux. On the morning of the 24th I rose unusually early, and started soon after daybreak; for I had a long day's journey before me, and hoped to reach Bayeux that night. I could not, however, take the direction road, being bound first for St Angely, a small coast-town lying near the mouth of the Aire, just opposite Portsmouth on the map. My only chance, therefore, was to make a long day, and, if possible, leave St Angely early enough to allow of my pushing on to Bayeux that afternoon. My route from Crépigny to St Angely lay across a bleak open country thinly planted with orchards, and scattered over here and there with villages, farms, and desolate, half-ruined country-houses. A thick white frost lay like snow upon the landscape. A grey mist brooded over the horizon. A

[53]

bitter wind swept every now and then across the plain, and shook the bare poplars that bordered the road on either side. Sometimes I passed a cart loaded with firewood, or a stout country wench in a warm cloak and *sabôts*; but I had all the road to myself, for the most part; and a very dreary road it was. It grew drearier, too, with every mile. Habitations became fewer and farther between. Every blast of wind brought with it a cloud of fine white dust; and now and then, as I reached the summit of a little eminence, or turned the shoulder of a sand slope, I caught distant glimpses of the sea.

'It was about eleven o'clock in the morning when I neared the end of my first stage, and came in sight of St Angely-sur-Aire; a melancholy riverside town, consisting of a singular irregular street about a mile in length, bordered by houses on one side and quays on the other.

'Having dashed along the quays, and pulled up, with my customary flourish, at the door of the principal inn, I alighted, ordered lunch, sent my horse to the stable, and went out into the town. I soon found, however, that there was no business to be done there. The place was too remote and too primitive; being peopled chiefly by small ship-owners, boat-builders, colliers, fishermen, and sailors. The inhabitants, besides, were not so friendly as in the more frequented towns. I could not help feeling that I was looked upon with disfavour as I walked along the streets. The children hooted after me. The shop-keepers were scarcely civil. It was evident that an Englishman was both an unusual and unwelcome visitor in the lonely little town of St Angely-sur-Aire.

'Going back, in no pleasant frame of mind, to the *Cheval Blanc*, I found my lunch prepared in a corner of the public-room, beside a window overlooking the river. A large wood fire blazed upon the hearth; a coloured print of Napoleon at Marengo hung over the chimney-piece; and at a long oak table in the centre of the sanded floor sat some five or six Frenchmen, drinking sour wine, smoking bad cigars, and playing dominoes.

'They looked up sullenly as I came in, and muttered among themselves. I could not distinguish what the words were; but I felt sure they related in some uncomplimentary manner to myself; and this, as you may well believe, did not help to make me more amiable. In short, being but a hot-tempered, conceited young fellow at the best of times, and being, moreover, on this occasion particularly annoyed by the reception I had met with in the town, I gave myself more airs than ever, found fault with the cutlets, abused the wine, worried the waiter, and made myself, I have no doubt, eminently disagreeable.

' "Call this Bordeaux, indeed!" said I, superciliously. "In England we would not buy it for vinegar. Have you nothing better?"

' "Nothing, monsieur," replied the waiter humbly, "We keep only two qualities, and monsieur ordered the best."

' "In England!" ejaculated one of the domino players—a shabby fellow in a faded uniform, who looked like a custom-house officer— "Bah! What do they know about wine in England? They grow no grapes. They are thankful over there for the washings of our vats."

'Stupid as the insult was, the blood rushed to my face, and tingled in my fingers. I longed to contradict the man; but it was of no use getting into a broil, if a little prudence would avert it. So I held my tongue, and affected not to hear. His companions laughed, and presently he spoke again.

' "What can you expect," pursued he, "in a country where the land is all swamp, and the air all fog, and every man keeps a shop? Monsieur there, you see, doesn't know wine from vinegar. How should he? The English drink nothing but beer and tea!"

'I could bear it no longer.

' "Stop there, friend," said I, boiling over with rage, but endeavouring to speak calmly. "It's a pity you should allow yourself to express opinions upon a subject of which you know nothing."

' "Did monsieur speak?"

' "I did speak. I said you expressed opinions on a subject of which you know nothing."

' "It appears to me, monsieur, that I have a right to express what opinions I please."

' "Not when they are offensive to others."

' "Pardon, monsieur—how could I tell that my opinions would offend? If I said that England was all swamp and fog, what then? Monsieur did not make the climate of his native country. If I said . . ."

' "You know nothing about either our customs or our climate," I interrupted, angrily.

' "And if I said that the English were a nation of shopkeepers," pursued he, "have I not the authority of the great Napoleon for that statement? Is not monsieur himself a commercial traveller?"

'The cool impertinence of the fellow, and the undisguised amusement of his friends, enraged me beyond all the bounds of prudence.

' "Shopkeepers or not," I retorted, "we have beaten the French too often to care for a nickname! Were they shopkeepers who routed you at Trafalgar? Were they shopkeepers before whom your Old Guard turned and fled at Waterloo? Were they—"

'My words were drowned in a torrent of imprecations. Furious and gesticulating, every Frenchman was instantly on his feet; whilst I, expecting nothing less than an immediate attack, snatched up a chair, and prepared for a desperate defence. At this moment, however, the landlord, alarmed by the noise, rushed in and placed himself between us.

' "Peace! peace, I say, gentlemen!" cried he. "I allow no quarrelling here. What! six against one? I am ashamed of you!"

' "Death of my life! shall we be insulted by a beggarly Englishman?" stormed one.

' "Or suffer the honour of France to be called in question?" shouted another.

' "Or the memory of our *grande armée* to be reviled?" added a third.

' "Nonsense—nonsense!" expostulated the landlord. "I'll bet a *louis d'or* that monsieur meant nothing of the kind. He is an Englishman; you are Frenchmen. You don't understand each other—*voilà tout!* Remember the duties of hospitality, gentlemen, and recollect that monsieur is a stranger. I'll be sworn that monsieur was not the first to begin."

' "*Parbleu!* I was the first to begin—I confess it," said the customs officer, good-temperedly. "I put monsieur out by abusing his country."

' "And I confess that I lost my temper too easily," replied I; "and said much that I should be ashamed to repeat."

' "Suppose, messieurs, you make your peace over another bottle of wine," suggested the landlord, rubbing his hands.

' "With all my heart," said I, "if these gentlemen will allow me to call for one!"

'The Frenchmen laughed, stroked their moustachios, shook hands, and forgot their anger as readily as if nothing had happened—all except one, a bronzed, grey-bearded man in a blue blouse and gaiters, who pulled his cap angrily over his eyes, muttered something about *maudit Anglais*, and strode out of the room.

' "*Peste!* that old François is as savage as a bear," said one of my late opponents.

' "He is an old soldier," observed another, apologetically. "He served under Napoleon, and he hates the English."

' "I am really sorry if I have hurt the feelings of a brave man," said I. 'Can we not induce him to come back and chink glasses with us?"

' "No—no; let him alone. He is a savage-tempered fellow, and best left to himself. Your health, monsieur, and a pleasant journey!"

'And with this, the good-natured *garçons* drew round the fire, pulled out their cigars, smacked their lips over their wine, and chatted away as pleasantly as if we had made each other's acquaintance under the most agreeable auspices in the world. When the first bottle was emptied, I called for another, and by the time we had done justice to the second, it was nearly three o'clock in the afternoon, and full time for me to begin my journey.

' "If monsieur is going to Crépigny," said a young farmer, whom his companions called Adolphe, "I will gladly take a seat in his chaise as far as the cross-roads."

' "Unfortunately, I came from Crépigny this morning, and am now bound for Bayeux," I replied.

' "For Bayeux? *Peste!* then monsieur has a good long road before him."

' "How far do you call it? I did not think it was more than three leagues."

' "Three leagues?—nearer five."

'Five French leagues, and only another hour of daylight before me! That was more than I had bargained for.

' "Monsieur had better let his horse go back to the stable, and stay with us to-night at the *Cheval Blanc*," suggested the landlord, obsequiously.

'I shook my head.

' "No, no," I said. "That will never do. I want to spend my Christmas-day at Bayeux to-morrow. Five leagues, you say?"

' "Full five by the road," answered the custom-house officer. "But there is a shorter way, if monsieur can only find it."

' "You would not send monsieur by the river?" interposed the landlord.

' "Why not? It will save him a good league."

' "Mon Dieu, it is not safe for a stranger—especially after dusk!"

' "Safe, Maître Pierre! Why it's as safe as the high road when the tide is out," replied the other, contemptuously. "Listen, monsieur. About five kilometres from St Angely, the Aire empties itself into the sea. It is but a narrow river, as you see it here—narrow and deep; but out there it gets wide and shallow; wider than the Seine at Paris. Eh *bien*, monsieur, about four kilometres from hence, and about one before you reach the mouth of the Aire, you come to a place called *L'Eau Perdu*. It is just an arm of the river—a reach in fact, which at high water feeds a small stream, over which you would have to cross by the bridge at Creuilly if you went round by the high road; but which, if you take the way by the coast, you can drive across as easily as possible when it is low tide. There is no danger in the world, monsieur may take my word for it; and it saves a *détour* of at least a league."

' "Monsieur had much better not attempt it," said mine host of the *Cheval Blanc*.

' "Nay, I am not afraid of attempting it, if I can but find my way," replied I. "My horse is no longer fresh, and a league is a league."

' "Monsieur cannot fail to go rightly," said the custom-house officer. "You drive straight forward, and take the first road to the left past the church. Follow that road till you come to a lane leading to a little inn called the *Bon Christophe*, and then ask any one to show you the best place to drive over. The house stands just on the brink of *L'Eau Perdu*, and in sight of the mouth of the Aire. If it is dusk, there is always a light burning at the revenue station on the opposite side."

' "A thousand thanks," said I, jumping into my chaise, and gathering up the reins. "You are quite sure the tide will be out?"

' "The tide is out now," replied the custom-house officer, taking out his watch, "and will not turn till ten minutes past four o'clock. If it had turned already, monsieur would still be in good time, for the reach does not fill till nearly high tide. Monsieur will have to drive over a quarter of a mile of muddy bottom. He will get his wheels dirty— *voilà tout!*"

' "I'm not afraid of that misfortune," said I, laughing. "Adieu, gentlemen. May we soon meet again to pledge our goodwill in another bottle of Maître Pierre's Bordeaux!"

'With this and a profusion of bows, adieux, and good wishes, we parted; I driving off at a rapid pace that brought the inhabitants of St Angely-sur-Aire to their windows as I rattled past, and my friends of the *Cheval Blanc* crowding round the threshold of that decent little hostelry, to do honour to my departure.

'I found my way easily enough past the church, and down the road to the left, along which I had been directed. It was not by any means a pleasant drive. The afternoon was dull and raw; the road was rough; the grey sea-mist thickened in the distance, and the wind was piercingly cold. The distance, too, proved greater than I had expected, and I was obliged, by the bad condition of the road, to drive very slowly. In the meantime the mist continued to thicken and the light to fade, so that by the time I reached the lane it was almost dusk. Such a lane as it was, too!—rough as a ploughed field and wet as a pond, with stones over which the horse stumbled, and ruts into which the wheels sank at every yard. Bad as the road had been, it was nothing to this. However, it was too late to turn back, so I dismounted, led my horse, and endeavoured to make the best of my position. The lane terminated presently in a broad space of waste ground, in the midst of which I saw the dark outline of a house and the glimmer of a lighted casement. Concluding that this must be the *auberge* of the good Christopher, I at once turned my horse's head in that direction, and led him, as well as I could, over the uneven ground that lay between. As I drew near the house I heard voices; but it was not till I came within a yard or two of the gate on which they were leaning that I could distinguish the forms of the two men who were speaking.

' "Holà!" said I, "is this the *auberge*, of the *Bon Christophe?*"

' "That it is, monsieur, and I am the landlord, at monsieur's service," replied the shorter of the two, stepping forward and holding the gate open. "Monsieur will please to enter? We have excellent beds—a good stable—every accommodation for travellers!"

' "Thanks; but I only want to be directed to the best place for driving over the reach here. The tide is out, I believe?"

' "Yes, monsieur, the tide is out—that is to say, it is just about to turn," replied the landlord in a tone of disappointment.

' "And I can cross with safety?"

'The landlord hesitated.

' "Because, if not," I added, suspecting that he would keep me if he could, "I shall drive back at once to St Angely-sur-Aire, and sleep at the *Cheval Blanc.*"

' "The reach is quite passable," said the taller man, abruptly.

' "Oh, yes—it is passable," admitted the landlord. "Monsieur has but to drive straight for the light at the revenue-station. He cannot go wrong."

' "Will you be so obliging, then, as to send some one just to put me in the right way?"

' "Certainly, monsieur; I will call . . ."

' "No need to call any one," interposed the other. "I am going by the beach. Follow me. Good night, friend Collet."

' "Good night, François," replied the landlord, somewhat sulkily. "Be sure you explain to monsieur the difference between the two lights."

' "Bah! do you take me for a fool?"

'Saying which, my guide pushed hastily forward, and I followed. It was too dark to see his features distinctly; but something in his height, in his gait, in the tone of his voice, struck me as not wholly unfamiliar. Then his name—the landlord called him François. Was not François the name of the old soldier whom I saw three hours since in the public room of the *Cheval Blanc?* It was quite possible that he might be the same man. Nay, the more I thought of it, the more I felt sure of his identity. And what if he were the same? Was it worth while to allude to the *fracas* of the afternoon? Surely not. He did not seem to have recognized me, and it might only lead to further disagreement. I deemed it better, on the whole, to say nothing. These thoughts flashed through my mind in less time than it takes to relate them. Just as I came to my decision, I found we were descending a sandy slope, beyond which lay what seemed to be a wide tract of mud and shingle. Far away across this waste, showing dimly through the mist, and distant, apparently, about half a mile from each other, gleamed two lights, one red and one white. My guide halted suddenly.

' "*Voilà,*" said he. "There are the two beacons—one on board the guard-ship at the mouth of the Aire; the other at the revenue-station across the reach. Do you see both?"

' "Yes, I see both plainly."

' "Then drive straight for the red one."

' "Thanks. Is the bottom tolerably level? Need I lead the horse?"

' "No; it is all smooth. Nothing but mud and sand."

' "Thanks again, *mon ami.* Good night."

'He made no answer, but turned and strode away, heavily and rapidly, into the darkness.

'I jumped into the chaise, wrapped a rug about my knees, lit a cigar, fixed my eyes steadily on the red light, and drove forward. In another moment, the wheels went off the shingly slope, and we were going smoothly and noiselessly along the bed of the reach. It was not by any means bad driving. The bottom, though somewhat yielding on the surface, was firm enough an inch below it; and the little pools through which we splashed now and then, or the shells, which grated occasionally under the wheels, offered no obstacle to our progress.

'The air, too, was fresh and salt, with a pleasant perfume of the sea; and there was something exciting after all, in driving out towards that red light, and remembering that in a few hours more it would be deep water in the channel between.

'All at once my horse neighed, and stood still. I spoke to him, stroked him gently with the whip, and succeeded in urging him forward some few yards farther, when he stopped again, more suddenly than before. It happened that we were at that moment in the midst of a pool deeper and more extensive than any through which I had yet driven; but for this I accounted by calculating that I had already traversed close upon half the distance, and that towards the mid-channel the deposit of water would naturally be somewhat greater. It was this, probably, that alarmed the horse. Whatever it was, however, I could not sit there for his pleasure; and so, finding persuasion useless, I administered three or four sharp cuts of the whip, which had the effect of making him start on again, though with evident reluctance.

'It was strange; but driving forward thus and steering ever for the red light ahead, I observed that the isolated pools had within the last few minutes become merged into one shallow sheet of water, extending under the wheels in every direction. In spite of myself, I grew nervous. Knowing that my best course must be to get out of the mid-channel as quickly as possible, I whipped the horse forward all the faster. Still the bottom seemed to decline lower and lower, and the water to rise higher at every yard. I looked eagerly round. The spot whence I had started was no longer distinguishable; but the red light, now larger and nearer than ever, glowed encouragingly through the mist. It was too late to turn back. Cost what it might, I *must* go forward!

'At this moment my horse flung himself back upon his haunches, planted his fore-legs firmly in the sand, and refused to stir a step farther. Was this fear, or instinct? I dared not ask myself the question. I dared not avow the terrible suspicion that had been gaining upon me during the last few minutes. I gathered up the reins, rose in my seat, and lashed him as I had never lashed him yet since the day I bought him. He resisted, snorted, then dashed on desperately, though the pool by this time rose within an inch of his knees.

'And now, quite suddenly, I became aware that there was a ripple on the surface of the water. From that moment I gave myself up for lost. From that moment I knew that the tide was upon me!

'I am amazed to this hour when I remember how calmly I took it. Every nerve, every thought, every feeling seemed bound up in the one aim of self-preservation. My only hope lay in the red light; now, apparently, some four hundred yards distant. And still the water rose higher, and the ripple grew stronger, till I felt the chaise undulate, and knew that my poor brute could not keep his legs two minutes longer.

[61]

My course was taken upon the instant. I knew that both he and I must now swim for our lives; so I took out my pocket-knife, deliberately pulled off my boots, coat, and waistcoat, jumped into the water, cut the horse free, and struck out in the direction of the beacon.

'I was but a poor swimmer at that time, and the current was setting dead against me. Still I kept my head to the red light, made what progress I could, and, though I felt the tide growing stronger every moment, made my mind up to fight it out doggedly to the last. A long time seemed to go by thus; I could not tell how long, for my thoughts, somehow, became confused. Then the water roared about my ears, and the red light came and went before my eyes, and I felt, with a despair beyond all words, that my strength was going! Then came a terrible moment when the beacon disappeared, as if swallowed up suddenly in the darkness—then something huge, black, shapeless, loomed up all at once before me, like a rock, and, fainting as I was, I knew it was a ship, and felt that in another moment I should be sucked under her bows! I shall never forget the horror of the next three or four seconds. I shall never forget how I tried to shout for help—how my hands glided over the wet hull—how, summoning all my strength for a last effort, I uttered one despairing shriek, felt the waves close over my head, and knew that I was going to the bottom!

'When I recovered consciousness, I found myself lying before a stove in a warm cabin, with a bottle of brandy to my lips, and a crowd of kind faces round me. I soon learnt that I was on board the guard-ship at the mouth of the Aire, a good two miles from land on any side. The sailor on watch had heard my drowning cry, jumped overboard as easily as a Newfoundland dog, and saved me as I rose the second time. I was very ill and exhausted, as you may suppose, and thankful to lie quietly in a hammock all that night, and a greater part of the Christmas-day that followed; and I can tell you that I shared those poor sailors' onion soup and salt beef with more thankfulness that I ever felt at the finest Christmas dinner to which it was my lot to be invited.'

'And what about the soldier, sir?' asked the schoolmaster, after the first excitement had subsided, and the stranger had relapsed into silence.

'Ay—what about that black villain François?' echoed the parish clerk.

'I don't know,' replied the stranger, abruptly. 'I never cared to ask. Either he knew that he was sending me to my death, or he mistook the lights. God forbid that I should accuse an innocent man of wilful murder. Error or no error, however, he cost me a good chaise and a valuable horse, neither of which did I ever see or hear of again. And now, gentlemen, I'll thank you for another glass of punch.'

HORROR:
A TRUE TALE

[Anonymous]

Many nineteenth-century stories were published
anonymously in magazines, and the authors'
identities were usually only revealed if they were
later reprinted in separate collections (as occurred
with Amelia B. Edwards, Mary Braddon, Mrs J.H.
Riddell, and their contemporaries). Sadly the
identity of the writer of 'Horror: A True Tale' was
never resolved in this way. This anonymous piece
was included by Julian Hawthorne in his selection
of the best Classic American Mystery and
Detective Stories, in The Lock and Key Library
(New York, 1909).

I was but nineteen years of age when the incident occurred which
has thrown a shadow over my life; and, ah me! how many and
many a weary year has dragged by since then! Young, happy,
and beloved I was in those long-departed days. They said that I was
beautiful. The mirror now reflects a haggard old woman, with ashen
lips and face of deadly pallor. But do not fancy that you are listening to
a mere puling lament. It is not the flight of years that has brought me
to be this wreck of my former self: had it been so I could have borne
the loss cheerfully, patiently, as the common lot of all; but it was no
natural progress of decay which has robbed me of bloom, of youth, of
the hopes and joys that belong to youth, snapped the link that bound
my heart to another's, and doomed me to a lone old age. I try to be
patient, but my cross has been heavy, and my heart is empty and

weary, and I long for the death that comes so slowly to those who pray to die.

I will try and relate, exactly as it happened, the event which blighted my life. Though it occurred many years ago, there is no fear that I should have forgotten any of the minutest circumstances: they were stamped on my brain too clearly and burningly, like the brand of a red-hot iron. I see them written in the wrinkles of my brow, in the dead whiteness of my hair, which was a glossy brown once, and has known no gradual change from dark to grey, from grey to white, as with those happy ones who were the companions of my girlhood, and whose honoured age is soothed by the love of children and grand-children. But I must not envy them. I only meant to say that the difficulty of my task has no connection with want of memory—I remember but too well. But as I take my pen my hand trembles, my head swims, the old rushing faintness and Horror comes over me again, and the well-remembered fear is upon me. Yet I will go on.

This, briefly, is my story: I was a great heiress, I believe, though I cared little for the fact; but so it was. My father had great possessions, and no son to inherit after him. His three daughters, of whom I was the youngest, were to share the broad acres among them. I have said, and truly, that I cared little for the circumstance; and, indeed, I was so rich then in health and youth and love that I felt myself quite indifferent to all else. The possession of all the treasures of earth could never have made up for what I then had—and lost, as I am about to relate. Of course, we girls knew that we were heiresses, but I do not think Lucy and Minnie were any the prouder or the happier on that account. I know I was not. Reginald did not court me for my money. Of *that* I felt assured. He proved it, Heaven be praised! when he shrank from my side after the change. Yes, in all my lonely age, I can still be thankful that he did not keep his word, as some would have done—did not clasp at the altar a hand he had learned to loathe and shudder at, because it was full of gold—much gold! At least he spared me that. And I know that I was loved, and the knowledge has kept me from going mad through many a weary day and restless night, when my hot eyeballs had not a tear to shed, and even to weep was a luxury denied me.

Our house was an old Tudor mansion. My father was very particular in keeping the smallest peculiarities of his home unaltered. Thus the many peaks and gables, the numerous turrets, and the mullioned windows with their quaint lozenge panes set in lead, remained very nearly as they had been three centuries back. Over and above the quaint melancholy of our dwelling, with the deep woods of its park and the sullen waters of the mere, our neighbourhood was thinly peopled and primitive, and the people round us were ignorant, and tenacious of ancient ideas and traditions. Thus it was a superstitious atmosphere that we children were reared in, and we heard, from our infancy, countless tales of horror, some mere fables doubtless, others legends of dark deeds of the olden time, exaggerated by credulity and the love of the marvellous. Our mother had died when we were young, and our other parent being, though a kind father, much absorbed in affairs of various kinds, as an active magistrate and landlord, there was no one to check the unwholesome stream of tradition with which our plastic minds were inundated in the company of nurses and servants. As years went on, however, the old ghostly tales partially lost their effects, and our undisciplined minds were turned more towards balls, dress, and partners, and other matters airy and trivial, more welcome to our riper age. It was at a county assembly that Reginald and I first met—met and loved. Yes, I am sure that he loved me with all his heart. It was not as deep a heart as some, I have thought in my grief and anger; but I never doubted its truth and honesty. Reginald's father and mine approved of our growing attachment; and as for myself, I know I was so happy then, that I look back upon those fleeting moments as on some delicious dream. I now come to the change. I have lingered on my childish reminiscences, my bright and happy youth, and now I must tell the rest—the blight and the sorrow.

It was Christmas, always a joyful and a hospitable time in the country, especially in such an old hall as our home, where quaint customs and frolics were much clung to, as part and parcel of the very dwelling itself. The hall was full of guests—so full, indeed, that there was great difficulty in providing sleeping accommodation for all. Several narrow and dark chambers in the turrets—mere pigeon-holes, as we irreverently called what had been thought good enough for the stately gentlemen of Elizabeth's reign—were now allotted to bachelor visitors, after having been empty for a century. All the spare rooms in the body and wings of the hall were occupied, of course; and the servants who had been brought down were lodged at the farm and at the keeper's, so great was the demand for space. At last the unexpected arrival of an elderly relative, who had been asked months before, but scarcely expected, caused great commotion. My aunts went about wringing their hands distractedly. Lady Speldhurst was a personage of some consequence; she was a distant cousin, and had been for years on cool terms with us all, on account of some fancied affront or slight when she had paid her *last* visit, about the time of my christening. She was seventy years old; she was infirm, rich, and testy; moreover, she was my godmother, though I had forgotten the fact; but it seems that though I had formed no expectations of a legacy in my favour, my aunts had done so for me. Aunt Margaret was especially eloquent on the subject. 'There isn't a room left,' she said; 'was ever anything so unfortunate! We cannot put Lady Speldhurst into the turrets, and yet where *is* she to sleep? And Rosa's godmother, too! Poor, dear child, how dreadful! After all these years of estrangement, and with a hundred thousand in the funds, and no comfortable, warm room at her own unlimited disposal—and Christmas, of all times in the year!' What *was* to be done? My aunts could not resign their own chambers to Lady Speldhurst, because they had already given them up to some of the married guests. My father was the most hospitable of men, but he was rheumatic, gouty, and methodical. His sisters-in-law dared not propose to shift his quarters; and, indeed, he would have far sooner dined on prison fare than have been translated to a strange bed. The matter ended in my giving up my room. I had a strange reluctance to making the offer, which surprised myself. Was it a boding of evil to come? I cannot say. We are strangely and wonderfully made. It *may* have been. At any rate, I do not think it was any selfish unwillingness to make an old and infirm lady comfortable by a trifling sacrifice. I was perfectly healthy and strong. The weather was not cold for the time of the year. It was a dark, moist Yule—not a snowy one, though snow brooded overhead in the darkling clouds. I *did* make the offer, which became me, I said with a laugh, as the youngest. My sisters laughed too, and made a jest of my evident wish to propitiate my godmother. 'She is a fairy godmother, Rosa,' said Minnie; 'and you know she was affronted at your christening, and went away muttering vengeance. Here she is coming back to see you; I hope she brings golden gifts with her.'

I thought little of Lady Speldhurst and her possible golden gifts. I cared nothing for the wonderful fortune in the funds that my aunts whispered and nodded about so mysteriously. But since then I have wondered whether, had I then showed myself peevish or obstinate— had I refused to give up my room for the expected kinswoman—it would not have altered the whole of my life? But then Lucy or Minnie would have offered in my stead, and been sacrificed—what do I say?

—better that the blow should have fallen as it did than on those dear ones.

The chamber to which I removed was a dim little triangular room in the western wing, and was only to be reached by traversing the picture-gallery, or by mounting a little flight of stone stairs which led directly upward from the low-browed arch of a door that opened into the garden. There was one more room on the same landing-place, and this was a mere receptacle for broken furniture, shattered toys, and all the lumber that *will* accumulate in a country-house. The room I was to inhabit for a few nights was a tapestry-hung apartment, with faded green curtains of some costly stuff, contrasting oddly with a new carpet and the bright, fresh hangings of the bed, which had been hurriedly erected. The furniture was half old, half new; and on the dressing-table stood a very quaint oval mirror, in a frame of black wood— unpolished ebony, I think. I can remember the very pattern of the carpet, the number of chairs, the situation of the bed, the figures on the tapestry. Nay, I can recollect not only the colour of the dress I wore on that fated evening, but the arrangement of every scrap of lace and ribbon, of every flower, every jewel, with a memory but too perfect.

Scarcely had my maid finished spreading out my various articles of attire for the evening (when there was to be a great dinner-party) when the rumble of a carriage announced that Lady Speldhurst had arrived. The short winter's day drew to a close, and a large number of guests were gathered together in the ample drawing-room, around the blaze of the wood-fire, after dinner. My father, I recollect, was not with us at first. There were some squires of the old, hard-riding, hard-drinking stamp still lingering over their port in the dining-room, and the host, of course, could not leave them. But the ladies and all the younger gentlemen—both those who slept under our roof, and those who would have a dozen miles of fog and mire to encounter on their road home—were all together. Need I say that Reginald was there? He sat near me—my accepted lover, my plighted future husband. We were to be married in the spring. My sisters were not far off; they, too, had found eyes that sparkled and softened in meeting theirs, had found hearts that beat responsive to their own. And, in their cases, no rude frost nipped the blossom ere it became the fruit; there was no canker in their flowerets of young hope, no cloud in their sky. Innocent and loving, they were beloved by men worthy of their esteem.

The room—a large and lofty one, with an arched roof—had somewhat of a sombre character, from being wainscoted and ceiled with polished black oak of a great age. There were mirrors, and there were pictures on the walls, and handsome furniture, and marble chimney-pieces, and a gay Tournay carpet; but these merely appeared as bright spots on the dark background of the Elizabethan woodwork. Many lights were burning, but the blackness of the walls and roof seemed absolutely to swallow up their rays, like the mouth of a cavern. A hundred candles could not have given that apartment the cheerful lightness of a modern drawing-room. But the gloomy richness of the panels matched well with the ruddy gleam from the enormous wood-fire, in which, crackling and glowing, now lay the mighty Yule log. Quite a blood-red lustre poured forth from the fire, and quivered on the walls and the groined roof. We had gathered round the vast antique hearth in a wide circle. The quivering light of the fire and candles fell upon us all, but not equally, for some were in shadow. I remember still how tall and manly and handsome Reginald looked that night, taller by the head than any there, and full of high spirits and gaiety. I, too, was in the highest spirits; never had my bosom felt lighter, and I believe it was my mirth that gradually gained the rest, for I recollect what a blithe, joyous company we seemed. All save one. Lady Speldhurst, dressed in grey silk and wearing a quaint head-dress, sat in her armchair, facing the fire, very silent, with her hands and her sharp chin propped on a sort of ivory-handled crutch that she walked with (for she was lame), peering at me with half-shut eyes. She was a little, spare old woman, with very keen, delicate features of the French type. Her grey silk dress, her spotless lace, old-fashioned jewels, and prim neatness of array, were well suited to the intelligence of her face, with its thin lips, and eyes of a piercing black, undimmed by age. Those eyes made me uncomfortable, in spite of my gaiety, as they followed my every movement with curious scrutiny. Still I was very merry and gay; my sisters even wondered at my ever-ready mirth, which was almost wild in its excess. I have heard since then of the Scottish belief that those doomed to some great calamity become *fey*, and are never so disposed for merriment and laughter as just before the blow falls. If ever mortal was *fey*, then I was so on that evening. Still, though I strove to shake it off, the pertinacious observation of old Lady Speldhurst's eyes *did* make an impression on me of a vaguely disagreeable nature. Others, too, noticed her scrutiny of me, but set it down as a mere eccentricity of a person always reputed whimsical, to say the least of it.

However, this disagreeable sensation lasted but a few moments. After a short pause my aunt took her part in the conversation, and we found ourselves listening to a weird legend, which the old lady told exceedingly well. One tale led to another. Everyone was called on in turn to contribute to the public entertainment, and story after story, always relating to demonology and witchcraft, succeeded. It was Christmas, the season for such tales; and the old room, with its dusky walls and pictures, and vaulted roof, drinking up the light so greedily, seemed just fitted to give effect to such legendary lore. The huge logs crackled and burned with glowing warmth; the blood-red glare of the Yule log flashed on the faces of the listeners and narrator, on the portraits, and the holly wreathed about their frames, and the upright old dame, in her antiquated dress and trinkets, like one of the originals of the pictures, stepped from the canvas to join our circle. It threw a shimmering lustre of an ominously ruddy hue upon the oaken panels. No wonder that the ghost and goblin stories had a new zest. No wonder that the blood of the more timid grew chill and curdled, that their flesh crept, that their hearts beat irregularly, and the girls peeped fearfully over their shoulders, and huddled close together like frightened sheep, and half fancied they beheld some impish and malignant face gibbering at them from the darkling corners of the old room. By degrees my high spirits died out, and I felt the childish tremors, long latent, long forgotten, coming over me. I followed each story with painful interest; I did not ask myself if I believed the dismal tales. I listened, and fear grew upon me—the blind, irrational fear of our nursery days. I am sure most of the other ladies present, young or middle-aged, were affected by the circumstances under which these traditions were heard, no less than by the wild and fantastic character of them. But with them the impression would die out next morning, when the bright sun should shine on the frosted boughs, and the rime on the grass, and the scarlet berries and green spikelets of the holly; and with me—but, ah! what was to happen ere another day dawn? Before we had made an end of this talk my father and the other squires came in, and we ceased our ghost stories, ashamed to speak of such matters before these new-comers—hard-headed, unimaginative men, who had no sympathy with idle legends. There was now a stir and bustle.

Servants were handing round tea and coffee, and other refreshments. Then there was a little music and singing. I sang a duet with Reginald, who had a fine voice and good musical skill. I remember that my singing was much praised, and indeed I was surprised at the power and pathos of my own voice, doubtless due to my excited nerves and mind. Then I heard someone say to another that I was by far the cleverest of the Squire's daughters, as well as the prettiest. It did not make me vain. I had no rivalry with Lucy and Minnie. But Reginald whispered some soft, fond words in my ear a little before he mounted his horse to set off homeward, which *did* make me happy and proud. And to think that the next time we met—but I forgave him long ago. Poor Reginald! And now shawls and cloaks were in request, and carriages rolled up to the porch, and the guests gradually departed. At last no one was left but those visitors staying in the house. Then my father, who had been called out to speak with the bailiff of the estate, came back with a look of annoyance on his face.

'A strange story I have just been told,' said he; 'here has been my bailiff to inform me of the loss of four of the choicest ewes out of that little flock of Southdowns I set such store by, and which arrived in the north but two months since. And the poor creatures have been destroyed in so strange a manner, for their carcasses are horribly mangled.'

Most of us uttered some expression of pity or surprise, and some suggested that a vicious dog was probably the culprit.

'It would seem so,' said my father; 'it certainly seems the work of a dog; and yet all the men agree that no dog of such habits exists near us, where, indeed, dogs are scarce, excepting the shepherds' collies and the sporting dogs secured in yards. Yet the sheep are gnawed and bitten, for they show the marks of teeth. Something had done this, and has torn their bodies wolfishly; but apparently it has been only to suck the blood, for little or no flesh is gone.'

'How strange!' cried several voices. Then some of the gentlemen remembered to have heard of cases when dogs addicted to sheep-killing had destroyed whole flocks, as if in sheer wantonness, scarcely deigning to taste a morsel of each slain wether.

My father shook his head. 'I have heard of such cases, too,' he said; 'but in this instance I am tempted to think the malice of some unknown enemy has been at work. The teeth of a dog have been busy, no doubt, but the poor sheep have been mutilated in a fantastic manner, as strange as horrible; their hearts, in especial, have been torn out, and left at some paces off, half-gnawed. Also, the men persist that they found the print of a naked human foot in the soft mud of the ditch, and near it—this.' And he held up what seemed a broken link of a rusted iron chain.

Many were the ejaculations of wonder and alarm, and many and shrewd the conjectures, but none seemed exactly to suit the bearings of the case. And when my father went on to say that two lambs of the same valuable breed had perished in the same singular manner three days previously, and that they also were found mangled and gore-stained, the amazement reached a higher pitch. Old Lady Speldhurst listened with calm, intelligent attention, but joined in none of our exclamations. At length she said to my father, 'Try and recollect— have you no enemy among your neighbours?' My father started, and knit his brows. 'Not one that I know of,' he replied; and indeed he was a popular man and a kind landlord. 'The more lucky you,' said the old dame, with one of her grim smiles. It was now late, and we retired to rest before long. One by one the guests dropped off. I was the member of the family selected to escort old Lady Speldhurst to her room—the room I had vacated in her favour. I did not much like the office. I felt a remarkable repugnance to my godmother, but my worthy aunts insisted so much that I should ingratiate myself with one who had so much to leave that I could not but comply. The visitor hobbled up the broad oaken stairs actively enough, propped on my arm and her ivory crutch. The room never had looked more genial and pretty, with its brisk fire, modern furniture, and the gay French paper on the walls. 'A nice room, my dear, and I ought to be much obliged to you for it, since my maid tells me it is yours,' said her ladyship; 'but I am pretty sure you repent your generosity to me, after all those ghost stories, and tremble to think of a strange bed and chamber, eh?' I made some commonplace reply. The old lady arched her eyebrows. 'Where have they put you, child?' she asked; 'in some cock-loft of the turrets, eh? or in a lumber-room—a regular ghost-trap? I can hear your heart beating with fear this moment. You are not fit to be alone.' I tried to call up my pride, and laugh off the accusation against my courage, all the more, perhaps, because I felt its truth. 'Do you want anything more that I can get you, Lady Speldhurst?' I asked, trying to feign a yawn of sleepiness. The old dame's keen eyes were upon me. 'I rather like you, my dear,' she said, 'and I liked your mamma well enough before she treated me so shamefully about the christening dinner. Now, I know you are frightened and fearful, and if an owl should but flap your window to-night, it might drive you into fits. There is a nice little sofa-bed in this dressing closet—call your maid to arrange it for you, and you can sleep there snugly, under the old witch's protection, and then no goblin dare harm you, and nobody will be a bit the wiser, or quiz you for being afraid.' How little I knew what hung in the balance of my refusal or acceptance of that trivial proffer! Had the veil of the future been lifted for one instant! but that veil is impenetrable to our gaze.

I left her door. As I crossed the landing a bright gleam came from another room, whose door was left ajar; it (the light) fell like a bar of golden sheen across my path. As I approached the door opened and my sister Lucy, who had been watching for me, came out. She was already in a white cashmere wrapper, over which her loosened hair hung darkly and heavily, like tangles of silk. 'Rosa, love,' she whispered, 'Minnie and I can't bear the idea of your sleeping out there, all alone, in that solitary room—the very room, too, Nurse Sherrard used to talk about! So, as you know Minnie has given up her room, and come to sleep in mine, still we should so wish you to stop with us tonight at any rate, and I could make up a bed on the sofa for myself or you—and—' I stopped Lucy's mouth with a kiss. I declined her offer. I would not listen to it. In fact, my pride was up in arms, and I felt I would rather pass the night in the churchyard itself than accept a proposal dictated, I felt sure, by the notion that my nerves were shaken by the ghostly lore we had been raking up, that I was a weak, superstitious creature, unable to pass a night in a strange chamber. So I would not listen to Lucy, but kissed her, bade her good-night, and went on my way laughing, to show my light heart. Yet, as I looked back in the dark corridor, and saw the friendly door still ajar, the yellow bar of light still crossing from wall to wall, the sweet, kind face still peering after me from amidst its clustering curls, I felt a thrill of sympathy, a wish to return, a yearning after human love and companionship. False shame was strongest, and conquered. I waved a gay adieu. I turned the corner, and peeping over my shoulder, I saw the door close; the bar of yellow light was there no longer in the darkness of the passage. I thought at that instant that I heard a heavy sigh. I looked sharply round. No one was there. No door was open, yet I fancied, and fancied with a wonderful vividness, that I did hear an actual sigh breathed not far off, and plainly distinguishable from the groan of the sycamore branches as the wind tossed them to and fro in the outer blackness. If ever a mortal's good angel had cause to sigh for sorrow, not sin, mine had cause to mourn that night. But imagination plays us strange tricks and my nervous system was not over-composed or very fitted for judicial analysis. I had to go through the picture-gallery. I had never entered this apartment by candle-light before and I was struck by the gloomy array of the tall portraits, gazing moodily from the canvas on the lozenge-paned or painted windows, which rattled to the blast as it swept howling by. Many of the faces looked stern, and very different from their daylight expression. In others a furtive, flickering smile seemed to mock me as my candle illumined them; and in all, the eyes, as usual with artistic portraits, seemed to follow my motions with a scrutiny and an interest the more marked for the apathetic immovability of the other features. I felt ill at ease under this stony gaze, though conscious how absurd were my apprehensions; and I called up a smile and an air of mirth, more as if acting a part under the eyes of human beings than of their mere shadows on the wall. I even laughed as I confronted them. No echo had my short-lived laughter but from the hollow armour and arching roof, and I continued on my way in silence.

By a sudden and not uncommon revulsion of feeling I shook off my aimless terrors, blushed at my weakness, and sought my chamber only too glad that I had been the only witness of my late tremors. As I entered my chamber I thought I heard something stir in the neglected lumber-room, which was the only neighbouring apartment. But I was determined to have no more panics, and resolutely shut my eyes to this slight and transient noise, which had nothing unnatural in it; for surely, between rats and wind, an old manor-house on a stormy night needs no sprites to disturb it. So I entered my room, and rang for my maid. As I did so I looked around me, and a most unaccountable repugnance to my temporary abode came over me, in spite of my efforts. It was no more to be shaken off than a chill is to be shaken off when we enter some damp cave. And, rely upon it, the feeling of dislike and apprehension with which we regard, at first sight, certain places and people, was not implanted in us without some wholesome purpose. I grant it is irrational—mere animal instinct—but is not instinct God's gift, and is it for us to despise it? It is by instinct that children know their friends from their enemies—that they distinguish with such unerring accuracy between those who like them and those who only flatter and hate them. Dogs do the same; they will fawn on one person, they slink snarling from another. Show me a man whom children and dogs shrink from, and I will show you a false, bad man— lies on his lips, and murder at his heart. No; let none despise the heaven-sent gift of innate antipathy, which makes the horse quail when the lion crouches in the thicket—which makes the cattle scent the shambles from afar, and low in terror and disgust as their nostrils snuff the blood-polluted air. I felt this antipathy strongly as I looked around me in my new sleeping-room, and yet I could find no reasonable pretext for my dislike. A very good room it was, after all, now that the green damask curtains were drawn, the fire burning bright and clear, candles burning on the mantel-piece, and the various familiar articles of toilet arranged as usual. The bed, too, looked peaceful and inviting—a pretty little white bed, not at all the gaunt funereal sort of couch which haunted apartments generally contain.

My maid entered, and assisted me to lay aside the dress and ornaments I had worn, and arranged my hair, as usual, prattling the while, in Abigail fashion. I seldom cared to converse with servants; but on that night a sort of dread of being left alone—a longing to keep some human being near me possessed me—and I encouraged the girl to gossip, so that her duties took her half an hour longer to get through than usual. At last, however, she had done all that could be done, and all my questions were answered, and my orders for the morrow reiterated and vowed obedience to, and the clock on the turret struck one. Then Mary, yawning a little, asked if I wanted anything more, and I was obliged to answer no, for very shame's sake; and she went. The shutting of the door, gently as it was closed, affected me unpleasantly. I took a dislike to the curtains, the tapestry, the dingy pictures—everything. I hated the room. I felt a temptation to put on a cloak, run, half-dressed to my sisters' chamber, and say I had changed my mind and come for shelter. But they must be asleep, I thought, and I could not be so unkind as to wake them. I said my prayers with unusual earnestness and a heavy heart. I extinguished the candles, and was just about to lay my head on my pillow, when the idea seized me that I would fasten the door. The candles were extinguished, but the firelight was amply sufficient to guide me. I gained the door. There was a lock, but it was rusty or hampered; my utmost strength could not turn the key. The bolt was broken and worthless. Baulked of my intention, I consoled myself by remembering that I had never had need of fastenings yet, and returned to my bed. I lay awake for a good while, watching the red glow of the burning coals in the grate. I was quiet now, and more composed. Even the light gossip of the maid, full of petty human cares and joys, had done me good—diverted my thoughts from brooding. I was on the point of dropping asleep, when I was twice disturbed. Once, by an owl, hooting in the ivy outside—no unaccustomed sound, but harsh and melancholy; once, by a long and mournful howling set up by the mastiff, chained in the yard beyond the wing I occupied. A long-drawn, lugubrious howling was this latter, and much such a note as the vulgar declare to herald a death in the family. This was a fancy I had never shared; but yet I could not help feeling that the dog's mournful moans were sad, and expressive of terror, not at all like his fierce, honest bark of anger, but rather as if something evil and unwonted were abroad. But soon I fell asleep.

How long I slept I never knew. I awoke at once with that abrupt start which we all know well, and which carries us in a second from utter unconsciousness to the full use of our faculties. The fire was still burning, but was very low, and half the room or more was in deep shadow. I knew, I felt, that some person or thing was in the room, although nothing unusual was to be seen by the feeble light. Yet it was a sense of danger that had aroused me from slumber. I experienced, while yet asleep, the chill and shock of sudden alarm, and I knew, even in the act of throwing off sleep like a mantle, *why* I awoke, and that some intruder was present. Yet, though I listened intently, no sound was audible, except the faint murmur of the fire — the dropping of a cinder from the bars — the loud, irregular beatings of my own heart. Notwithstanding this silence, by some intuition I knew that I had not been deceived by a dream, and felt certain that I was not alone. I waited. My heart beat on; quicker, more sudden grew its pulsations, as a bird in a cage might flutter in presence of the hawk. And then I heard a sound, faint, but quite distinct, the clank of iron, the rattling of a chain! I ventured to lift my head from the pillow. Dim and uncertain as the light was, I saw the curtains of my bed shake, and caught a glimpse of something beyond, a darker spot in the darkness. This confirmation of my fears did not surprise me so much as it shocked me. I strove to cry aloud, but could not utter a word. The chain rattled again, and this time the noise was louder and clearer. But though I strained my eyes, they could not penetrate the obscurity that shrouded the other end of the chamber whence came the sullen clanking. In a moment several distinct trains of thought, like many-coloured strands of thread twining into one, became palpable to my mental vision. Was it a robber? Could it be a supernatural visitant? Or was I the victim of a cruel trick, such as I had heard of, and which some thoughtless persons love to practise on the timid, reckless of its dangerous results? And then a new idea, with some ray of comfort in it, suggested itself. There was a fine young dog of the Newfoundland breed, a favourite of my father's, which was usually chained by night in an outhouse. Neptune might have broken loose, found his way to my room, and, finding the door imperfectly closed, have pushed it open and entered. I breathed more freely as this harmless interpretation of the noise forced itself upon me. It was—it must be—the dog, and I was distressing myself uselessly. I resolved to call to him; I strove to utter his name—'Neptune, Neptune', but a secret apprehension restrained me, and I was mute.

Then the chain clanked nearer and nearer to the bed, and presently I saw a dusky, shapeless mass appear between the curtains on the opposite side to where I was lying. How I longed to hear the whine of the poor animal that I hoped might be the cause of my alarm. But no; I heard no sound save the rustle of the curtains and the clash of the iron chains. Just then the dying flame of the fire leaned up, and with one sweeping, hurried glance I saw that the door was shut, and, horror! it is not the dog! it is the semblance of a human form that now throws itself heavily on the bed, outside the clothes, and lies there, huge and swart, in the red gleam that treacherously died away after showing so much to affright, and sinks into dull darkness. There was now no light left, though the red cinders yet glowed with a ruddy gleam like the eyes of wild beasts. The chain rattled no more. I tried to speak, to scream wildly for help; my mouth was parched, my tongue refused to obey. I could not utter a cry, and, indeed, who could have heard me, alone as I was in that solitary chamber, with no living neighbour, and the picture-gallery between me and any aid that even the loudest, most piercing shriek could summon. And the storm that howled without would have drowned my voice, even if help had been at hand. To call aloud—to demand who was there—alas! how useless, how perilous! If the intruder were a robber, my outcries would but goad him to fury; but what robber would act thus? As for a trick, that seemed impossible. And yet, *what* lay by my side, now wholly unseen? I strove to pray aloud as there rushed on my memory a flood of weird legends— the dreaded yet fascinating lore of my childhood. I had heard and read of the spirits of the wicked men forced to revisit the scenes of their earthly crimes—of demons that lurked in certain accursed spots—of the ghoul and vampire of the east, stealing amidst the graves they rifled for their ghostly banquets; and then I shuddered as I gazed on the blank darkness where I knew it lay. It stirred—it moaned hoarsely; and again I heard the chain clank close beside me—so close that it must almost have touched me. I drew myself from it, shrinking away in loathing and terror of the evil thing—what, I knew not, but felt that something malignant was near.

And yet, in the extremity of my fear, I dared not speak; I was strangely cautious to be silent, even in moving farther off; for I had a wild hope that it—the phantom, the creature, whichever it was—had not discovered my presence in the room. And then I remembered all the events of the night—Lady Speldhurst's ill-omened vaticinations, her half-warnings, her singular look as we parted, my sister's persuasions, my terror in the gallery, the remark that 'this was the room nurse Sherrard used to talk of'. And then memory, stimulated by fear, recalled the long-forgotten past, the ill-repute of this disused chamber, the sins it had witnessed, the blood spilled, the poison administered by unnatural hate within its walls, and the tradition which called it haunted. The green room—I remembered now how fearfully the servants avoided it—how it was mentioned rarely, and in whispers, when we were children, and how we had regarded it as a mysterious region, unfit for mortal habitation. Was It—the dark form with the chain—a creature of this world, or a spectre? And again—more dreadful still—could it be that the corpses of wicked men were forced to rise and haunt in the body the places where they had wrought their evil deeds? And was such as these my grisly neighbour? The chain faintly rattled. My hair bristled; my eyeballs seemed starting from their sockets; the damps of a great anguish were on my brow. My heart laboured as if I were crushed beneath some vast weight. Sometimes it appeared to stop its frenzied beatings, sometimes its pulsations were fierce and hurried; my breath came short and with extreme difficulty, and I shivered as if with cold; yet I feared to stir. It moved, it moaned, its fetters clanked dismally, the couch creaked and shook. This was no phantom, then—no air-drawn spectre. But its very solidity, its palpable presence, were a thousand times more terrible. I felt that I was in the very grasp of what could not only affright but harm; of something whose contact sickened the soul with deathly fear. I made a desperate resolve: I glided from the bed, I seized a warm wrapper, threw it around me, and tried to grope, with extended hands, my way to the door. My heart beat high at the hope of escape. But I had scarcely taken one step before the moaning was renewed—it changed into a threatening growl that would have suited a wolf's throat, and a hand clutched at my sleeve. I stood motionless. The muttering growl sank to a moan again, the chain sounded no more, but still the hand held its grip of my garment, and I feared to move. It knew of my presence, then. My brain reeled, the blood boiled in my ears, and my knees lost all strength, while my heart panted like that of a deer in the wolf's jaws. I sank back, and the benumbing influence of excessive terror reduced me to a state of stupor.

[78]

When my full consciousness returned I was sitting on the edge of
the bed, shivering with cold, and barefooted. All was silent, but I felt
that my sleeve was still clutched by my unearthly visitant. The silence
lasted a long time. Then followed a chuckling laugh that froze my very
marrow, and the gnashing of teeth as in demoniac frenzy; and then a
wailing moan, and this was succeeded by silence. Hours may have
passed—nay, though the tumult of my own heart prevented my
hearing the clock strike, must have passed—but they seemed ages to
me. And how were they passed? Hideous visions passed before the
aching eyes that I dared not close, but which gazed ever into the dumb
darkness where It lay—my dread companion through the watches of
the night. I pictured It in every abhorrent form which an excited fancy
could summon up: now as a skeleton; with hollow eye-holes and
grinning, fleshless jaws; now as a vampire, with livid face and bloated
form, and dripping mouth wet with blood. Would it never be light!
And yet, when day should dawn I should be forced to see It face to
face. I had heard that spectre and fiend were compelled to fade as
morning brightened, but this creature was too real, too foul a thing of
earth, to vanish at cock-crow. No! I should see it—the Horror—face
to face! And then the cold prevailed, and my teeth chattered, and
shiverings ran through me, and yet there was the damp of agony on my
bursting brow. Some instinct made me snatch at a shawl or cloak that
lay on a chair within reach, and wrap it round me. The moan was
renewed, and the chain just stirred. Then I sank into apathy, like an
Indian at the stake, in the intervals of torture. Hours fled by, and
I remained like a statue of ice, rigid and mute. I even slept, for I
remember that I started to find the cold grey light of an early winter's
day was on my face, and stealing around the room from between the
heavy curtains of the window.

Shuddering, but urged by the impulse that rivets the gaze of the bird
upon the snake, I turned to see the Horror of the night. Yes, it was no
fevered dream, no hallucination of sickness, no airy phantom unable
to face the dawn. In the sickly light I saw it lying on the bed, with its
grim head on the pillow. A man? Or a corpse arisen from its
unhallowed grave, and awaiting the demon that animated it? There it
lay—a gaunt, gigantic form, wasted to a skeleton, half-clad, foul with
dust and clotted gore, its huge limbs flung upon the couch as if at
random, its shaggy hair streaming over the pillows like a lion's mane.
His face was toward me. Oh, the wild hideousness of that face, even in
sleep! In features it was human, even through its horrid mask of mud

and half-dried bloody gouts, but the expression was brutish and savagely fierce; the white teeth were visible between the parted lips, in a malignant grin; the tangled hair and beard were mixed in leonine confusion, and there were scars disfiguring the brow. Round the creature's waist was a ring of iron, to which was attached a heavy but broken chain—the chain I had heard clanking. With a second glance I noted that part of the chain was wrapped in straw to prevent its galling the wearer. The creature—I cannot call it a man—had the marks of fetters on its wrists, the bony arm that protruded through one tattered sleeve was scarred and bruised; the feet were bare, and lacerated by pebbles and briers, and one of them was wounded, and wrapped in a morsel of rag. And the lean hands, one of which held my sleeve, were armed with talons like an eagle's. In an instant the horrid truth flashed upon me—I was in the grasp of a madman. Better the phantom that scares the sight than the wild beast that rends and tears the quivering flesh—the pitiless human brute that has no heart to be softened, no reason at whose bar to plead, no compassion, naught of man save the form and the cunning. I gasped in terror. Ah! the mystery of those ensanguined fingers, those gory, wolfish jaws! that face, all besmeared with blackening blood, is revealed!

The slain sheep, so mangled and rent—the fantastic butchery—the print of the naked foot—all, all were explained; and the chain, the broken link of which was found near the slaughtered animals—it came from his broken chain—the chain he had snapped, doubtless, in his escape from the asylum where his raging frenzy had been fettered and bound. In vain! in vain! Ah me! how had this grisly Samson broken manacles and prison bars—how had he eluded guardian and keeper and a hostile world, and come hither on his wild way, hunted like a beast of prey, and snatching his hideous banquet like a beast of prey, too! Yes, through the tatters of his mean and ragged garb I could see the marks of the severities, cruel and foolish, with which men in that time tried to tame the might of madness. The scourge—its marks were there; and the scars of the hard iron fetters, and many a cicatrice and welt, that told a dismal tale of hard usage. But now he was loose, free to play the brute—the baited, tortured brute that they had made him—now without the cage, and ready to gloat over the victims his strength should overpower. Horror! horror! I was the prey—the victim—already in the tiger's clutch; and a deadly sickness came over me, and the iron entered into my soul, and I longed to scream, and was dumb! I died a thousand deaths as that morning wore on. I *dared not* faint. But words cannot paint what I suffered as I waited—waited till the moment when he should open his eyes and be aware of my presence; for I was assured he knew it not. He had entered the chamber as a lair, when weary and gorged with his horrid orgy; and he had flung himself down to sleep without a suspicion that he was not alone. Even his grasping my sleeve was doubtless an act done betwixt sleeping and waking, like his unconscious moans and laughter, in some frightful dream.

Hours went on; then I trembled as I thought that soon the house would be astir, that my maid would come to call me as usual, and awake that ghastly sleeper. And might he not have time to tear me, as he tore the sheep, before any aid could arrive? At last what I dreaded came to pass—a light footstep on the landing—there is a tap at the door. A pause succeeds, and then the tapping is renewed, and this time more loudly. Then the madman stretched his limbs, and uttered his moaning cry, and his eyes slowly opened—very slowly opened and met mine. The girl waited a while ere she knocked for the third time. I trembled lest she should open the door unbidden—see that grim thing, and bring about the worst.

I saw the wondering surprise in his haggard, bloodshot eyes; I saw him stare at me half vacantly, then with a crafty yet wondering look; and then I saw the devil of murder begin to peep forth from those hideous eyes, and the lips to part as in a sneer, and the wolfish teeth to bare themselves. But I was not what I had been. Fear gave me a new and a desperate composure—a courage foreign to my nature. I had heard of the best method of managing the insane; I could but try; I *did* try. Calmly, wondering at my own feigned calm, I fronted the glare of those terrible eyes. Steady and undaunted was my gaze—motionless my attitude. I marvelled at myself, but in that agony of sickening terror I was *outwardly* firm. They sink, they quail, abashed, those dreadful eyes, before the gaze of a helpless girl; and the shame that is never absent from insanity bears down the pride of strength, the bloody cravings of the wild beast. The lunatic moaned and drooped his shaggy head between his gaunt, squalid hands.

I lost not an instant. I rose, and with one spring reached the door, tore it open, and, with a shriek, rushed through, caught the wondering girl by the arm, and crying to her to run for her life, rushed like the wind along the gallery, down the corridor, down the stairs. Mary's screams filled the house as she fled beside me. I heard a long-drawn, raging cry, the roar of a wild animal mocked of its prey, and I knew what was behind me. I never turned my head—I flew rather than ran. I was in the hall already; there was a rush of many feet, an outcry of many voices, a sound of scuffling feet, and brutal yells, and oaths, and heavy blows, and I fell to the ground crying, 'Save me!' and lay in a swoon. I awoke from a delirious trance. Kind faces were around my bed, loving looks were bent on me by all, by my dear father and dear sisters; but I scarcely saw them before I swooned again.

When I recovered from that long illness, through which I had been nursed so tenderly, the pitying looks I met made me tremble. I asked for a looking-glass. It was long denied me, but my importunity prevailed at last—a mirror was brought. My youth was gone at one fell swoop. The glass showed me a livid and haggard face, blanched and bloodless as of one who sees a spectre; and in the ashen lips, and wrinkled brow, and dim eyes, I could trace nothing of my old self. The hair, too, jetty and rich before, was now as white as snow; and in one night the ravages of half a century had passed over my face. Nor have my nerves ever recovered their tone after that dire shock. Can you wonder that my life was blighted, that my lover shrank from me, so sad a wreck was I?

I am old now—old and alone. My sisters would have had me to live with them, but I chose not to sadden their genial homes with my phantom face and dead eyes. Reginald married another. He has been dead many years. I never ceased to pray for him, though he left me when I was bereft of all. The sad weird is nearly over now. I am old, and near the end, and wishful for it. I have not been bitter or hard, but I cannot bear to see many people, and am best alone. I try to do what good I can with the worthless wealth Lady Speldhurst left me, for, at my wish, my portion was shared between my sisters. What need had I of inheritance?—I, the shattered wreck made by that one night of horror!

A PIPE OF MYSTERY

by G. A. Henty

The life of George Alfred Henty (1832–1902)
spanned the Victorian era, and his imperialist
stories of British expansion influenced successive
generations of devoted readers. India, which
dominated Victorian imperial thinking, was the
setting of several Henty novels including *The Tiger
of Mysore, In Times of Peril*, and *At the Point of the
Bayonet*; plus various short stories including 'A Pipe
of Mystery' (from *Tales of Daring and Danger*).

Ajovial party were gathered round a blazing fire in an old
grange near Warwick. The hour was getting late; the very
little ones had, after dancing round the Christmas-tree,
enjoying the snap-dragon, and playing a variety of games, gone off to
bed; and the elder boys and girls now gathered round their uncle
Colonel Harley, and asked him for a story—above all, a ghost story.

'But I have never seen any ghosts,' the colonel said, laughing; 'and,
moreover, I don't believe in them one bit. I have travelled pretty well
all over the world, I have slept in houses said to be haunted, but
nothing have I seen—no noises that could not be accounted for by rats
or the wind have I ever heard. I have never'—and here he paused—
'never but once met with any circumstances or occurrence that could
not be accounted for by the light of reason, and I know you prefer
hearing stories of my own adventures to mere invention.'

'Yes, uncle. But what was the "once" when circumstances happened
that you could not explain?'

'It's rather a long story,' the colonel said, 'and it's getting late.'

'Oh! no, no, uncle; it does not matter a bit how late we sit up on Christmas Eve, and the longer the story is, the better; and if you don't believe in ghosts, how can it be a story of something you could not account for by the light of nature?'

'You will see when I have done,' the colonel said. 'It is rather a story of what the Scotch call second sight, than one of ghosts. As to accounting for it, you shall form your own opinion when you have heard me to the end.

'I landed in India in '50, and after going through the regular drill work, marched with a detachment up country to join my regiment, which was stationed at Jubbalpore, in the very heart of India. It has become an important place since; the railroad across India passes through it and no end of changes have taken place; but at that time it was one of the most out-of-the-way stations in India, and, I may say, one of the most pleasant. It lay high, there was capital boating on the Nerbudda, and, above all, it was a grand place for sport, for it lay at the foot of the hill country, an immense district, then but little known, covered with forests and jungle, and abounding with big game of all kinds.

'My great friend there was a man named Simmonds. He was just of my own standing; we had come out in the same ship, had marched up the country together, and were almost like brothers. He was an old Etonian, I an old Westminster, and we were both fond of boating, and, indeed, of sport of all kinds. But I am not going to tell you of that now. The people in these hills are called Gonds, a true hill tribe — that is to say, aborigines, somewhat of the negro type. The chiefs are of mixed blood, but the people are almost black. They are supposed to accept the religion of the Hindus, but are in reality deplorably ignorant and superstitious. Their priests are a sort of compound of a Brahmin priest and a negro fetish man, and among their principal duties is that of charming away tigers from the villages by means of incantations. There, as in other parts of India, were a few wandering fakirs, who enjoyed an immense reputation for holiness and wisdom. The people would go to them from great distances for charms or predictions, and believed in their power with implicit faith.

'At the time when we were at Jubbalpore, there was one of these fellows, whose reputation altogether eclipsed that of his rivals, and nothing could be done until his permission had been asked and his blessing obtained. All sorts of marvellous stories were constantly coming to our ears of the unerring foresight with which he predicted the termination of diseases, both in men and animals; and so generally was he believed in that the colonel ordered that no one connected with the regiment should consult him, for these predictions very frequently brought about their own fulfilment; for those who were told that an illness would terminate fatally, lost all hope, and literally lay down to die.

'However, many of the stories that we heard could not be explained on these grounds, and the fakir and his doings were often talked over at mess, some of the officers scoffing at the whole business, others maintaining that some of these fakirs had, in some way or another, the power of foretelling the future, citing many well authenticated anecdotes upon the subject.

'The older officers were the believers, we young fellows were the scoffers. But for the well-known fact that it is very seldom indeed that these fakirs will utter any of their predictions to Europeans, some of us would have gone to him, to test his powers. As it was, none of us had ever seen him.

'He lived in an old ruined temple, in the middle of a large patch of jungle at the foot of the hills, some ten or twelve miles away.

'I had been at Jubbalpore about a year, when I was woke up one night by a native, who came in to say that at about eight o'clock a tiger had killed a man in his village, and had dragged off the body.

'Simmonds and I were constantly out after tigers, and the people in all the villages within twenty miles knew that we were always ready to pay for early information. This tiger had been doing great damage, and had carried off about thirty men, women, and children. So great was the fear of him, indeed, that the people in the neighbourhood he frequented scarcely dared stir out of doors, except in parties of five or six. We had had several hunts after him, but, like all man-eaters, he was old and awfully crafty; and although we got several snap shots at him, he had always managed to save his skin.

'In a quarter of an hour after the receipt of the message, Charley Simmonds and I were on the back of an elephant, which was our joint property; our shekarry, a capital fellow, was on foot beside us, and with the native trotting on ahead as guide we went off at the best pace of old Begaum, for that was the elephant's name. The village was fifteen miles away, but we got there soon after daybreak, and were received with delight by the population. In half an hour the hunt was organized; all the male population turned out as beaters, with sticks, guns, tom-toms, and other instruments for making a noise.

'The trail was not difficult to find. A broad path, with occasional smears of blood, showed where he had dragged his victim through the long grass to a cluster of trees a couple of hundred yards from the village.

'We scarcely expected to find him there, but the villagers held back, while we went forward with cocked rifles. We found, however, nothing but a few bones and a quantity of blood. The tiger had made off at the approach of daylight into the jungle, which was about two miles distant. We traced him easily enough, and found that he had entered a large ravine, from which several smaller ones branched off.

'It was an awkward place, as it was next to impossible to surround it with the number of people at our command. We posted them at last all along the upper ground, and told them to make up in noise what they wanted in numbers. At last all was ready, and we gave the signal. However, I am not telling you a hunting story, and need only say that we could neither find nor disturb him. In vain we pushed Begaum through the thickest of the jungle which clothed the sides and bottom of the ravine, while the men shouted, beat their tom-toms, and showered imprecations against the tiger himself and his ancestors up to the remotest generations.

'The day was tremendously hot, and, after three hours' march, we gave it up for a time, and lay down in the shade, while the shekarries made a long examination of the ground all round the hillside, to be sure that he had not left the ravine. They came back with the news that no traces could be discovered, and that, beyond a doubt, he was still there. A tiger will crouch up in an exceedingly small clump of grass or bush, and will sometimes almost allow himself to be trodden on before moving. However, we determined to have one more search, and if that should prove unsuccessful, to send off to Jubbalpore for some more of the men to come out with elephants, while we kept up a circle of fires, and of noises of all descriptions, so as to keep him a prisoner until the arrival of the reinforcements. Our next search was no more successful than our first had been; and having, as we imagined, examined every clump and crevice in which he could have been concealed, we had just reached the upper end of the ravine, when we heard a tremendous roar, followed by a perfect babel of yells and screams from the natives.

'The outburst came from the mouth of the ravine, and we felt at once that he had escaped. We hurried back to find, as we had expected, that the tiger was gone. He had burst out suddenly from his hiding-place, had seized a native, torn him horribly, and had made across the open plain.

'This was terribly provoking, but we had nothing to do but follow him. This was easy enough, and we traced him to a detached patch of wood and jungle, two miles distant. This wood was four or five hundred yards across, and the exclamations of the people at once told us that it was the one in which stood the ruined temple of the fakir of whom I have been telling you. I forgot to say, that as the tiger broke out one of the village shekarries had fired at, and, he declared, wounded him.

'It was already getting late in the afternoon, and it was hopeless to attempt to beat the jungle that night. We therefore sent off a runner with a note to the colonel, asking him to send the work-elephants, and to allow a party of volunteers to march over at night, to help surround the jungle when we commenced beating it in the morning.

'We based our request upon the fact that the tiger was a notorious man-eater, and had been doing immense damage. We then had a talk with our shekarry, sent a man off to bring provisions for the people out with us, and then set them to work cutting sticks and grass to make a circle of fires.

'We both felt much uneasiness respecting the fakir, who might be seized at any moment by the enraged tiger. The natives would not allow that there was any cause for fear, as the tiger would not dare to touch so holy a man. Our belief in the respect of the tiger for sanctity was by no means strong, and we determined to go in and warn him of the presence of the brute in the wood. It was a mission which we could not intrust to anyone else, for no native would have entered the jungle for untold gold; so we mounted old Begaum again, and started. The path leading towards the temple was pretty wide, and as we went along almost noiselessly, for the elephant was too well trained to tread upon fallen sticks, it was just possible we might come upon the tiger suddenly, so we kept our rifles in readiness in our hands.

'Presently we came in sight of the ruins. No one was at first visible; but at that very moment the fakir came out from the temple. He did not see or hear us, for we were rather behind him and still among the trees, but at once proceeded in a high voice to break into a sing-song prayer. He had not said two words before his voice was drowned in a terrific roar, and in an instant the tiger had sprung upon him, struck him to the ground, seized him as a cat would a mouse, and started off with him at a trot. The brute evidently had not detected our presence, for he came right towards us. We halted old Begaum, and with our fingers on the triggers, awaited the favourable moment. He was a hundred yards from us when he struck down his victim; he was not more than fifty when he caught sight of us. He stopped for an instant in surprise. Charley muttered, "Both barrels, Harley," and as the beast turned to plunge into the jungle, and so showed us his side, we sent four bullets crashing into him, and he rolled over lifeless.

'We went up to the spot, made old Begaum give him a kick, to be sure that he was dead, and then got down to examine the unfortunate fakir. The tiger had seized him by the shoulder, which was terribly torn, and the bone broken. He was still perfectly conscious.

'We at once fired three shots, our usual signal that the tiger was dead, and in a few minutes were surrounded by the villagers, who hardly knew whether to be delighted at the death of their enemy, or to grieve over the injury to the fakir. We proposed taking the latter to our hospital at Jubbalpore, but this he positively refused to listen to. However we finally persuaded him to allow his arm to be set and the wounds dressed in the first place by our regimental surgeon, after which he could go to one of the native villages and have his arm dressed in accordance with his own notions. A litter was soon improvised, and away we went to Jubbalpore, which we reached about eight in the evening.

'The fakir refused to enter the hospital, so we brought out a couple of trestles, laid the litter upon them, and the surgeon set his arm and dressed his wounds by torch-light, when he was lifted into a dhoolie, and his bearers again prepared to start for the village.

'Hitherto he had only spoken a few words; but he now briefly expressed his deep gratitude to Simmonds and myself. We told him that we would ride over to see him shortly, and hoped to find him getting on rapidly. Another minute and he was gone.

'It happened that we had three or four fellows away on leave or on staff duty, and several others knocked up with fever just about this time, so that the duty fell very heavily upon the rest of us, and it was over a month before we had time to ride over to see the fakir.

'We had heard he was going on well; but we were surprised, on reaching the village, to find that he had already returned to his old abode in the jungle. However, we had made up our minds to see him, especially as we had agreed that we would endeavour to persuade him to do a prediction for us; so we turned our horses' heads towards the jungle. We found the fakir sitting on a rock in front of the temple, just where he had been seized by the tiger. He rose as we rode up.

' "I knew that you would come today, sahibs, and was joyful in the thought of seeing those who have preserved my life."

' "We are glad to see you looking pretty strong again, though your arm is still in a sling," I said, for Simmonds was not strong in Hindustani.

' "How did you know that we were coming?" I asked, when we had tied up our horses.

' "Siva has given to his servant to know many things," he said quietly.

' "Did you know beforehand that the tiger was going to seize you?" I asked.

' "I knew that a great danger threatened, and that Siva would not let me die before my time had come."

' "Could you see into our future?" I asked.

'The fakir hesitated, looked at me for a moment earnestly to see if I was speaking in mockery, and then said:

' "The sahibs do not believe in the power of Siva or of his servants. They call his messengers impostors, and scoff at them when they speak of the events of the future."

' "No, indeed," I said. "My friend and I have no idea of scoffing. We have heard of so many of your predictions coming true, that we are really anxious that you should tell us something of the future."

'The fakir nodded his head, went into the temple, and returned in a minute or two with two small pipes used by the natives for opium-smoking, and a brazier of burning charcoal. The pipes were already charged. He made signs to us to sit down, and took his place in front of us. Then he began singing in a low voice, rocking himself to and fro, and waving a staff which he held in his hand. Gradually his voice rose, and his gesticulations and actions became more violent. So far as I could make out, it was a prayer to Siva that he would give some glimpse of the future which might benefit the sahibs who had saved the life of his servant. Presently he darted forward, gave us each a pipe, took two pieces of red-hot charcoal from the brazier in his fingers, without seeming to know that they were warm, and placed them in the pipes; then he recommenced his singing and gesticulations.

[89]

'A glance at Charley, to see if, like myself, he was ready to carry the thing through, and then I put the pipe to my lips. I felt at once that it was opium, of which I had before made experiment, but mixed with some other substance, which was, I imagine, hashish, a preparation of hemp. A few puffs, and I felt a drowsiness creeping over me. I saw, as through a mist, the fakir swaying himself backwards and forwards, his arms waving, and his face distorted. Another minute, and the pipe slipped from my fingers, and I fell back insensible.

'How long I lay there I do not know. I woke with a strange and not unpleasant sensation, and presently became conscious that the fakir was gently pressing, with a sort of shampooing action, my temples and head. When he saw that I opened my eyes he left me, and performed the same process upon Charley. In a few minutes he rose from his stooping position, waved his hand in token of adieu, and walked slowly back into the temple.

'As he disappeared I sat up; Charley did the same.

'We stared at each other for a minute without speaking, and then Charley said:

' "This is a rum go, and no mistake, old man."

' "You're right, Charley. My opinion is, we've made fools of ourselves. Let's be off out of this."

'We staggered to our feet, for we both felt like drunken men, made our way to our horses, poured a mussuk of water over our heads, took a drink of brandy from our flasks, and then feeling more like ourselves, mounted and rode out of the jungle.

' "Well, Harley, if the glimpse of futurity which I had is true, all I can say is that it was extremely unpleasant."

' "That was just my case, Charley."

' "My dream, or whatever you like to call it, was about a mutiny of the men."

' "You don't say so, Charley; so was mine. This is monstrously strange, to say the least of it. However, you tell your story first, and then I will tell mine."

' "It was very short," Charley said. "We were at mess—not in our present mess-room—we were dining with the fellows of some other regiment. Suddenly, without any warning, the windows were filled with a crowd of Sepoys, who opened fire right and left into us. Half the fellows were shot down at once; the rest of us made a rush to our swords just as the devils came swarming into the room. There was a desperate fight for a moment. I remember that Subadar Pirán—one of

[90]

the best native officers in the regiment, by the way—made a rush at me, and I shot him through the head with a revolver. At the same moment a ball hit me, and down I went. At the moment a Sepoy fell dead across me, hiding me partly from sight. The fight lasted a minute or two longer. I fancy a few fellows escaped, for I heard shots outside. Then the place became quiet. In another minute I heard a crackling, and saw that the devils had set the mess-room on fire. One of our men, who was lying close by me, got up and crawled to the window, but he was shot down the moment he showed himself. I was hesitating whether to do the same or to lie still and be smothered, when suddenly I rolled the dead Sepoy off, crawled into the ante-room half-suffocated by smoke, raised the lid of a very heavy trap-door, and stumbled down some steps into a place, half store-house half cellar, under the mess-room. How I knew about it being there I don't know. The trap closed over my head with a bang. That is all I remember."

' "Well, Charley, curiously enough my dream was also about an extraordinary escape from danger, lasting, like yours, only a minute or two. The first thing I remember—there seems to have been something before, but what, I don't know—I was on horseback, holding a very pretty but awfully pale girl in front of me. We were pursued by a whole troop of Sepoy cavalry, who were firing pistol-shots at us. We were not more than seventy or eighty yards in front, and they were gaining fast, just as I rode into a large deserted temple. In the centre was a huge stone figure. I jumped off my horse with the lady, and as I did so she said, "Blow out my brains, Edward; don't let me fall alive into their hands."

' "Instead of answering, I hurried her round behind the idol, pushed against one of the leaves of a flower in the carving, and the stone swung back, and showed a hole just large enough to get through, with a stone staircase inside the body of the idol, made no doubt for the priest to go up and give responses through the mouth. I hurried the girl through, crept in after her, and closed the stone, just as our pursuers came clattering into the courtyard. That is all I remember."

' "Well, it is monstrously rum," Charley said, after a pause. "Did you understand what the old fellow was singing about before he gave us the pipes?"

' "Yes; I caught the general drift. It was an entreaty to Siva to give us some glimpse of futurity which might benefit us."

'We lit our cheroots and rode for some miles at a brisk canter without remark. When we were within a short distance of home we reined up.

' "I feel ever so much better," Charley said. "We have got that opium out of our heads now. How do you account for it all, Harley?"

' "I account for it in this way, Charley. The opium naturally had the effect of making us both dream, and as we took similar doses of the same mixture, under similar circumstances, it is scarcely extraordinary that it should have affected the same portion of the brain, and caused a certain similarity in our dreams. In all nightmares something terrible happens, or is on the point of happening; and so it was here. Not unnaturally in both our cases, our thoughts turned to soldiers. If you remember there was a talk at mess some little time since, as to what would happen in the extremely unlikely event of the Sepoys mutinying in a body. I have no doubt that was the foundation of both our dreams. It is all natural enough when we come to think it over calmly. I think, by the way, we had better agree to say nothing at all about it in the regiment."

' "I should think not," Charley said. "We should never hear the end of it; they would chaff us out of our lives."

'We kept our secret, and came at last to laugh over it heartily when we were together. Then the subject dropped, and by the end of a year had as much escaped our minds as any other dream would have done. Three months after the affair the regiment was ordered down to Allahabad, and the change of place no doubt helped to erase all memory of the dream. Four years after we had left Jubbalpore we went to Beerapore. The time is very marked in my memory, because the very week we arrived there, your aunt, then Miss Gardiner, came out from England, to her father, our colonel. The instant I saw her I was impressed with the idea that I knew her intimately. I recollected her face, her figure, and the very tone of her voice, but wherever I had met her I could not conceive. Upon the occasion of my first introduction to her, I could not help telling her that I was convinced that we had met, and asking her if she did not remember it. No, she did not remember, but very likely she might have done so, and she suggested the names of several people at whose houses we might have met. I did not know any of them. Presently she asked how long I had been out in India?

' "Six years," I said.

' "And how old, Mr Harley," she said, "do you take me to be?"

'I saw in one instant my stupidity, and was stammering out an apology, when she went on, —

' "I am very little over eighteen, Mr Harley, although I evidently look ever so many years older; but papa can certify to my age; so I was only twelve when you left England."

'I tried in vain to clear matters up. Your aunt would insist that I took her to be forty, and the fun that my blunder made rather drew us together, and gave me a start over the other fellows at the station, half of whom fell straightway in love with her. Some months went on, and when the mutiny broke out we were engaged to be married. It is a proof of how completely the opium-dreams had passed out of the minds of both Simmonds and myself, that even when rumours of general disaffection among the Sepoys began to be current, they never once recurred to us; and even when the news of the actual mutiny reached us, we were just as confident as were the others of the fidelity of our own regiment. It was the old story, foolish confidence and black treachery. As at very many other stations, the mutiny broke out when we were at mess. Our regiment was dining with the 34th Bengalees. Suddenly, just as dinner was over, the window was opened, and a tremendous fire poured in. Four or five men fell dead at once, and the poor colonel, who was next to me, was shot right through the head. Every one rushed to his sword and drew his pistol—for we had been ordered to carry pistols as part of our uniform. I was next to Charley Simmonds as the Sepoys of both regiments, headed by Subadar Pirán, poured in at the windows.

' "I have it now," Charley said; "it is the scene I dreamed."

'As he spoke he fired his revolver at the subadar, who fell dead in his tracks.

'A Sepoy close by levelled his musket and fired. Charley fell, and the fellow rushed forward to bayonet him. As he did so I sent a bullet through his head, and he fell across Charley. It was a wild fight for a minute or two, and then a few of us made a sudden rush together, cut our way through the mutineers, and darted through an open window on to the parade. There were shouts, shots, and screams from the officers' bungalows, and in several places flames were already rising. What became of the other men I knew not; I made as hard as I could tear for the colonel's bungalow. Suddenly I came upon a sowar sitting on his horse watching the rising flames. Before he saw me I was on him, and ran him through. I leapt on his horse and galloped down to Gardiner's compound. I saw lots of Sepoys in and around the bungalow, all engaged in looting. I dashed into the compound.

' "May! May!" I shouted. "Where are you?"

'I had scarcely spoken before a dark figure rushed out of a clump of bushes close by with a scream of delight.

'In an instant she was on the horse before me, and shooting down a couple of fellows who made a rush at my reins, I dashed out again. Stray shots were fired after us. But fortunately the Sepoys were all busy looting, most of them had laid down their muskets, and no one really took up the pursuit. I turned off from the parade-ground, dashed down between the hedges of two compounds, and in another minute we were in the open country.

'Fortunately, the cavalry were all down looting their own lines, or we must have been overtaken at once. May happily had fainted as I lifted her on to my horse—happily, because the fearful screams that we heard from the various bungalows almost drove me mad, and would probably have killed her, for the poor ladies were all her intimate friends.

'I rode on for some hours, till I felt quite safe from any immediate pursuit, and then we halted in the shelter of a clump of trees.

'By this time I had heard May's story. She had felt uneasy at being alone, but had laughed at herself for being so, until upon her speaking to one of the servants he had answered in a tone of gross insolence, which had astonished her. She at once guessed that there was danger, and the moment that she was alone caught up a large, dark carriage rug, wrapped it round her so as to conceal her white dress, and stole out into the verandah. The night was dark, and scarcely had she left the house than she heard a burst of firing across at the mess-house. She at once ran in among the bushes and crouched there, as she heard the rush of men into the room she had just left. She heard them searching for her, but they were looking for a white dress, and her dark rug saved her. What she must have suffered in the five minutes between the firing of the first shots and my arrival, she only knows. May had spoken but very little since we started. I believe that she was certain that her father was dead, although I had given an evasive answer when she asked me; and her terrible sense of loss, added to the horror of that time of suspense in the garden, had completely stunned her. We waited in the tope until the afternoon and then set out again.

'We had gone but a short distance when we saw a body of the rebel cavalry in pursuit. They had no doubt been scouring the country generally, and the discovery was accidental. For a short time we kept away from them, but this could not be for long, as our horse was carrying double. I made for a sort of ruin I saw at the foot of a hill half a mile away. I did so with no idea of the possibility of concealment. My intention was simply to get my back to a rock and to sell my life as dearly as I could, keeping the last two barrels of the revolver for ourselves. Certainly no remembrance of my dream influenced me in any way, and in the wild whirl of excitement I had not given a second thought to Charley Simmonds' exclamation. As we rode up to the ruins only a hundred yards ahead of us, May said, —

' "Blow out my brains, Edward; don't let me fall alive into their hands."

'A shock of remembrance shot across me. The chase, her pale face, the words, the temple—all my dream rushed into my mind.

' "We are saved," I cried, to her amazement, as we rode into the courtyard, in whose centre a great figure was sitting.

'I leapt from the horse, snatched the mussuk of water from the saddle, and then hurried May round the idol, between which and the rock behind, there was but just room to get along.

'Not a doubt entered my mind but that I should find the spring as I had dreamed. Sure enough there was the carving, fresh upon my memory as if I had seen it but the day before. I placed my hand on the leaflet without hesitation, a solid stone moved back, I hurried my amazed companion in, and shut to the stone. I found, and shot to, a massive bolt, evidently placed to prevent the door being opened by accident or design when anyone was in the idol.

'At first it seemed quite dark, but a faint light streamed in from above; we made our way up the stairs, and found that the light came through a number of small holes pierced in the upper part of the head, and through still smaller holes lower down, not much larger than a good-sized knitting-needle could pass through. These holes, we afterwards found, were in the ornaments round the idol's neck. The holes enlarged inside, and enabled us to have a view all round.

'The mutineers were furious at our disappearance, and for hours searched about. Then, saying that we must be hidden somewhere, and that they would wait till we came out, they proceeded to bivouac in the courtyard of the temple.

'We passed four terrible days, but on the morning of the fifth a scout came in to tell the rebels that a column of British troops marching on Delhi would pass close by the temple. They therefore hastily mounted and galloped off.

'Three quarters of an hour later we were safe among our own people. A fortnight afterwards your aunt and I were married. It was no time for ceremony then; there were no means of sending her away; no place where she could have waited until the time for her mourning for her father was over. So we were married quietly by one of the chaplains of the troops, and, as your story-books say, have lived very happily ever after."

'And how about Mr Simmonds, uncle? Did he get safe off too?"

'Yes, his dream came as vividly to his mind as mine had done. He crawled to the place where he knew the trap-door would be, and got into the cellar. Fortunately for him there were plenty of eatables there, and he lived there in concealment for a fortnight. After that he crawled out, and found the mutineers had marched for Delhi. He went through a lot, but at last joined us before that city. We often talked over our dreams together, and there was no question that we owed our lives to them. Even then we did not talk much to other people about them, for there would have been a lot of talk, and inquiry, and questions, and you know fellows hate that sort of thing. So we held our tongues. Poor Charley's silence was sealed a year later at Lucknow, for on the advance with Lord Clyde he was killed.

'And now, boys and girls, you must run off to bed. Five minutes more and it will be Christmas-day. So you see, Frank, that although I don't believe in ghosts, I have yet met with a circumstance which I cannot account for.'

'It is very curious anyhow, uncle, and beats ghost stories into fits.'

'I like it better, certainly,' one of the girls said, 'for we can go to bed without being afraid of dreaming about it.'

'Well, you must not talk any more now. Off to bed, off to bed,' Colonel Harley said, 'or I shall get into terrible disgrace with your fathers and mothers, who have been looking very gravely at me for the last three quarters of an hour.'

ON THE DOWN LINE

by George Manville Fenn

George Manville Fenn (1831–1909), Henty's
biographer, was one of his most successful fellow-
writers, responsible for at least a hundred
adventure stories for boys. In his early career, Fenn
was a close adherent of the Dickensian literary
tradition, and probably wrote more seasonal
Christmas stories than any other author—exciting
thrillers as well as ghostly yarns—and a selection of
these were published as *Christmas Penny Readings,
original sketches for the season.*
'On the Down Line' is taken
from this very scarce volume.

I couldn't stop indoors, for I couldn't bear to see them all. The
children didn't seem to mind it so much, for they ran about and
played, and their little hearts were light; but there was some one
sitting by the wretched little fire, looking so pale and worn and
miserable, that it went quite to one's heart.

Christmas morning, with the bright sun shining in through the
dirty windows, while from everywhere the rays went flashing as
they lighted upon the frost, rime, or snow. Such of the blue sky as
we could see from our court, was as bright and clear a blue as could be
seen out in the country, while the pavement looked dry, and you
could hear the snow crunch under the people's feet. But there was
no brightness with us, and at last I went out, for I couldn't stop
indoors.

Was it my fault? I kept asking myself; had I tried hard enough to get took on again; or ought we to have been more saving when I had a situation? Ah! I asked myself all this again and again as I went out, leaving them at home in a regular state of beggary; for we had come down to the last shilling.

I've always noticed as poor men keep their hands in their pockets; and I did mine that sharp, cold morning, and went sauntering along the streets, wondering what it would all come to, and how we were to manage. There was every one I met looking cheerful and bright; here and there shops a little way open, just as if they were winking at you, because they were so full of all sorts of good things; people were going in and coming out with loaded baskets; while, when I got near the baker's, it was enough to make a hungry man savage to see the stream of people, with their happy, jolly faces, bearing in geese, turkeys, and great fat mottled pieces of beef; and all looking as though there wasn't such a thing as poverty.

Every body seemed in a hurry, and every face seemed twinkling and bright with the thoughts of good things to come, till at last, from feeling low and miserable, I got to be reckless and savage, and felt as if I should have liked to have had it out with the world there on the spot.

Every one you met in the big streets was like nature that morning— dressed in the best clothes; some bound for church, some out visiting; and do what I would, I couldn't find one face that looked miserable. There were the cabs and carriages rattling along; 'buses loaded; the bells ringing merrily; while there seemed to be a something in the air that made you feel bright in spite of yourself; and after being savage for an hour and a half, I seemed to catch the infection from the people about, and more than once I caught myself going to whistle.

But the thoughts of what I'd left at home made me stop short, with my face all screwed up, and from going to one extreme, I got to another; and at last, ready to break down, I found myself sitting on the stone-setting of the railings of one of the West End churches.

Beadle comes out after a bit and has a look at me, as much as to say, 'Are you a beggar, or ain't you?' but he never says nothing; and after a bit he goes in again. Policeman comes by beating his white gloves together, and he looks very suspiciously at me, as if he couldn't quite make up his mind; and then he goes on, and says nothing. And there I sat in the cold, feeling nothing but the misery gripping at my heart, and at last, seeing nothing but a pale worn face in a bare room, where a troop of hungry children were wanting bread.

Sounds strange that, and some may think it stretched. But let them climb some of the dirty stairs at the East End, and they can find such sights any day and every day.

No; I could see nothing then, but the place we called home; and I might have sat there till I froze, if all at once something that seemed almost like a vision had not come before me; for as I sat there with my head upon my hands, there came a light touch, and looking up, there stood a little bright-eyed, golden-haired child before me, her beautiful cheeks ruddy with the keen air, while a tiny bright tear was in each eye, as with a pitying look she pushed a penny into my hand; when I was so utterly took aback, that her bright scarlet cloak was some distance off as she tripped along beside a tall stately lady, before I could recover myself.

That did it. It seemed to bear down pride, anger, everything, and taking me so suddenly, I couldn't bear it, but there in that open street my head went down again upon my hands, and in the hopeless misery of my heart I cried like a child.

But only for a minute, when I jumped up and hurried along the street to catch one more sight of the bright pitying little angel; but she was gone, and at last, making sure that she had gone into one of the houses, I walked slowly back to the churchyard.

When I got there the people were beginning to come out of the big church: carriages were drawing up; from out of the open doors there came the rolling sound of the organ; and as I stood there against the railings, watching the happy-looking crowd, it seemed to me that I must be a sort of impostor, for to see how folks were dressed there couldn't be such a thing as misery in the world.

All at once I started, and took hold of the railing, for I heard a voice that put me in mind of the time when I was sacked from the Great Central line. Just in front of me, and coming towards a carriage that a lad held open, were a lady and gentleman dressed tip-top, and he was laughing and chatting to her. But I only just saw that she was very handsome, for I was watching the gentleman's eyes—bright, piercing blue eyes, such as you seldom see; and in a regular state of muddle in my own mind, and wondering about where those eyes had come across me before, I leaned forward right in the way, staring fixed-like at him.

'Stand back, my good fellow,' he says, and then, just as the lady lightly stepped into the carriage, he stops short, fixes those eyes of his on to mine, and then, with his hand playing with his big brown moustache, he burst out laughing, when I knew him in a moment. It *was* him; and as I thought of the misery of the past year that he had caused, something seemed to rise up in me, and for a moment I felt as if I could have knocked him down. But the clenching of my fist made me feel that penny, and that brought up another face, when turning dejected once more, I turned aside, saying—

'Ah! it's fun for you, but pretty nigh death for me;' but before I'd got two steps off, he had his hand on my shabby blackened moleskin jacket, and he says—

'Gently, my friend, I must introduce you;' and before I knew what he was about, he had me at the door of the carriage, and he says— 'Look, Marian, here's our honest charioteer, the Vulcan who drove us down to Moreton;' and then he whispered something that made the lady smile, and a bright colour come all over her handsome face. 'Do you drive the mail now?' he says, turning to me.

'Never touched a handle since, sir,' I says. 'They had me afore the board two mornings after, and discharged me.' And then the thoughts of it all seemed too much for me, and I turned husky and choky, and couldn't speak for a minute, when I says, with a sort of gulp, 'Can't help it, sir; I've been werry hard drove since—wife—children—' and then I choked again as I shunted off what I was saying.

'Stand back a bit,' says the gentleman to his servant, and then, in so kind and gentle a way, he says to me—'Why, my poor fellow, I wouldn't have had this happen on any account'; and then I saw a tear or two in his lady's beautiful eyes, and they both stopped talking to me a good quarter of an hour, free as could be, telling me that they had me to thank for much happiness, as theirs was a runaway match. And at last, when they drove off, nodding and smiling at me, I had the gentleman's card, so as to call on him next morning, when he said his father, being a railway director, I should be took on the line at once; and, what was more to the purpose then, there were five sovereigns in my hand.

I didn't know what to do, whether to laugh or cry; and I'm sure I must have looked like a madman as I tore through the streets, and rushed upstairs into our room, when the first thing I did was to scrape up every bit of coal at the bottom of the cupboard and put it atop of the fire.

'Lay the cloth, my lass,' I says, seizing a dish; 'and, Lord bless you, look alive!' The children stared, and then laughed and clapped their hands, while I rushed out to the cook's shop in the lane, looking like a wolf.

There was a roast goose just up, and cissing away in the big pewter dish all amongst the gravy, with the stuffing a-smelling that rich, it was enough to drive you mad.

Just as I slipped into the door, the waiter—red-nosed chap—with a dirty white wisp of a handkercher round his neck, looking like a seedy undertaker—the waiter says: 'Two goose—apple sauce—and taters;' and the master sticks his fork into the buzzum, and makes a cut as sent the stuffing all out of a gush.

'Hold hard,' I says, 'that's mine;' and ketching hold of one leg, before he knew what I was up to, it was on my dish. 'Now then, ladle on that gravy,' I says, 'and lets have the setrers;' and saying that, I dabs a sovrin down on the edge of the pewter.

I think they were going to send out for a policeman, but the sight of that little bit of metal settled it, and five minutes after I was carrying the change—not much of it neither—the goose under a cover, and the waiter following behind with a tray, with vegetables, sauce, and aside the great wedge of pudding, a pot of half-and-half.

When the waiter had gone out of the room, and the little ones were hooraying and tapping with their knives, I got to the top of the table, the wife went to the bottom, and I began to say grace, when our eyes met, she ran to me, and then for a good ten minutes she was a sobbing in my arms; while I—there; that's private, and I think I've confessed enough.

There; I don't care whose it was, or where it was, all I know is this, that there wasn't such a dinner eaten or enjoyed anywhere that day throughout the length and breadth of our old country; and though sometimes it was hard to see where I stuck the fork, or cut with the knife, I was smiling all the time. As for the wife, she would keep breaking down till I shouted at her, when she went at it and helped me keep the young ones going; and at last of all I'd have taken a shilling for what was left of the goose, and whoever bought it wouldn't have been the best off in the bargain.

The very next week I was took on the London, Highshare, and Ploughshare railway, and that through the gent who got me discharged from the Great Central, which happened this way.

The Christmas Eve afore what I've told you was one of those yaller, smoky, foggy times, when trains are all later than they should be, even worse than might be expected at Christmas time. The lamps were burning in the booking offices all day, while the steam hung like a cloud in the roof of the terminus. I was sitting in the engine-shed on our horse—steam-horse you know— waiting to run the mail down to the north, when Ben Davis, my stoker, says:

'There they goes again, "bang, bang," I wonder what it's cost the company today in fog signals;' and then as I didn't say nothing, he says, 'Ah! this is just such a night as it was four years agone, when poor Tom Harris was cut up the night afore the pitch in'—smash you know. 'Poor Tom; he knowed it was acomin' to that, and he told me all about it; for I stoked him.'

Just then time was up, and all hot and hissing, I runs out to the switches, and comes back on to the down line, where we were coupled on to the train, when Ben goes on:

'Poor chap; he'd been outer sorts for some time, and I do think he took more than he should; but one way and another, he was horribly low-spirited, and would quite upset you with the way he'd talk. The last night as I stoked him, he got telling me his reg'lar tale, about a run down he had, and one as he had never forgotten about, being on full swing in a terribly dark foggy night, he heard a whistle, and looking back he could see a train coming on at an awful rate just behind him, when of course he put on more steam. But that didn't seem no good; for coming round the curve, he could see the train closing up fast; and at last, when half mad with fear, and ready to jump off, he saw that the train was on the up line, and the next minute it was alongside his; and there they two were racing abreast of each other; when he slackened, the other slackened; and when he did t'other, they did t'other. Same length train; same size engine; same lights; and fire door open like his; so that he could see the driver's face; and he says, says he, "I nearly dropped; for it was me as was driving that t'other train." On they goes together into the tunnel, and out they goes together. When he looked back, there was all the carriages lit up, and all just as if it was his own train; but whistling at the short stations when he did, and keeping an exactly same pace. It was like being in a cloud, the fog was so heavy; while the steam from both funnels mixed together.

'It was Christmas-eve, just like this; and yet cold as it was, he said, poor chap, the water dripped from his face as they rushed on. He knew it couldn't last long, for there'd be an up-train directly, and then there must be a fearful smash; but yet something seemed to tell him as there wouldn't; and watching as they went by station after station, he stood trembling at his post. All at once he could see the up-train coming; and then he put on a spurt so as to be ahead when the smash came; but that was no use, for the train kept aside his, and then all at once there was a shriek, and a rush, and the up-train was right behind; while along side his, there was that same engine just in the same place, and him a-driving it. Poor Tom use to make me creep when he told that tale, and he didn't live long arter; for one night there was something wrong in front of our engine, when he wouldn't wait till we stopped, but got along as we were going, and when I was expecting him to come back, and looked—for I'd been putting on more coal— there was some blood splashed all about the screen, and when I stopped and run back, there was poor Tom lying all to bits in the six foot. And they do say as he's been seen by some of the chaps a-running a ghost engine along the line at express rate, sometimes one line, and sometimes the other; and when he meets another train, there's a whistle and shriek, and he's gone.'

'That's werry pretty,' I says. 'I'd have that put in a book, if I was you;' and just then there was a bit of door banging, the second bell rang, the guard's whistle chirrupped, and then with a scream we started, the steam puffing out of the funnel in round white balls, and slowly spreading overhead till it came faster, and hanging over us like a plume of white feathers, it streamed back over the train.

Such a night: thick as thick; and every now and then it was 'bang, bang' as we went over the fog signals, and had to pull up and go very slowly, so that we were a good ten minutes going the first half-mile; and then past the first short station we went very slowly.

Thirty-five miles down was our first stoppage, where we took in water, and then another forty took us to Moreton, which was our next stoppage. By degrees we got on faster and faster, but the darkness was something terrible; while the signal lights at the short stations were almost useless, for I couldn't see them till we were close up, so being already very late through its being Christmas time I pushed her along, trusting to the line being all clear.

'Ah!' says Ben all at once, 'we're jest a-coming to the spot where poor Tom was cut up. Poor old chap,' he says; 'and it was just here as he first saw that train running by his side.'

Now, of course, I knew well enough that it was all gammon; but Ben talked so serious that it give me quite a shiver, and as we came suddenly upon the lights of a station, and raced through, my heart gave a jump, for it almost seemed as if a train was aside us; and even after passing the station, I looked out, for there was the train lights reflected on the fog on each side; but directly after I laughed at myself.

'It was just about here as he must have gone down,' says Ben to me—shouting in my ear, for we were going fast; 'and they do say as sometimes he mounts an engine and—*Yah—h—h!*' cried the poor fellow, falling down upon his hands and knees; while regularly took aback, I shrunk trembling up in the corner of the screen, and there stopped staring at a horrible looking figure, as seemed to start all at once into the light just as if he'd rose out of the coals. And then he came right up to me, for poor Ben had fainted.

As we were staring at one another I could see as the figure was buttoned up in an oilskin coat, while a close fur cap covered its head, and a handkercher was round the lower part of the face, so that I could see nothing but a pair of fierce bright eyes; and there it stood with one hand holding the side of the screen.

As long as I kept quiet it never moved; but directly I tried to get to my place it motioned me back. At last, half-desperate, I faced it; for a bit of thinking told me it must be a man, though Ben's story had a bit upset me.

'Here's Richford close here,' I shouts, 'where we stops;' but in a moment I saw the barrel of a pistol flashing in the light of the fire, and then I shrunk back again into the corner. If he would only have turned his back for a moment I should have pinned him, but he only glanced round once, when Ben shuffled back into the far corner of the tender; and there we were five minutes after rushing through Richford at full speed.

'Now,' he says, leaning down to me, 'rouse up, and push on faster; and don't you dare to stop till we get to Moreton:' and when a man says this to you with a pistol in his hand, why, what else can you do but mind.

'Now,' thinks I, 'this is a pretty go;' and then I kicks up Ben to come and stoke; but he wouldn't move, and what wanted doing I had to do myself; and so we raced on, for he made me put on more steam, seeing through my dodge in a moment, when I slackened instead; and on we went, with the night seeming to grow darker every moment. But it was race on, past station after station like a flash; and, one way and another, I began to grow excited. The guard had been letting go at the gong, but of course I could take no notice; no doubt, too, he had screwed down his break, but that seemed to make very little difference, with the metals in such a greasy state with the heavy frosty mist; and we raced along at such a rate as I've never been at since.

More than once, I made sure we should be crash into the tail of some goods-train; but though we passed several coming up, nothing was in our way, and at last, after the wildest ride I ever had, we began to get near Moreton, just as the water was beginning to get low. 'And now,' he says, fiercely, 'draw up just this side of the station;' and I nodded: but, for all that, I meant to have run right in, but he was too quick for me, and screwed down the break so that we stopped a good fifty yards short of the platform, when he leaped down, and I was going to follow, but a rough voice said, 'Stand back,' and I could see some one in front of me; while, by the lights of the train, I just saw a carriage next the tender opened, and some one hurried off to where a couple of lights were shining; and I could hear horses stamping; and then—it all didn't take a minute—there was the trampling of hoofs and the rolling of wheels, and the man who stopped me from getting down was gone.

'Get up,' I says to Ben, as we run into the station; 'it warn't a ghost:' but Ben seemed anything but sure on that point. While, as we finished our journey that night, I put that and that together, and made out as this chap, who must have been a plucky fellow, got from the next carriage on to the tender while we were crawling through the fog just outside London; and all to prevent stopping at Richford, where, no doubt, somebody had telegraphed for him to be taken; while, though the message would perhaps be repeated to Moreton, it was not sure to be so, and his dodge of stopping short where a conveyance was in waiting made that all right.

I drove the up-mail next day to town; but that was my last on the Great Central, for, when summoned before the Board, it was pay off, and go; and that, too, without a character.

AN EXCITING
CHRISTMAS EVE

by A. Conan Doyle

In the decade leading up to the immortal A *Study in
Scarlet*, Arthur Conan Doyle (1859–1930), a
struggling young doctor in Southsea, was churning
out a long line of short stories and thrillers for
numerous magazines and periodicals. 'An Exciting
Christmas Eve' was first published in the Christmas
number of the *Boy's Own Paper* (1883).

I t has often seemed to me to be a very strange and curious thing
that danger and trouble should follow those who are most anxious
to lead a quiet and uneventful life. I myself have been such a one,
and I find on looking back that it was in those very periods of my
existence which might have been most confidently reckoned on as
peaceful that some unexpected adventure has befallen me, like the
thunder-bolt from an unclouded sky which shook the nerves of old
Horace. Possibly my experience differs from that of other men, and I
may have been especially unfortunate. If so, there is the more reason
why I should mourn over my exceptional lot, and record it for the
benefit of those more happily circumstanced.

Just compare my life with that of Leopold Walderich, and you will
see what I complain of. We both come from Mulhausen, in Baden,
and that is why I single him out as an example, though many others
would do as well. He was a man who professed to be fond of
adventure. Now listen to what occurred. We went to Heidelberg

University together. I was quiet, studious, and unassuming; he was impetuous, reckless, and idle. For three years he revelled in every sort of riot, while I frequented the laboratories, and rarely deserted my books save for a hurried walk into the country when a pain in my head and ringing in my ears warned me that I was trifling with my constitution.

Yet during that period his life was comparatively uneventful, while my whole existence was a series of hairbreadth perils and escapes. I damaged my eyesight and nearly choked myself by the evolution of a poisonous gas. I swallowed a trichina in my ham, and was prostrated for weeks. I was hurled out of a second-floor window by an English lunatic because I ventured to quote the solemn and serious passage in Schoppheim's 'Weltgeschichte' which proves Waterloo to have been a purely Prussian victory, and throws grave doubts on the presence of any British force nearer than Brussels! Twice I was nearly drowned, and once I should have been precipitated from the parapet of the *schloss* but for the assistance of this same Englishman. These are a few of the incidents which occurred to me while endeavouring to read in seclusion for my degree.

Even in smaller matters this luck of mine held good. I can well remember, for example, that on one occasion the wilder spirits of the Badischer Corps ventured upon an unusually hare-brained escapade. There was a farmer about a couple of miles from the town whose name was Nicholas Bodeck. This man had made himself obnoxious to the students, and they determined to play a prank upon him in return. An enormous number of little caps were accordingly made with the colours of the corps upon them, and the conspirators invaded his premises in the middle of the night and gummed them upon the heads of all the fowls.

They certainly had a very comical effect, as I had an opportunity of judging, for I happened to pass that way in the morning. I supposed that Walderich and his friends carried out their little joke for excitement, knowing the farmer to be a resolute man. *They* got no excitement from it, however; it was I who got that. Activity was never my strong point, but certainly I ran those two miles that morning with incredible speed—and so did the five men with pitch-forks who ran behind me!

These things may seem trivial, but, as you say in England, a straw shows which way the wind blows, and these were only indications of what was to come.

I took my degree in medicine, and found myself Herr Doctor Otto von Spee. I then graduated in science, receiving much applause for my thesis, 'On the Explosive Compounds of the Tri-methyl Series'. I was quoted as an authority in works of science, and my professors prophesied that a great career lay before me. My studies, however, were suddenly put an end to by the outbreak of the great war with France.

Walderich volunteered into one of the crack regiments, fought in nearly every engagement, covered himself with glory, and came back unhurt to be decorated with the cross for valour. I was stationed in an ambulance which never even crossed the frontier, yet I succeeded in breaking my arm by tumbling over a stretcher, and in contracting erysipelas from one of the few wounds which came under my care. I got no medal or cross, and went back quietly to Berlin after it was all over, and there I settled as *privat docent* of chemistry and physics.

You will naturally ask what all this has to do with my Christmas story. You shall see in time that it is necessary I should tell you this, in order that you may appreciate that crowning event in my long list of misfortunes. You must remember also that I am a German and therefore somewhat long-winded perhaps, as my nation has the reputation of being. I have often admired the dashing, rattling manner of English story-tellers, but I fear if I were to attempt to imitate this it would be as if one of our own ponderous old Mulhausen storks were to adopt the pretty graceful airs of your Christmas robins. You shall hear in time all that I have to say about my Christmas Eve.

After I had settled in Berlin I endeavoured to combine the private practice of medicine with my labours as a *privat docent*, which corresponds to what you call a 'coach' in England. For some years I pursued this plan, but I found that my practice, being largely among the lower classes, favoured my unfortunate propensity for getting into trouble, and I determined to abandon it.

I took a secluded house, therefore, in a quiet quarter of the city, and there I gave myself up to scientific research, pursuing principally the same train of investigation which had originally attracted me— namely, the chemistry of explosive compounds.

My expenses were small, and all the money which I could spare was laid out on scientific instruments and mechanical contrivances of different sorts. Soon I had a snug little laboratory which, if not as pretentious as that at Heidelberg, was quite as well fitted to supply my wants. It is true that the neighbours grumbled, and that Gretchen, my housekeeper, had to be quieted with a five-mark piece, after having been blown up three separate times, and blown down once while engaged in fixing an electric wire upon the summit of an outhouse. These little matters, however, were easily settled, and I found my life rapidly assuming a peaceful complexion, of which I had long despaired.

I was happy—and what is more I was becoming famous. My 'Remarks on Cacodyl' in the 'Monthly Archives of Science' created no small sensation, and Herr Raubenthal of Bonn characterised them as, 'meisterlich,' though dissenting from many of my deductions. I was enabled, however, in a later contribution to the same journal to recount certain experiments which were sufficient to convince that eminent *savant* that my view of the matter was the correct one.

After this victory I was universally recognised as an authority in my own special branch, and as one of the foremost living workers at explosives. The Government appointed me to the torpedo commission at Kiel, and many other honours were bestowed upon me. One of the consequences of this sudden accession of celebrity was that I found myself in great request as a lecturer, both at scientific gatherings and at those meetings for the education of the people which have become so common in the metropolis. By these means my name got into the daily papers as one learned in such matters, and to this it is that I ascribe the events which I am about to narrate.

It was a raw windy Christmas Eve. The sleet pattered against the window panes, and the blast howled among the skeleton branches of the gaunt poplar-trees in my garden. There were few people in the street, and those few had their coats buttoned up, and their chins upon their breasts, and hurried rapidly homewards, staggering along against the force of the storm. Even the big policeman outside had ceased to clank up and down, and was crouching in a doorway for protection.

Many a lonely man might have felt uncomfortable upon such a night, but I was too interested in my work to have time for any sympathy with the state of the weather. A submarine mine was engaging my attention, and in a leaden tank in front of me I had stuck a small pellet of my new explosive. The problem was how far its destructive capacities would be modified by the action of the water. The matter was too important to allow me to feel despondent. Besides, one of Gretchen's lovers was in the kitchen, and his gruff expressions of satisfaction, whether with her charms or my beer, or both, were sufficiently audible to banish any suspicion of loneliness.

I was raising my battery on to the table, and was connecting the wires carefully so as to explode the charge, when I heard a short, quick step outside the window, and immediately afterwards a loud knock at the outer door.

Now I very seldom had a call from any of my limited number of acquaintances, and certainly never upon such a night as this. I was astonished for a moment; then concluding that it was a visitor of Gretchen's, I continued to work at my apparatus.

To my very great surprise, after Gretchen had opened the door there was some muttering in the hall, and then a quiet tap at the entrance of my sanctum, followed by the appearance of a tall lady whom I could vow that I had never seen in my life before.

Her face was covered by a thick dark veil, and her dress was of the same sombre colour, so that I concluded her to be a widow. She walked in with a decisive energetic step, and after glancing round, seated herself quietly upon the sofa between the voltaic pile and my stand of reagents—all this without saying a word, or apparently taking the slightest notice of my presence.

'Good evening, madam,' I remarked, when I had somehow recovered my composure.

'Would you do me a favour, doctor?' she replied, brusquely, in a harsh voice, which harmonised with her gaunt angular figure.

'Surely, madam,' I answered, in my most elegant manner. I remember a girl at Heidelberg used to say that I had a very fascinating way sometimes. Of course it was only a joke, but still something must have put it into her head or she would never have said it. 'What can I do for you?' I asked.

'You can send away that servant of yours, who is listening at the door.'

At this moment, before I could move hand or foot, there were a succession of tremendous bumps, followed by a terrible crash and a prolonged scream. It was evident that my unhappy domestic had fallen downstairs in her attempt to avoid detection. I was about to rise, but the stranger arrested me.

'Never mind now,' she said. 'We can proceed to business.'

I bowed my head to show that I was all attention.

'The fact is, doctor,' she continued, 'that I wish you to come back with me and give me your opinion upon a case.'

'My dear madam,' I answered, 'I have long retired from the practice of my profession. If you go down the street, however, you will see the surgery of Doctor Benger, who is a most competent man, and who will be happy to accompany you.'

'No, no,' cried my companion, in great distress. 'You or no one! You or no one! My poor dear husband cried out as I left him that Otto von Spee was the only man who could bring him back from the tomb. They will all be broken-hearted if I return without you. Besides, the professors at the hospital said that you were the only one in Europe who would be capable of dealing with it.'

Now, devoted as I was to scientific research, I had always had a conviction in my mind that I had the makings in me of a first-class practical physician. It was inexpressibly consoling to hear that the heads of the profession had endorsed this opinion by referring a curious case to my judgment. The more I thought of it, however, the more extraordinary did it seem. 'Are you sure?' I asked.

'Oh yes, quite sure.'

'But I am a specialist—a student of explosives. I have had very little experience in practice. What is the matter with your husband?'

'He has a tumour.'

'A tumour? I know nothing of tumours.'

'Oh come, dear Doctor von Spee; come and look at it!' implored the female, producing a handkerchief from her pocket and beginning to sob convulsively.

It was too much. I had lived a secluded life, and had never before seen a female in distress.

'Madam,' I said, 'I shall be happy to accompany you.'

I regretted that promise the moment it was uttered. There was a wild howl of wind in the chimney which reminded me of the inclemency of the night. However, my word was pledged, and there was no possibility of escape. I left the room with as cheerful an aspect as possible, while Gretchen wrapped a shawl round my neck and muffled me up to the best of her ability.

What could there be about this tumour, I wondered, which had induced the learned surgeons to refer it to my judgment—I who was rather an artillerist than a physician? Could it be that the growth was of such stony hardness that no knife could remove it, and that explosives were necessary for extraction? The idea was so comical that I could scarce refrain from laughing.

'Now, madam,' I said re-entering the study, 'I am at your disposal.' As I spoke I knocked against the electric machine, causing a slight transmission of the current along the wires, so that the submarine mine exploded with a crash, blowing a little column of water into the air. Accustomed as I was to such accidents, I confess that I was considerably startled by the suddenness of the occurrence. My companion, however, sat perfectly impassive upon the sofa, and then rose without the slightest sign of surprise or emotion, and walked out of the room.

'She has the nerves of a grenadier,' I mentally ejaculated, as I followed her into the street.

'Is it far?' I asked, as we started off through the storm.

'Not very far,' she answered; 'and I took the liberty of bringing a cab for you, for fear Herr Doctor might catch cold. Ah, here it comes.'

As she spoke, a closed carriage dashed along the road, and pulled up beside us.

'Have you got Otto von Spee?' asked a sallow-faced man, letting down the window and protruding his head.

'Yes, here he is.'

'Then shove him in.'

For the moment I was inclined to regard the expression as a playful figure of speech, but my companion soon dispelled the delusion by seizing me by the collar and hurling me, with what seemed superhuman strength, into the vehicle. I fell upon the floor, and was dragged on to a seat by the man, while the other sprang in, slammed the door, and the horses dashed off at a furious gallop.

I lay back in a state of bewilderment, hardly able to realise what had occurred. It was pitch dark inside the carriage, but I could hear my two companions conversing in low whispers. Once I attempted to expostulate and demand an explanation of their conduct, but a threatening growl, and a rough hand placed over my mouth, warned me to be silent. I was neither a wealthy man nor particularly well connected, nor was I a politician. What then, could be the object of these people in kidnapping me in such an elaborate fashion? The more I pondered over it, the more mysterious did it seem.

Once we halted for a moment, and a third man got into the carriage, who also inquired anxiously whether Otto von Spee had been secured, and expressed his satisfaction on being answered in the affirmative. After this stoppage we rattled along even more quickly than before, the vehicle rocking from side to side with the velocity, and the clatter of the horses' hoofs sounding above the howling of the gale. It seemed to me that we must have passed through every street in Berlin before, with a sudden jar, the coachman pulled up, and my captors intimated that I was to descend.

I had hardly time to look about me and realise the fact that I was in a narrow street in some low quarter of the city. A door opened in front of us, and the two men led me through it, while the herculean female followed us, effectually cutting off any hopes of escape.

We were in a long passage or corridor, feebly illuminated by a couple of flickering lamps, whose yellow glare seemed to intensity the darkness around them. After walking about twenty metres or more we came to a massive door, blocking our passage. One of my guardians struck it a blow with a stick which he carried in his hand, when it reverberated with a metallic clang, and swung open, closing with a snap behind us.

At this point I ventured to stop and expostulate with my companions once again. My only answer, however, was a shove from the individual behind me, which shot me through a half-opened door into a comfortable little chamber beyond. My captors followed in a more leisurely manner, and after turning the lock, they proceeded to seat themselves, motioning to me that I should do the same.

The room in which I found myself was small, but elegantly furnished. A fire was sparkling in the grate, and the bright colours of the handsome suite of furniture and variegated carpet helped to give it a cheering aspect. The pictures on the walls, however, went far towards neutralising this effect. They were very numerous, but every one of them treated of some unpleasant or murderous passage of history. Many of them were so distant that I was unable to decipher the inscriptions. To a scholar like myself, however, the majority were able to tell their own story. There was the lunatic Schtaps in the garden, making his attempt upon the life of the First Napoleon. Above it was a sketch of Orsini with his cowardly bomb, waiting silently among the loungers at the opera. A statuette of Ravaillac was placed upon a pedestal in the corner, while a large oil-painting of the strangling of the unhappy Emperor Paul in his bedchamber occupied the whole of one wall of the apartment.

These things did not tend to raise my spirits, and the appearance of my three companions was still less calculated to do so. I had several times doubted the sex of the individual who had seduced me from my comfortable home, but the veil had now been removed and revealed a dark moustache and sunburnt countenance, with a pair of searching, sinister eyes, which seemed to look into my very soul. Of the others, one was gaunt and cadaverous, the other insignificant-looking, with a straggling beard and unhealthy complexion.

[113]

'We are very sorry, Doctor von Spee, to be reduced to this necessity,' said the last-mentioned individual, 'but unhappily we had no other method of securing the pleasure of your society.'

I bowed—a little sulkily, I am afraid.

'I must apologise for any little liberties I have taken, above all for having deprived you of the satisfaction of beholding my husband's remarkable tumour,' said my original acquaintance.

I thought of the manner in which he had bundled me about like an empty portmanteau, and my bow was even more sulky than before.

'I trust, gentlemen,' I remarked, 'that since your practical joke has been so admirably carried out, you will now permit me to return to the studies which you have interrupted.'

'Not so fast, Herr Doctor—not so fast,' said the tall man, rising to his feet. 'We have a little duty which you shall perform before you leave us. It is nothing more nor less than to give a few inquirers into the truth a lesson upon your own special subject. Might I beg you to step in this direction?'

He walked over to a side door, painted of the same colour as the paper on the wall, and held it persuasively open. Resistance was useless, as the other confederates had also risen, and were standing on either side of me. I yielded to circumstances, and walked out as directed.

We passed down a second passage, rather shorter than the first, and much more brilliantly illuminated. At the end of it a heavy velvet curtain was hung, which covered a green baize folding-door. This was swung open, and I found myself, to my astonishment, in a large room in which a considerable number of people were assembled. They were arranged in long rows, and sat so as to face a raised platform at one end of the apartment, on which was a single chair, with a small round table, littered with a number of objects.

My companions ushered me in, and our entrance was greeted with considerable applause. It was clear that we had been awaited, for there was a general movement of expectation throughout the assembly. Glancing round, I could see that the majority of the company were dressed as artisans or labourers. There were some, however, who were respectably and even fashionably attired, and a few whose blue coats and gilt shoulder-bands proclaimed them to be officers in the army. Their nationalities seemed almost as varied as their occupations. I could distinguish the dolichocephalic head of the Teuton, the round, curl-covered cranium of the Celt, and the prognathous jaw and savage features of the Slav. I could almost have imagined myself looking into one of the cabinets of casts in my friend Landerstein's anthropological museum.

However, I had not much time for wonder or reflection. One of my guardians led me across the room, and I found myself standing at the table, which I have already mentioned as being situated upon a raised dais. My appearance in this situation was the signal for a fresh outburst of applause, which, with clapping of hands and drumming of sticks upon the floor, lasted for some considerable time.

When it had subsided, the gaunt man who had come with me in the carriage walked up to the dais and addressed a few words to the audience. 'Gentlemen,' he said, 'you will perceive that the committee have succeeded in keeping their promise and of bringing the celebrated — ('beruhmte' was the word he used) — Doctor Otto von Spee to address you.' Here there was renewed applause.

'Doctor,' he continued, turning to me, 'I think a few words of public explanation will not be amiss in this matter. You are well known as an authority upon explosives. Now all these gentlemen and myself have an interest in this subject, and would gladly listen to your views upon it. We are particularly anxious that you should give us clear and precise directions as to the method of preparing dynamite, guncotton, and other such substances, as we sometimes have a little difficulty in obtaining such things for our experiments. You shall also tell us about the effect of temperature, water, and other agents upon these substances, the best method of storing them, and the way of using them to the greatest advantage. For our part, we shall listen attentively and treat you well, always provided that you make no attempt to summon aid or to escape. Should you be so ill-advised as to do either'—here he slapped his pocket—'you shall become as intimately acquainted with projectiles as you now are with explosives.' I cannot say that this struck me as a good joke, but it seemed to meet considerable favour among the audience.

'I wish to add a few words to the remarks of our learned president,' said a small man, rising up from among the first line of the company. 'I have placed upon the table such materials as I could lay my hands upon in order that the learned doctor may be able to illustrate his discourse by any experiments which he may think appropriate. I may warn him, in conclusion, to speak somewhat slowly and distinctly, as some of his hearers are but imperfectly acquainted with the German language.'

Here was my old luck again with a vengeance! At a time when Walderich and every gay dog in Berlin were snoring peacefully in their beds, I—I, Doctor Otto von Spee, the modest man of science—was lecturing to a murderous secret organisation—for my audience could be nothing else—and teaching them to forge the weapons with which they were to attack society and everything which should be treasured and revered. And on such a night as this too! Should I, then, put it in their power to convert a house into an arsenal, to destroy the stability of the Fatherland, and even perhaps attempt the life of my beloved kaiser? Never! I swore it—never!

Most small men who wear spectacles are obstinate. I am a small man with spectacles, and I was no exception to the rule. I clenched my teeth, and felt that *ruat cœlum*, never a word should pass my lips that might be of any help to them. I should not refuse to lecture, but I was determined to avoid those very points upon which they desired to be instructed.

I was not allowed much time for meditation. An ominous murmur among the audience, and a shuffling of feet upon the floor, betokened their impatience. I must say, however, that many of them seemed actuated with rather kindly feelings towards me, more particularly one stoutish individual of a well-marked Celtic type, who, not content with smiling all over his florid countenance, waved his arms occasionally in motions intended to indicate sympathy and inspire confidence.

I stepped up to the table, which was covered all over with such objects as were thought to have a bearing upon my subject. Some of them were rather curious—a lump of salt, an iron teapot, part of the broken axle of a wheel, and a large pair of kitchen bellows. Others were more appropriate. There was a piece of guncotton which could not have weighed less than a couple of pounds, coarse cotton, starch, various acids, a Bunsen burner, tubes of fulminate of mercury, some dynamite powder, and a large pitcher of water. There was also a carafe and tumbler for my own use, should I feel so disposed.

'Meine herren,' I began, with perhaps a slight quaver in my voice, 'we have met here tonight for the purpose of studying dynamite and other explosives.' It flowed naturally from my lips, as it was the stereotyped formula with which my discourses at the Education-ische Institut were usually commenced. My audience seemed, however, to be much amused, and the florid Celt was convulsed with admiration and merriment. Even the forbidding-looking man who had been referred to as the president condescended to smile his approval and remark that I adapted myself readily to my circumstances.

'These substances,' I continued, 'are powerful agents either for good or for evil. For good when used for the quarrying of rocks, the removal of impediments to navigation, or the destruction of houses during a conflagration. For evil—'

'I think you had better pass on to something more practical,' said the president, grimly.

'On dipping starch into certain liquids,' I resumed, 'it is found to assume an explosive property. The attention of a learned countryman of ours, the chemist Schönbein, was directed to the fact, and he found that by treating cotton in a similar manner the effect was enormously increased. Schönbein was a man respected among his contemporaries, devoted to his country, and loyal—'

'Pass on!' said the president.

'After being treated in this fashion,' I continued, 'the cotton is found to gain eighty per cent. in weight. This substance is more susceptible to an increase of temperature than gunpowder, igniting at 300° Fahrenheit, while the latter requires a heat of 560° for its explosion. Guncotton can also be exploded by a blow, which is not the case with a mixture of carbon, sulphur, and saltpetre.'

Here there were some angry murmurs among the company, and the president interrupted me for the third time.

'These gentlemen complain,' he said, 'that you have left no definite impression upon their minds as to how the substance is manufactured. Perhaps you will kindly dwell more fully upon the point.'

'I have no further remarks to make,' I said.

There was another threatening murmur, and the president took something out of the pocket of his coat, and toyed with it negligently. 'I think you had better reconsider your decision,' he remarked.

Most little men with spectacles are timid. Again I was no exception to the rule. I am ashamed to say that the peril of my Fatherland and even of my kaiser suddenly vanished from my recollection. I only realised that I, Otto von Spee, was standing upon the brink of eternity. After all, I argued, they could find out for themselves in any book upon chemistry. Why should my valuable life be sacrificed for such a trifle? I resumed my lecture with somewhat undignified haste.

'Guncotton is manufactured by steeping cotton waste in nitric acid. The explosion is caused by the oxygen of the acid combining with the carbon of the wool. It should be well cleaned with water after manufacture, otherwise the superfluous nitric acid acts directly upon the wool, charring it and gradually reducing it to a gummy mass.

During this process heat is often evolved sufficient to explode the cotton, so that it is a dangerous matter to neglect the cleaning. After this a little sulphuric acid may be used to get rid of the moisture, when the substance is ready for use.'

There was considerable applause at this point of my discourse, several of the audience taking notes of my remarks.

While I had been speaking I had been making a careful survey of the room in the hope of seeing some possibility of escape. The dais upon which I stood extended as far as the side wall, in which there was a window. The window was half open, and, could I reach it, there appeared to be a deserted looking garden outside, which might communicate with the street. No one could intercept me before I reached the window, but then there was the deadly weapon with which my cadaverous acquaintance was still trifling. He was sitting on the other side, and the table would partially protect me should I venture upon a dash. Could I screw up my courage to make an attempt? Not yet, at any rate.

'General von Link,' I continued, 'the Austrian artillerist, is one of our leading authorities upon guncotton. He experimented upon it in field-pieces, but—'

'Never mind that,' said the president.

'After being manufactured, guncotton may be compressed under water. When compressed it is perfectly safe, and cannot be discharged. This sample which we have upon the table is not compressed. No amount of heat will have any effect upon the wet cotton. In an experiment tried in England a storehouse containing guncotton was burned down without there being any explosion. If, however, a charge of fulminated mercury, or a small piece of dry cotton, be fired in connection with a damp disc, it will be sufficient to discharge it. I shall now proceed to demonstrate this to you by an experiment.'

An idea had come into my mind. Upon the table there was lying a mixture of sugar and chlorate of potash, used with sulphuric acid as a fuse for mining purposes. A bottle of the acid was also ready to my hand. I knew the white dense cloud of smoke which is raised by the imperfect combustion of these bodies. Could I make it serve as a screen between the weapon of the president and myself?

For a moment the plan seemed wild and unfeasible; still, it offered some chance of escape, and the more I thought it over the more reconciled I became to it. Of course, even after getting through the window there was the possibility that the garden might prove to be a *cul-de-sac,* and that my pursuers might overtake me. But then, on the other hand, I had no guarantee that I might not be murdered at the conclusion of my lecture. From what I knew of the habits of such men I considered it to be extremely probable. It was better to risk—but no, I would not think of what I was risking.

'I am now going to show you the effect of fulminate of mercury upon a small piece of damp cotton,' I said, shaking out the sugar and chlorate of potash upon the edge of the table and pushing the large piece of cotton to the other end to be out of danger from the effects of the explosion.

'You will observe that the fact of the substance having been soaked with water does not in any way hinder its action.' Here I poured the sulphuric acid over the mixture, dropped the bottle, and fled for the window amid a perfect cloud of smoke.

Most little men with spectacles are not remarkable for activity. Ha! there at last I proved myself to be an exception. I seemed hardly to put my foot to the ground between leaving the table and shooting out through the window as the equestrians fly through hoops in the circus. I was well outside before the sharp crack which I was expecting sounded in the chamber behind me, and then—

Ah! what then? How can I ever hope to describe it? There was a low, deep rumble, which seemed to shake the ground, swelling and swelling in sound until it culminated in a roar which split the very heavens. Flames danced before my eyes, burning wood and stones and *débris* came clattering down around me, and as I stared about me in bewilderment I received a crushing blow upon the head, and fell.

How long I may have remained unconscious it is difficult to say. Some time, at any rate, for when I came to myself I was stretched upon the bed in my own little chamber at home, while the devoted Gretchen bathed my temples with vinegar and water. In the doorway were standing a couple of stalwart *polizei diener,* who bobbed their helmeted heads and grinned their satisfaction on seeing that I was returning to consciousness.

It was some while before I could recall anything of what had passed. Then gradually came the recollection of my mysterious visitor, of the wild drive through the storm, of the impromptu lecture on dynamite, and lastly of some strange and unaccountable accident. Strange it still remains, but I think that when we reflect that the table was between the bullet and me, and that on that table were two pounds of guncotton liable to ignition at a blow, we have not very far to go for an explanation. I have fired a pistol at a distance into a small piece of the same substance since that occasion with very much the same result.

And where was the house? you will ask, and what was the fate of its inmates? Ah! there my lips are sealed. The police of the Fatherland are active and cunning, and they have commanded me to say nothing—not even to my dearest friend—upon either point. No doubt they have their reasons for it, and I must obey. Perhaps they wish other conspirators to imagine that more has been found out than is actually the case. I may say, however, that it is not conducive to long life or perfect health to be present on such an occasion. That, at least, no one can object to.

I am nearly well again now, thanks to Gretchen and Dr Benger, who lives down the road. I can hobble about, and my neighbours are already beginning to complain of the noxious vapours which I evolve. I fear I have not quite the same enthusiasm, however, upon the subject of explosives as I entertained before my midnight lecture on dynamite. The subject seems to have lost many of its charms. It may be that in the course of time I may return to my first love once again; at present, however, I remain a quiet *privat docent* of the more elementary branches of chemistry. It is that very quietness which weighs upon my mind. I fear that I am on the verge of some other unexpected adventure. There is one thing, however, upon which I am unalterably determined. Should every relative that I have in the world, with the Imperial family and half the population of Berlin, be clamouring at my door for medical advice, I shall never again protrude my head after nightfall. I am content to work away in my own little groove, and have laid aside for ever the pretensions to be looked upon as a practical physician which I entertained before that eventful Christmas Eve.

REMORSELESS VENGEANCE

by Guy Boothby

A young Australian writer who achieved
quick and early success, and became extremely
prolific, was Guy Boothby (1867–1905). When
his first book, *On the Wallaby*, a record of his
journey across Australia in 1892, was a runaway
bestseller, he moved to England and produced a
series of exciting fast-paced thrillers for Ward Lock
and the *Windsor* magazine. His best-known
creation was the mysterious Dr Nikola, who
featured in five novels. 'Remorseless Vengeance'
appeared in his collection
Uncle Joe's Legacy (1902).

To use that expressive South Sea phrase, I have had the misfortune to be 'on the beach' in a variety of places in my time. There are people who say that it is worse to be stranded in Trafalgar Square than, shall we say, Honolulu or Rangoon. Be that as it may, the worst time I ever had was that of which I am now going to tell you. I had crossed the Pacific from San Francisco before the mast on an American mail boat, had left her in Hong Kong, and had made my way down to Singapore on a collier. As matters did not look very bright there, I signed aboard a Dutch boat for Batavia, intending to work my way on to Australia. It was in Batavia, however, that the real trouble began. As soon as I arrived I fell ill, and the little money I had managed to scrape together melted like snow before the mid-day sun. What to do I knew not—I was on my beam ends. I had nothing to sell, even if there were anyone to buy, and horrible visions of Dutch gaols began to obtrude themselves upon me.

It was on the night of the 23rd of December, such a night as I'll be bound they were not having in the old country. There was not a cloud in the sky, and the stars shone like the lamps along the Thames Embankment when you look at them from Waterloo Bridge. I was smoking in the brick-paved verandah of the hotel and wondering how I was going to pay my bill, when a man entered the gates of the hotel and walked across the garden and along the verandah towards where I was seated. I noticed that he was very tall, very broad-shouldered, and that he carried himself like a man who liked his own way and generally managed to get it.

'I wonder who he can be?' I said to myself, and half expected that he would pass me and proceed in the direction of the manager's office. My astonishment may be imagined, therefore, when he picked up a chair from beside the wall and seated himself at my side.

'Good evening,' he said, as calmly as you might address a friend on the top of a bus.

'Good evening,' I replied in the same tone.

'Frank Riddington is your name, I believe?' he continued, still with the same composure.

'I believe so,' I answered, 'but I don't know how you became aware of it.'

'That's neither here nor there,' he answered; 'putting other matters aside for the moment, let me give you some news.'

He paused for a moment and puffed meditatively at his cigar.

'I don't know whether you're aware that there's an amiable plot on hand in this hotel to kick you into the street in the morning,' he went on. 'The proprietor seems to think it unlikely that you will be able to settle your account.'

'And, by Jove, he is not far wrong,' I replied. 'It's Christmas time, I know, and I am probably in bed and dreaming. You're undoubtedly the fairy godmother sent to help me out of my difficulty.'

He laughed—a short, sharp laugh.

'How do you propose to do it?'

'By putting a piece of business in your way. I want your assistance, and if you will give it to me I am prepared to hand you sufficient money not only to settle your bill, but to leave a bit over. What's more, you can leave Batavia, if you like.'

'Provided the business of which you speak is satisfactory,' I replied, 'you can call it settled. What am I to do?'

He took several long puffs at his cigar.

'You have heard of General Van der Vaal?'

'The man who, until lately, has been commanding the Dutch forces up in Achin?'

'The same. He arrived in Batavia three days ago. His house is situated on the King's Plain, three-quarters of a mile or so from here.'

'Well, what about him?'

Leaning a little towards me, and sinking his voice, he continued:

'I want General Van der Vaal—badly—and tonight!'

For a moment I had doubts as to his sanity.

'I'm afraid I haven't quite grasped the situation,' I said. 'Do I understand that you are going to abduct General Van der Vaal?'

'Exactly!' he replied. 'I am going to deport him from the island. You need not ask why, at this stage of the proceedings. I shouldn't have brought you into the matter at all, but that my mate fell ill, and I had to find a substitute.'

'You haven't told me your name yet,' I replied.

'It slipped my memory,' he answered, 'but you are welcome to it now. I am Captain Berringer!'

You may imagine my surprise. Here I was sitting talking face to face with the notorious Captain Berringer, whose doings were known from Rangoon to Vladivostock—from Nagasaki to Sourabaya. He and his brother—of whom, by the way, nothing had been heard for some time past—had been more than suspected of flagrant acts of piracy. They were well known to the Dutch as pearl stealers in prohibited waters. The Russians had threatened to hang them for seal-stealing in Behring Straits, while the French had some charges against them in Tonkin that would ensure them a considerable sojourn there should they appear in that neighbourhood again.

'Well, what do you say to my proposal?' he asked. 'It will be as easy to accomplish as it will be for them to turn you into the street in the morning.'

I knew this well enough, but I saw that if he happened to fail I should, in all probability, be even worse off than before.

'Where's your vessel,' I asked, feeling sure that he had one near at hand.

'Dodging about off the coast,' he said. 'We'll pick her up before daylight.'

[123]

'And you'll take me with you?'

'That's as you please,' he answered.

'I'll come right enough. Batavia will be too hot for me after tonight. But first you must hand over the money. I must settle with that little beast of a proprietor tonight.'

'I like your honesty,' he said, with a sneer. 'Under the circumstances it is so easy to run away without paying.'

'Captain Berringer,' said I, 'whatever I may be now, I was once a gentleman.'

A quarter-of-an-hour later the bill was paid, and I had made my arrangements to meet my employer outside the Harmonic Club punctually at midnight. I am not going to say that I was not nervous, for it would not be the truth. Van der Vaal's reputation was a cruel one, and if he got the upper hand of us we should be likely to receive but scant mercy. Punctually to the minute I reached the rendezvous, where I found the captain awaiting me. Then we set off in the direction of the King's Plain, as you may suppose keeping well in the shadow of the trees. We had not walked very far before Berringer placed a revolver into my hand, which I slipped into my pocket.

'Let's hope we shan't have to use them,' he said; 'but there's nothing like being prepared.'

By the time we had climbed the wall and were approaching the house, still keeping in the shadow of the trees, I was beginning to think I had had enough of the adventure, but it was too late to draw back, even had the Captain permitted such a thing.

Suddenly the Captain laid his hand on my arm.

'His room is at the end on this side,' he whispered. 'He sleeps with his window open, and his bed is in the furthest corner. His lamp is still burning, but let us hope that he is asleep. If he gives the alarm we're done for.'

I won't deny that I was too frightened to answer him. My fear, however, did not prevent me from following him into the clump of trees near the steps that led to the verandah. Here we slipped off our boots, made our preparations, and then tiptoed with the utmost care across the path, up the steps, and in the direction of the General's room. That he was a strict disciplinarian we were aware, and that, in consequence, we knew that his watchman was likely to be a watchman in the real sense of the word.

The heavy breathing that came from the further corner of the room told us that the man we wanted was fast asleep. A faint light, from a wick which floated in a bowl of cocoanut oil, illuminated the room, and showed us a large bed of the Dutch pattern, closely veiled with mosquito curtains. Towards this we made our way. On it, stretched out at full length, was the figure of a man. I lifted the netting while the Captain prepared for the struggle. A moment later he leapt upon his victim, seized him by the throat and pinioned him. A gag was quickly thrust into his mouth, whilst I took hold of his wrists. In less time than it takes to tell he was bound hand and foot, unable either to resist or to summon help.

'Bundle up some of his clothes,' whispered Berringer, pointing to some garments on a chair. 'Then pick up his heels, while I'll take his shoulders. But not a sound as you love your life.'

In less than ten minutes we had carried him across the grounds, had lifted him over the wall, where we found a native cart waiting for us, and had stowed him and ourselves away in it.

'Now for Tanjong Prick,' said the Captain. 'We must be out of the islands before daybreak.'

At a prearranged spot some four or five miles from the port we pulled up beneath a small tope of palms.

'Are you still bent upon accompanying me?' asked the Captain, as we lifted the inanimate General from the cart and placed him on the ground.

'More than ever,' I replied. 'Java shall see me no more.'

Berringer consulted his watch, and found the time to be exactly half-past two. A second later a shrill whistle reached us from the beach.

'That's the boat,' said Berringer. 'Now let's carry him down to her.'

We accordingly set off in the direction indicated. It was not, however, until we were alongside a smart-looking brig, and I was clambering aboard, that I felt in any way easy in my mind.

'Pick him up and bring him aft to the cuddy,' said the skipper to two of the hands, indicating the prostrate General. Then turning to the second mate, who was standing by, he added: 'Make sail, and let's get out of this. Follow me, Mr Riddington.'

I accompanied him along the deck, and from it into the cuddy, the two sailors and their heavy burden preceding us. Once there the wretched man's bonds were loosed. They had been tight enough, goodness knows, for when we released him he was so weak that he could not stand, but sank down on one of the seats beside the table, and buried his face in his hands.

'What does this mean?' he asked at last, looking up at us with a pitiable assumption of dignity. 'Why have you brought me here?'

'That's easily told,' said the Captain. 'Last Christmas you were commanding in Achin. Do you remember an Englishman named Bernard Watson who threw in his lot with them?'

'I hanged him on Christmas Day,' said the other, with a touch of his old spirit.

'Exactly,' said Berringer. 'And that's why you're here tonight. He was my brother. We will cry "quits" when I hang you on the yard-arm on Christmas morning.'

'Good heavens, Captain!' I cried, 'you're surely not going to do this?'

'I am,' he answered, with a firmness there was no mistaking. The idea was too horrible to contemplate. I tried to convince myself that, had I known what the end would be, I should have taken no part in it.

A cabin had already been prepared for the General, and to it he was forthwith conducted. The door having been closed and locked upon him, the Captain and I were left alone together. I implored him to reconsider his decision.

'I never reconsider my decisions,' he answered. 'The man shall hang at sunrise the day after tomorrow. He hanged my brother in cold blood, and I'll do the same for him. That's enough. Now I must go and look at my mate, he's been ailing this week past. If you want food the steward will bring it to you, and if you want a bunk—well, you can help yourself.'

With that he turned on his heel, and left me.

Here I was in a nice position. To all intents and purposes I had aided and abetted a murder, and if any of Berringer's crew should care to turn Queen's evidence I should find myself in the dock, a convicted murderer. In vain I set my wits to work to try and find some scheme which might save the wretched man and myself. I could discover none, however.

All the next day we sailed on, heading for the Northern Australian Coast, so it seemed to me. I met the Captain at meals, and upon the deck, but he appeared morose and sullen, gave his orders in peremptory jerks, and never once, so far as I heard, alluded to the unhappy man below. I attempted to broach the subject to the mate, in the hope that he might take the same view of it as I did, but I soon found that my advances in that quarter were not likely to be favourably received. The crew, as I soon discovered, were Kanakas, with two exceptions, and devoted to their Captain. I was quite certain that they would do nothing but what he wished. Such a Christmas Eve I sincerely trust I may never spend again.

Late in the afternoon I bearded the Captain in his cabin, and once more endeavoured to induce him to think well before committing such an act. Ten minutes later I was back in the cuddy, a wiser and sadder man. From that moment I resigned myself to the inevitable.

At half-past six that evening the Captain and I dined together in solitary state. Afterwards I went on deck. It was a beautiful moonlight night with scarcely enough wind to fill the canvas. The sea was as smooth as glass, with a long train of phosphorous light in our wake. I had seen nothing of the skipper since eight bells. At about ten o'clock, however, and just as I was thinking of turning in, he emerged from the companion. A few strides brought him to my side.

'A fine night, Riddington,' he said, in a strange, hard voice, very unlike his usual tone.

'A very fine night,' I answered.

'Riddington,' he began again, with sudden vehemence, 'do you believe in ghosts?'

'I have never thought much about the matter,' I answered. 'Why do you ask?'

'Because I've seen a ghost tonight,' he replied. 'The ghost of my brother Bernard, who was hanged by that man locked in the cabin below, exactly a year ago, at daybreak. Don't make any mistake about what I'm saying. You can feel my pulse, if you like, and you will find it beating as steady as ever it has done in my life. I haven't touched a drop of liquor today, and I honestly believe I'm as sane a man as there is in the world. Yet I tell you that, not a quarter of an hour ago, my brother stood beside me in my cabin.'

Not knowing what answer to make, I held my tongue for the moment. At last I spoke.

'Did he say anything?' I inquired.

'He told me that I should not be permitted to execute my vengeance on Van der Vaal! It was to be left to him to deal with him. But I've passed my word, and I'll not depart from it. Ghost or no ghost, he hangs at sunrise.'

So saying, he turned and walked away from me, and went below.

I am not going to pretend that I slept that night. Of one thing I am quite certain, and that is that the Captain did not leave his cabin all night. Half an hour before daybreak, however, he came to my cabin.

'Come on deck,' he said. 'The time is up.'

I followed him, to find all the ghastly preparations complete. Once more I pleaded for mercy with all the strength at my command, and once more I failed to move him. Even the vision he had declared he had seen seemed now to be forgotten.

'Bring him on deck,' he said at last, turning to the mate and handing him the key of the cabin as he spoke. The other disappeared, and I, unable to control myself, went to the side of the vessel and looked down at the still water below. The brig was scarcely moving. Presently I heard the noise of feet in the companion, and turning, with a white face, no doubt, I saw the mate and two of the hands emerge from the hatchway. They approached the Captain, who seemed not to see them. To the amazement of everyone, he was looking straight before him across the poop, with an expression of indescribable terror on his face. Then, with a crash, he lost his balance and fell forward upon the deck. We ran to his assistance, but were too late. He was dead.

Who shall say what he had seen in that terrible half-minute? The mate and I looked at each other in stupefied bewilderment. I was the first to find my voice.

'The General?'

'Dead,' the other replied. 'He died as we entered the cabin to fetch him out. God help me—you never saw such a sight! It looked as if he were fighting with someone whom we could not see, and was being slowly strangled.'

I waited to hear no more, but turned and walked aft. I am not a superstitious man, but I felt that the Captain's brother had been right after all, when he had said that he would take the matter of revenge into his own hands.

THE VANISHING HOUSE

by Bernard Capes

Bernard Capes (1854–1918) was another equally
popular and busy author at the turn of the century,
equally adept in the genres of romantic and mystery
fiction, especially the bizarre and the supernatural.
This unusual story, concerning a musician who
plays before a strange house that suddenly appears
in the snow, is taken from the first (and best)
of Capes's six collections, *At A Winter's
Fire* (1899).

'**M**y grandfather,' said the banjo, 'drank "dog's-nose," my father drank "dog's-nose," and I drink "dog's-nose." If that ain't heredity, there's no virtue in the board schools.'

'Ah!' said the piccolo, 'you're always a-boasting of your science. And so, I suppose, your son'll drink "dog's-nose," too?'

'No,' retorted the banjo, with a rumbling laugh, like wind in the bung-hole of an empty cask; 'for I ain't got none. The family ends with me; which is a pity, for I'm a full-stop to be proud on.'

He was an enormous, tun-bellied person—a mere mound of expressionless flesh, whose size alone was an investment that paid a perpetual dividend of laughter. When, as with the rest of his company, his face was blackened, it looked like a specimen coal on a pedestal in a museum.

There was Christmas company in the Good Intent, and the sanded tap-room, with its trestle tables and sprigs of holly stuck under sooty beams reeked with smoke and the steam of hot gin and water.

'How much could you put down of a night, Jack?' said a little grinning man by the door.

'Why,' said the banjo, 'enough to lay the dustiest ghost as ever walked.'

'*Could* you, now?' said the little man.

'Ah!' said the banjo, chuckling. 'There's nothing like settin' one sperit to lay another; and there I could give you proof number two of heredity.'

'What! Don't you go for to say you ever see'd a ghost!'

'Haven't I? What are you whisperin' about, you blushful chap there by the winder?'

'I was only remarkin', sir, 'twere snawin' like the devil.'

'*Is* it? Then the devil has been misjudged these eighteen hundred and ninety odd years.'

'But *did* you ever see a ghost?' said the little grinning man, pursuing his subject.

'No, I didn't, sir,' mimicked the banjo, 'saving in coffee grounds. But my grandfather in *his* cups see'd one; which brings us to number three in the matter of heredity.'

'Give us the story, Jack,' said the 'bones,' whose agued shins were extemporizing a rattle on their own account before the fire.

'Well, I don't mind,' said the fat man. 'It's seasonable; and I'm seasonable, like the blessed plum-pudden, I am; and the more burnt brandy you set about me, the richer and headier I'll go down.'

'You'd be a jolly old pudden to digest,' said the piccolo.

'You blow your aggravation into your pipe and sealing-wax the stops,' said his friend.

He drew critically at his 'churchwarden' a moment or so, leaned forward, emptied his glass into his capacious receptacles, and, giving his stomach a shift, as if to accommodate it to its new burden, proceeded as follows: —

'Music and malt is my nat'ral inheritance. My grandfather blew his "dog's-nose," and drank his clarinet like a artist; and my father—'

'What did you say your grandfather did?' asked the piccolo.

'He played the clarinet.'

'You said he blew his "dog's-nose." '

'Don't be a ass, Fred!' said the banjo, aggrieved. 'How the blazes could a man blow his dog's nose, unless he muzzled it with a handkercher, and then twisted its tail? He played the clarinet, I say;

and my father played the musical glasses, which was a form of harmony pertiklerly genial to him. Amongst us we've piped out a good long century—ah! we have, for all I look sich a babby bursting on sops and spoon meat.'

'What!' said the little man by the door. 'You don't include them cockt hatses in your expeerunce?'

'My grandfather wore 'em, sir. He wore a play-actin' coat, too, and buckles to his shoes, when he'd got any; and he and a friend or two made a permanency of "waits" (only they called 'em according to the season), and got their profit goin' from house to house, principally in the country, and discoursin' music at the low rate of whatever they could get for it.'

'Ain't you comin' to the ghost, Jack?' said the little man hungrily.

'All in course, sir. Well, gentlemen, it was hard times pretty often with my grandfather and his friends, as you may suppose; and never so much as when they had to trudge it across country, with the nor'-easter buzzin' in their teeth and the snow piled on their cockt hats like lemon sponge on entry dishes. The rewards, I've heard him say—for he lived to be ninety, nevertheless—was poor compensation for the drifts, and the inflienza, and the broken chilblains; but now and again they'd get a fair skinful of liquor from a jolly squire, as 'd set 'em up like boggarts mended wi' new broomsticks.'

'Ho-haw!' broke in a hurdle-maker in a corner; and then, regretting the publicity of his merriment, put his fingers bashfully to his stubble lips.

'Now,' said the banjo, 'it's of a pertikler night and a pertikler skinful that I'm a-going to tell you; and that night fell dark, and that skinful were took a hundred years ago this December, as I'm a Jack-pudden!'

He paused a moment for effect, before he went on:—

'They were down in the sou'-west country, which they little knew; and were anighing Winchester city, or should 'a' been. But they got muzzed on the ungodly downs, and before they guessed, they was off the track. My good hat! there they was, as lost in the snow as three nutshells a-sinkin' into a hasty pudden. Well, they wandered round; pretty confident at first, but getting madder and madder as every sense of their bearings slipped from them. And the bitter cold took their vitals, so as they saw nothing but a great winding sheet stretched abroad for to wrap their dead carcases in.

'At last my grandfather he stopt and pulled hisself together with an awful face, and says he: "We're Christmas pie for the carrying-on

[131]

crows if we don't prove ourselves human. Let's fetch out our pipes and blow our trouble into 'em." So they stood together, like as if they was before a house, and they played "Kate of Aberdare" mighty dismal and flat, for their fingers froze to the keys.

'Now, I tell you, they hadn't climbed over the first stave, when there come a skirl of wind and spindrift of snow as almost took them off of their feet; and, on the going down of it, Jem Sloke, as played the hautboy, dropped the reed from his mouth, and called out, "Sakes alive! if we fools ain't been standin' outside a gentleman's gate all the time, and not known' it!"

'You might 'a' knocked the three of 'em down wi' a barley straw, as they stared and stared, and then fell into a low, enjoyin' laugh. For they was standin' not six fut from a tall iron gate in a stone wall, and behind these was a great house showin' out dim, with the winders all lighted up.

' "Lord!" chuckled my grandfather, "to think o' the tricks o' this vagarious country! But, as we're here, we'll go on and give 'em a taste of our quality."

'They put new heart into the next movement, as you may guess; and they hadn't fair started on it, when the door of the house swung open, and down the shaft of light that shot out as far as the gate there come a smiling young gal, with a tray of glasses in her hands.

'Now she come to the bars; and she took and put a glass through, not sayin' nothin', but invitin' some one to drink with a silent laugh.

'Did any one take that glass? Of course he did, you'll be thinkin'; and you'll be thinkin' wrong. Not a man of the three moved. They was struck like as stone, and their lips was gone the colour of sloe berries. Not a man took the glass. For why? The moment the gal presented it, each saw the face of a thing lookin' out of the winder over the porch, and the face was hidjus beyond words, and the shadder of it, with the light behind, stretched out and reached to the gal, and made her hidjus, too.

'At last my grandfather give a groan and put out his hand; and, as he did it, the face went, and the gal was beautiful to see agen.

' "Death and the devil!" said he. "It's one or both, either way; and I prefer 'em hot to cold!"

'He drank off half the glass, smacked his lips, and stood staring a moment.

' "Dear, dear!" said the gal, in a voice like falling water, "you've drunk blood, sir!"

'My grandfather gave a yell, slapped the rest of the liquor in the faces of his friends, and threw the cup agen the bars. It broke with a noise like thunder, and at that he up'd with his hands and fell full length into the snow.'

There was a pause. The little man by the door was twisting nervously in his chair.

'He came to—of course, he came to?' said he at length.

'He come to,' said the banjo solemnly, 'in the bitter break of dawn; that is, he come to as much of hisself as he ever was after. He give a squiggle and lifted his head; and there was he and his friends a-lyin' on the snow of the high downs.'

'And the house and the gal?'

'Narry a sign of either, sir, but just the sky and the white stretch; and one other thing.'

'And what was that?'

'A stain of red sunk in where the cup had spilt.'

There was a second pause, and the banjo blew into the bowl of his pipe.

'They cleared out of that neighbourhood double quick, you'll bet,' said he. 'But my grandfather was never the same man agen. His face took purple, while his friends' only remained splashed with red, same as birth marks; and, I tell you, if he ever ventur'd upon "Kate of Aberdare," his cheeks swelled up to the reed of his clarinet, like as a blue plum on a stalk. And forty year after, he died of what they call solution of blood to the brain.'

'And you can't have better proof than that,' said the little man.

'That's what I say,' said the banjo. 'Next player, gentlemen, please.'

THE WHITE RAVEN

by Dick Donovan

*'Dick Donovan' was the pseudonym and alter ego of
J.E.P. Muddock (1843–1934), author of more
than fifty mystery and detective volumes—many
starring Donovan himself—and a frequent
contributor to the Strand and most other popular
magazines of the period. 'The White Raven'
is taken from Donovan's rare
collection of horror stories, Tales of Terror (1899).*

THE STORY AS TOLD BY LYDIA STAINSBY.

It was generally said of my father—who was a son of the late Sir John Mark Stainsby—that he was somewhat of an oddity. He certainly had original ideas, and it was a favourite remark of his that he did not care to baa, because the great family of human sheep baaed in chorus. It was due, no doubt, to this faculty of originality that he became the owner of Moorland Grange, which was situated on the edge of wild Dartmoor. My father was a widower; I was his only daughter, but I had four brothers, and I doubt if any girl's brothers were more devoted to her than mine were to me. We were a very united family, and had for many years resided in London, and as my father had ample means we found life very enjoyable. I was considered to be an exceedingly fortunate young woman. My friends all too flatteringly told me I was beautiful, and I know that when I looked into my mirror the reflection that met my gaze was certainly not one to make me shudder. Of course this was vanity, but then that is a woman's especial privilege, and so I don't intend to make any apology for the remark, for I am quite sure that I never was a plain-looking girl.

[134]

When my father purchased Moorland Grange I was just turned twenty years of age, and was looking forward with eager pleasure— what girl does not?—to my marriage with one of the dearest and most devoted of men. His name was Herbert Wilton. By profession he was a civil engineer, and for some time he had been in the Brazils, surveying for a new line of railroad which an English company had undertaken to construct. Herbert's engagement had nearly expired, and we were to be married on the New Year's Day following his return.

My father had some relatives in Devonshire; he was exceedingly fond of that part of the country. And on one occasion, after having been on a visit there, he said:

'Lydia, how would you like to go and live in Devonshire?'

I told him that hardly anything could give me greater pleasure, and then he astonished me by telling me that he had bought one of the 'queerest, tumble-down, romantic, ghost-haunted old houses imaginable.' It was known as 'Moorland Grange,' and he had got it for, as he said, 'an old song,' as it had been without a tenant for twenty-five years. The cause of this was, as I learnt, mainly attributable to an evil reputation it had acquired, owing to a remarkable murder that had been committed in the house at some remote period. That at least was the current legend, and it certainly affected the interests of the owners of the property. It was another instance of the truth of the adage about giving a dog a bad name. This house had got a bad name, and people shunned it as they might have shunned a leper. For some time the estate had been in Chancery, and as no purchaser could be found for it, my father had been able to secure it at a ridiculously low figure, and he intended—as he told me cheerfully—to purge it of its evil reputation.

At this time only my two younger brothers—who were mere boys— were at home, the others being in India; and so they, my father and I, with three servants, started for Moorland Grange, so as to get it in order, as we intended to reside there permanently.

The time of year was April, and the nearest station to the Grange was Tavistock, where we arrived about five in the afternoon, on as wild, bleak, and windy a day as our fickle and varying climate is capable of giving us even in tearful April. From the station we had a drive of over three miles. My father had deputed an old man named Jack Bewdley to meet us with a trap. Jack had been promised work on our new estate as handy man, woodcutter, or anything else in which he could be useful. He had nearly reached the allotted span, and was gnarled and twisted like an ancient oak. Born and bred in the neighbourhood of Dartmoor, he had never been fifty miles away from his native place in his life. He was a blunt, rugged, honest rustic, very superstitious and very simple: and as soon as he saw me he exclaimed, as he opened his bleared old eyes to their fullest capacity:

'By goom, miss, but you be powerful handsome! I hope as how you won't be a seeing of the White Raven in th' owd Grange.'

This compliment made me blush, and I asked him what the White Raven was, whereupon he looked very melancholy, and answered:

'Ah, I woan't be the chap to make your pretty face white wi' fright, so doan't ye ask me, please.'

As I was in no way a nervous or superstitious girl, I was amused rather than otherwise at old Jack's mysterious air, and I did not question him further then, as I felt pretty sure when we had become better acquainted he would be more communicative. We reached the Grange after a very cold and windy drive. The day was done, but there was just light enough lingering in the angry sky to outline the place in ghostly silhouette. It was a house of many gables, with all sorts of angles and projecting eaves, and a grotesque gothic porch that was approached by a flight of steps with stone balustrades. The whole building was covered with a mantling of dense ivy, which obscured the windows and hung down in ragged streamers, that swayed and rasped mournfully in the chill wind. All around were gloomy woods, and the garden was a forlorn wilderness of rank weeds. Old Jack's wife had got a few of the rooms cleaned out for our immediate use, and some furniture had been sent in, so that we were enabled to make ourselves tolerably comfortable on this the first night in our strange abode.

The next day I set to work with my brothers to explore the house, and soon I was quite able to endorse my father's opinion that it was the queerest, oddest, most romantic and ghostly place imaginable. I have already said that I was neither nervous nor superstitious, but I honestly confess that the rambling, draughty, echoing building quite depressed me. The Grange was said to be over 400 years old, though in some respects it had been modernised; nevertheless it was full of surprises in the shape of nooks and corners, deep, dark recesses, strange angles, dimly-lighted passages, winding staircases, and wainscoted and raftered rooms. One of these rooms was long and narrow, tapering away at one end almost to a point. The walls were wainscoted right to the ceiling, and the ceiling itself panelled with oak. There was a wide open fireplace, and a very massive carved mantel. Two diamond-paned windows lighted the room, one of the windows being filled in with blue and red glass. But at this time the windows were so obscured by the hanging ivy that we had to cut it away to let in the light. I became greatly interested in this antique chamber, and in a spirit of fun and ridicule I at once dubbed it 'the haunted chamber,' and declared I would use it as my bedroom. Afterwards, when talking about it to my father, I said laughingly:

. 'If that room, pa, hasn't got a ghost, it will have to have one, and we must invent one for it.'

'Oh,' he added, 'according to old Jack Bewdley that's the room where the White Raven shows itself.'

A little later I went to Jack, who was busy trying to clear some of the weeds away from the long-neglected grounds, and I said to him:

'Look here, Bewdley, what's this story about the White Raven? Come, now, you must tell me.'

He paused in his work, leaned his grizzled chin on the handle of his spade, and as a scared look spread itself over his shrivelled face, he answered me thus:

'There be zum foak in these parts, miss, as vow they've seen th' White Raven, and they doa say as how them as sees it dies within th' week. But I doan't know if them as said they've seen it died or not.'

'Have you seen it, Jack?' I asked, trying to look very serious, though I could scarcely keep from laughing.

'Noa, noa, thank God, noa!' he exclaimed with startling earnestness, and mopping his bald head with his red handkerchief, although the weather was cold, while his tanned and weather-beaten cheeks seemed to me to become pale. Then he asked, 'Have you been in what we foak call the oak chamber?'

Guessing what room he referred to I told him that I had, and he at once said that it was in that chamber that the mysterious White Raven always showed itself to the doomed person.

Of course I was incredulous, and ridiculed the whole idea; nor can I say I was more deeply impressed when on a subsequent and more critical examination of the chamber I found the following doggerel carved in old English on one of the panels—

'The stranger who beneath this roof shall lie,
And sees the White Raven is sure to die;
For a curse rests on the unhallowed place,
And the blood that was shed you here may trace.

So, stranger, beware, sleep not in the room,
Lest you should meet with a terrible doom.'

From people in the neighbouring villages I learned that in this very room, which I had been prompted to call the haunted chamber, tradition said that at some distant period a very beautiful lady had been brutally done to death by a jealous and dissipated husband, who gave out that she had eloped. He allowed her body to fester and moulder away in the room, and many years afterwards her skeleton was found, and that since then she had haunted the place in the shape of a white raven, while to anyone to whom she appeared it was a fatal sign. But why that should have been so nobody attempted to explain.

Now I will honestly confess that the gruesomeness of the story—which, however, I did not believe in its entirety—so far affected me that I changed my mind about occupying the room myself, and my father said he would take it for his own bedroom. But he also, for some reason or other, did not occupy it, although it was made into a most luxurious sleeping apartment. In the course of a few weeks the Grange began to present a very different appearance, and where gloom and melancholy had reigned, cheerfulness and light spread themselves. Under the fostering care of three or four gardeners the gardens blazed with flowers; some of the timber that encroached too much on the house was cut away, and the windows of the building were cleared of the ivy. I came at last to love the old place, for it was so bizarre, so unlike anything else I had ever seen: and in spite of all the predictions and croakings of the ignorant peasantry round about, who declared that sooner or later the curse which had affected everyone who had ever lived there since the poor lady was murdered would affect us, we were very comfortable and very happy. The summer lingered long that year, but the autumn was short, and winter set in with quite startling suddenness; by the end of the first week in December snow began to fall, and it continued snowing more or less for several days until the country round about was buried.

During all the year I had been pining for my love, who came not, although I knew that he was on his way home. But he had remained in Brazil longer than he intended, owing to the death from yellow fever of one of the surveying party, so that Herbert had been induced to renew his engagement for another six months, to do the dead man's work. With painful suspense and anxiety I had for days been scanning the papers for a report of the vessel which was bearing him to me, for she was overdue, but the weather at sea had been fearful, and old seamen said that vessels making for the Channel would have a hard time of it. As she was to call at Plymouth I persuaded my father to take me there in order that we might welcome Herbert as soon as ever he touched English soil again. As papa denied me nothing, he readily consented to this, but it was not until three days before Christmas that the welcome news came to me that the vessel had entered the Sound.

Need I dwell upon the joy I experienced when, after our long separation, I felt Herbert's dear arms around me once more. How handsome and manly he looked! The sun had tanned him brown, the fine sea voyage home had braced him up after the enervating Brazilian climate, and he declared that he had never been in better health in his life. He was possessed of a wonderful constitution, and during the whole time he had been in Brazil had never had a day's illness.

Of course I told him that, selfish as it seemed, I was going to keep him for Christmas Day, and on New Year's Day I was to become his bride, according to the long prior arrangement. He said that it was necessary for him to go to London to see his friends and to make some preparations, but he promised that he would be with me again on Christmas Eve. And so I parted from him, and as we were to meet again so soon, and in less than a fortnight he was to be my husband, I was verily at that moment one of the happiest girls alive.

As my father was thoroughly imbued with the spirit of old-fashioned English hospitality he generally kept open house at Christmas time, and this being our first Christmas at the Grange we had a large number of visitors, so that the house was quite full. In order that Herbert, when he came, might be fittingly bestowed as the bridegroom-elect, we decided that he should occupy the haunted chamber, for it certainly was the best sleeping room in the house; and though some silly and unusual nervousness—as I believed then—had prevented my occupying it as I intended, neither I nor my father attached the slightest importance to the supernatural stories current in the district. With my own hands I arranged the room for Herbert, filling it with nick-nacks and odds and ends, and everything I could think of that was likely to give him pleasure or add to his comfort.

Christmas Eve of that year was marked by a snowstorm such as, the country people said, had not been known for forty years. The train that brought my love from London was very late, and I had become quite anxious, but all anxiety was forgotten when I helped him to divest himself of his snow-laden topcoat in the hall, and taking me in his arms he kissed me in his hearty, cheery way. We were a very jovial party, and that night was a happy, gladsome night, the memory of which will never leave me. Nor shall I ever forget dear Herbert's words, as he kissed me good-night on the stairs as the great hall clock struck one.

'Darling little woman,' he whispered, 'what joy, what happiness, what ecstasy, to think that in a week's time you will belong to me!'

I had no words. I could only sigh in token of the supreme happiness that filled my heart to overflowing.

Christmas morning broke bright, clear, and beautiful. The snow had ceased to fall, and a hard frost had set in. It was veritable Canadian weather—crisp, crystalline, and invigorating. As soon as breakfast was over Herbert took me on one side and said:

'You know, Lydia, I am about one of the most practical men that you could find in a day's march, and hitherto I have been without, as I believe, a scrap of superstition in my composition. But, by Jove! after last night's experience I'll be hanged if I don't believe with Shakespeare that there are more things in heaven and earth than are dreamt of in our philosophy.'

At these words I turned deadly pale. I scarcely knew why, but such was the case, and I gasped out:

'What—what do you mean?'

'Well,' he answered, with a laugh that wasn't sincere, for it was obviously forced, 'I believe that room in which I slept is positively haunted.'

Now, I may state here that not a word of any kind had been mentioned to Herbert about the stories that were current with regard to the house. Both my father and I had resolved that the subject should be strictly avoided, so that none of our lady guests might be alarmed. As he spoke, I looked up into his brown face, and I saw that it was filled with a puzzled and troubled expression, while his splendid eyes had an unusual expression in them.

'Tell me,' I said quickly, 'what did you see or hear?'

'Oh, don't let us talk about it,' he answered lightly. 'Perhaps, after all, I have simply been dreaming.'

'Yes, yes—tell me—you must tell me, Herbert,' I exclaimed. 'You know that I am strong-nerved.'

He seemed to hesitate; but laughing again, though it was the same forced laugh, he said:

'Well, the fact is, if ever I saw a raven in my life, I saw one last night, only it was white.'

At this I almost fainted, and he caught me by the arm. I made a desperate effort, however, and recovered myself.

'Go on; tell me all about it,' I said peremptorily.

And the sum and substance of what he told me was this. He had seen a white raven, or what appeared to be a white raven, flying round and round the room. It made no noise, which amazed him and, as he confessed, startled him. He tried to catch this mysterious and noiseless bird, but it had no substantiality—it was an airy phantom; but once or twice, when he appeared to grasp it, a deep groan and sigh broke upon his ears.

Although a strange fear seemed to turn my heart cold, I endeavoured not to show it, nor could I bring myself to tell my lover of the tradition so common all over the country side about the murdered lady and the White Raven.

If the extraordinary apparition had any real effect on Herbert, he soon shook it off, and his hearty ringing laughter made music in the house, and his eyes were filled again with the old look of love with which they always greeted me. It had been arranged that the gentlemen were to form a shooting party, to go out on to the moor and try and bag some wild ducks. At first I was disposed to dissuade Herbert from going—ah, would that I had done so!—but it seemed to me weak and foolish. Moreover, he was so anxious to go for the novelty of the thing, and so I whispered in his ear as he was standing on the steps:

'Take care of yourself, love, for my sake.'

'Of course I will, darling; and you do the same,' he answered cheerily.

I watched his manly form until he was hidden from my sight by the trees. He looked splendid in his perfect health, and his magnificent physique was set off to every possible advantage by the superb coat of Russian sable that he wore. How proud I felt of him! for truly he was a man to be proud of.

Three hours later the party returned, minus Herbert. They said he had got separated from them in some way, and they quite thought he had come back. Although a sense of something being wrong over-came me for the moment, I tried to think that it was simply nervousness. Of course, the gentlemen at once hurried back to the moor, and when they came again they brought my lover mangled and shattered, and, as it seemed then, in the agony of death. Oh, my God! how awful it was! I thought I should have gone raving mad. It appears that Herbert had been found in a hollow, whither he had fallen by the breaking away of the snow under his feet. In his fall he had not only fractured an arm and some of his ribs, but his gun had gone off full in his face, and, besides disfiguring him frightfully, had destroyed both his eyes.

It can be imagined what a terrible shock it was to the household, and how the joy and mirth were turned to lamentations and moaning. Doctors were procured, but they pronounced the sufferer's condition as critical; they left us no room to hope that the sight would be restored under any circumstances.

Ah, what a fearful dark Christmas that became to me! I think in my agony of mind I cursed my fate, my God; and how I hated the house, and shuddered as I thought of the horrible room where my beloved had seen the strange apparition of the White Raven.

Up to a short time previously, it would have been difficult to have found a girl more sceptical than I was about anything that savoured of superstition; but now I was filled with a strange dread, and feared my own shadow.

When I saw old Jack for the first time after the accident, he said to me:

'Is it true, miss, that Meester Wilton's been asleeping in the haunted room?'

'Yes, Jack; it is,' I answered, in heartbroken tones.

'Then, maybe, he's seen the White Raven?'

'He has,' I replied; whereupon I thought the old man would have fallen down in a fit, so scared did he seem; and he mumbled out:

'God bless us and preserve us all! I wouldn't sleep in that room, miss, not if Queen Victoriey was to give me her golden crown. That there room, miss, ought to be shut up, and no one ever allowed to go anigh it agen.'

The shadow that had so suddenly and cruelly fallen upon us rendered the Christmas festivities out of the question, and most of the guests sorrowfully departed the following day. Many long weeks ensued—dark, torturing weeks to me, for my loved one was suspended, as it were, by a single hair over that profound abyss into which all living atoms finally fall, and from which no sound ever comes to break the mystery. But if they were dark weeks to me, how much, how infinitely, how unspeakably darker to him who, in the pride of his manhood, had been deprived of the power of ever again beholding the wonders of God's creation. And yet he murmured not, nor uttered complaint nor groan. To me the one consolation I had in this hideous calamity was being near him, being able to tend him, and hear his voice, which had lost none of its old cheerfulness. Slowly, very slowly, as the summer drifted by, he began to regain some of his lost strength, and we led him out beneath the trees and into the sunlight, though it was ever, ever night to him, for not a glimmer of vision remained. And as I looked at his sightless orbs and his maimed and torn face, from which no human power could banish the cruel and ghastly scars, I hated the Grange with a hate that hath no words.

One day he asked to be taken to where my father was, and, putting his arm in mine, we entered my father's presence.

'Mr Stainsby,' he began, with an attempt at a smile, 'I am not quite the same man I was when I came here last Christmas. But in my misfortune an angel has watched over me in the person of your daughter, who, but for this mishap, would now have been my wife. She has brought me out of the shadow of the grave, and I owe a duty to her no less than to you. That duty is to release her from all promises and vows, and leave her perfectly free to bestow her heart on some one who is whole and sound. I am now but a battered wreck, and all I can hope for is to break up soon and drift away into the great and mysterious ocean of eternal silence. But let me ask you, sir, to see to it that the man upon whom you bestow your daughter is as near perfection as a man may come; for no more perfect woman than she is walks the world. I have nothing more to add further than, in such poor words as well up from my stricken heart, to thank you for your hospitality.'

He had tried so hard to be strong and collected, and show no sign of the awful despair that was crushing him. But is the man born who could go through such an ordeal unmoved? His lips quivered, his voice grew weak, and something like a spasm caught his breath.

My own eyes were filled with blinding, scalding tears, and my heart fluttered like the wing of a bird in pain. Gliding over to where he stood, I placed my arms about his neck, and laying my cheek against his scarred face, I found voice to say to my father, who was also deeply affected and moved:

'Father, the man whom Herbert would have you choose for me need be sought no further than this room. He is here. My heart beats to his heart; my face is pressed to his.'

My father came to us. He laid one hand on Herbert's shoulder, and the other on my head; and thus he spoke:

'A woman's love that clings not to a man when calamity overtakes him is worthless. Freely do I bestow her upon you, Herbert, if it is her wish and your wish that you should be united.'

'My husband,' I murmured, as I clung closer to him, and it was my only answer.

Herbert tried to persuade me that it was to my happiness and my interest to abandon him; but he might as well have tried to convince the winds of heaven that they should not blow. Externally the Herbert as I had first known him had changed. His handsome face was handsome no longer, and his wondrous eyes were sightless for ever. But his heart was the same. What could change that—the bravest, truest, tenderest that ever beat in man's breast? And so ere the next Christmas had dawned I was Herbert's wife, and soon after that my father abandoned the accursed Grange to the gloom and the silence and the melancholy from which he had reclaimed it, and a little later it was burned to the ground. We never knew how the fire originated; but it was generally supposed that some of the superstitious people in the neighbourhood wilfully set it alight, under the impression that a place that was accursed by the spilling of human blood should no longer be allowed to encumber the earth. When I heard of its destruction I confess that I rejoiced, and I said to myself:

'Never again will the White Raven bring calamity to a household as it has brought to ours.'

For five years I walked with my husband in his darkness, and let him see the world through my eyes. Two children blessed—literally blessed—our union, a girl and a boy. But my beloved husband never fully recovered from the shock of the awful accident on that dark and memorable Christmas Day; and, though he uttered no moan, his blindness preyed upon his mind, and a short, brief illness took him from me.

For long years the grass has waved over his grave. Other men have praised my face and sought my hand; but to all I have turned a deaf ear, for my love was buried in Herbert's grave. But in my son the father lives again, and when I gaze upon his handsome face and splendid figure, I feel that God is very good, and that He chastens us to make us more perfect is His sight.

THE STRANGE STORY OF NORTHAVON PRIORY

by F. Frankfort Moore

Frank Frankfort Moore (1855–1931) served as a
roving reporter and journalist in Africa and the
Colonies for several years before achieving great
success with his novel *I Forbid the Banns* (1893).
Like his fellow Irishman and brother-in-law Bram
Stoker, creator of *Dracula*, Moore settled in London
and was an extremely popular writer (specialising
in 18th century romances) for more than thirty
years. His weird and supernatural stories were
collected together in *The Other World* (1904).

When Arthur Jephson wrote to me to join his Christmas
party at Northavon Priory, I was set wondering where I had
heard the name of this particular establishment. I felt certain
that I had heard the name before, but I could not recollect for the
moment whether I had come upon it in a newspaper report of a breach
of promise of marriage or in a Blue-Book bearing upon Inland Fisheries:
I rather inclined to the belief that it was in a Blue Book of some sort. I
had been devoting myself some years previously to an exhaustive study
of this form of literature; for being very young, I had had a notion that
a Blue-Book education was essential to any one with parliamentary
aspirations. Yes, I had, I repeat, been very young at that time, and I had
not found out that a Blue-Book is the *oubliette* of inconvenient facts.

It was not until I had promised Arthur to be with him on Christmas Eve that I recollected where I had read something about Northavon Priory, and in a moment I understood how it was I had acquired the notion that the name had appeared in an official document. I had read a good deal about this Priory in a curious manuscript which I had unearthed at Sir Dennis le Warden's place in Norfolk, known as Marsh Towers. The document, which, with many others, I found stowed away in a wall-cupboard in the great library, purported to be a draft of the evidence taken before one of the Commissions appointed by King Henry VIII to inquire into the abuses alleged to be associated with certain religious houses throughout England. An ancestor of Sir Dennis's had, it appeared, been a member of one of these Commissions, and he had taken a note of the evidence which he had in the course of his duties handed to the King.

The parchments had, I learned, been preserved in an iron coffer with double padlocks, but the keys had been lost at some remote period, and then the coffer had been covered over with lumber in a room in the east tower overlooking the moat, until an outbreak of fire had resulted in an overturning of the rubbish and a discovery of the coffer. A blacksmith had been employed to pick the locks, which he did with a sledge-hammer; but it was generally admitted that his energy had been wasted when the contents of the box were made known. Sir Dennis cared about nothing except the improvement of the breed of horses through the agency of race meetings, so the manuscripts of his painstaking ancestor were bundled into one of the presses in the library, some, however, being reserved by the intelligent housekeeper in the still-room to make jam-pot covers—a purpose for which, as she explained to me at considerable length, they were extremely well adapted.

I had no great difficulty in deciphering those that came under my hand, for I had had considerable experience of the tricks of early English writers; and as I read I became greatly interested in all the original 'trustie and well-beelou'd Sir Denice le Warden' had written. The frankness of the evidence which he had collected on certain points took away my breath, although I had been long accustomed to the directness with which some of the fifteenth-century people expressed themselves.

Northavon Priory was among the religious houses whose practices had formed the subject of the inquiry, and it was the summary of Sir Denice's notes regarding the Black Masses alleged to have been

[146]

celebrated within its walls that proved so absorbing to me. The bald account of the nature of these orgies would of itself have been sufficient, if substantiated, to bring about the dissolution of all the order in England. The Black Mass was a pagan revel, the details of which were unspeakable, though their nature was more than hinted at by the King's Commissioner. Anything so monstrously blasphemous could not be imagined by the mind of man, for with the pagan orgy there was mixed up the most solemn rite of the Mass. It was celebrated on the night of Christmas Eve, and at the hour of midnight the celebration culminated in an invocation to the devil, written so as to parody an office of the Church, and, according to the accounts of some witnesses, in a human sacrifice. Upon this latter point, however, Sir Denice admitted there was a diversity of opinion.

One of the witnesses examined was a man who had entered the Priory grounds from the river during a fearful tempest, on one Christmas Eve, and had, he said, witnessed the revel through a window to which he had climbed. He declared that at the hour of midnight the candles had been extinguished, but that a moment afterwards an awful red light had floated through the room, followed by the shrieks of a human being at the point of strangulation, and then by horrible yells of laughter. Another man who was examined had been a wood-cutter in the service of the Priory, and he had upon one occasion witnessed the celebration of a Black Mass; but he averred that no life was sacrificed, though he admitted that in the strange red light, which had flashed through the room, he had seen what appeared to be two men struggling on the floor. In the general particulars of the orgy there was, however, no diversity of opinion, and had the old Sir Denice le Warden been anything of a comparative mythologist, he could scarcely fail to have been greatly interested in being brought face to face with so striking an example of the survival of an ancient superstition within the walls of a holy building.

During a rainy week I amused myself among the parchments dealing with Northavon Priory, and although what I read impressed me greatly at the time, yet three years of pretty hard work in various parts of the world had so dulled my memory of any incident so unimportant as the deciphering of a mouldy document that, as I have already stated, it was not until I had posted my letter to Arthur Jephson agreeing to spend a day or two with his party, that I succeeded in recalling something of what I had read regarding Northavon Priory.

I had taken it for granted that the Priory had been demolished when Henry had superintended the dissolution of the religious establishments throughout the country: I did not think it likely that one with such a record as was embodied in the notes would be allowed to remain with a single stone on another. A moment's additional reflection admitted of my perceiving how extremely unlikely it was that, even if Northavon Priory had been spared by the King, it would still be available for visitors during the latter years of the nineteenth century. I had seen many red-brick 'abbeys' and 'priories' in various parts of the country, not more than ten years old, inhabited mostly by gentlemen who had made fortunes in iron, or perhaps lard, which constitutes, I understand, an excellent foundation for a fortune. There might be, for all I knew, a score of Northavon Priories in England. Arthur Jephson's father had made his money by the judicious advertising of a certain oriental rug manufactured in the Midlands, and I thought it very likely that he had built a mansion for himself which he had called Northavon Priory.

A letter which I received from Arthur set my mind at rest. He explained to me very fully that Northavon Priory was a hotel built within the walls of an ancient religious house. He had spent a delightful month fishing in the river during the summer—I had been fishing in the Amazon at that time—and had sojourned at the hotel, which he had found to be a marvel of comfort in spite of its picturesqueness. This was why, he said, he had thought how jolly it would be to entertain a party of his friends at the place during the Christmas week.

That explanation was quite good enough for me. I had a week or two to myself in England before going to India, and so soon as I recalled what I had read regarding Northavon Priory, I felt glad that my liking for Jephson had induced me to accept his invitation.

It was not until we were travelling together to the station nearest to the Priory that he mentioned to me, quite incidentally, that during the summer he had been fortunate enough to make the acquaintance of a young woman who resided in a spacious mansion within easy distance of the Priory Hotel, and who was, so far as he was capable of judging—and he considered that in such matters his judgment was worth something—the most charming girl in England.

'I see,' I remarked before his preliminary panegyric had quite come to a legitimate conclusion—'I see all now: you haven't the courage— to be more exact, the impudence—to come down alone to the hotel—

she has probably a brother who is a bit of an athlete—but you think that Tom Singleton and I will form a good enough excuse for an act on your part which parents and guardians can construe in one way only.'

'Well, perhaps—Hang it all, man, you needn't attribute to me any motives but those of the purest hospitality,' laughed my companion. 'Isn't the prospect of a genuine old English Christmas—the Yule log, and that sort of thing—good enough for you without going any further?'

'It's quite good enough for me,' I replied. 'I only regret that it is not good enough for you. You expect to see her every day?'

'Every day? Don't be a fool, Jim. If I see her more than four times in the course of the week—I think I should manage to see her four times—I will consider myself exceptionally lucky.'

'And if you see her less than four times you will reckon yourself uncommonly unlucky?'

'O, I think I have arranged for four times all right: I'll have to trust to luck for the rest.'

'What! you mean to say that the business has gone as far as that?'

'As what?'

'As making arrangements for meetings with her?'

My friend laughed complacently.

'Well, you see, old chap, I couldn't very well give you this treat without letting her know that I should be in the neighbourhood,' said he.

'Oh, indeed. I don't see, however, what the—'

'Great heavens! You mean to say that you don't see—Oh, you will have your joke.'

'I hope I will have one eventually; I can't say that I perceive much chance of one at present, however. You'll not give us much of your interesting society during the week of our treat, as you call it.'

'I'll give you as much of it as I can spare—more than you'll be likely to relish, perhaps. A week's a long time, Jim.'

' "Time travels at divers paces with divers persons," my friend. I suppose she's as lovely as any of the others of past years?'

'As lovely! Jim, she's just the—'

'Don't trouble yourself over the description. I have a vivid recollection of the phrases you employed in regard to the others. There was Lily, and Gwen, and Bee, and—yes, by George! there was a fourth; her name was Nelly, or—'

'All flashes in the pan, my friend. I didn't know my own mind in those old days; but now, thank heaven!—Oh, you'll agree with me when you see her. This is the real thing and no mistake.'

He was good enough to give me a genuine lover's description of the young woman, whose name was, he said, Sylvia St Leger; but it did not differ materially from the descriptions which had come from him in past days, of certainly four other girls for whom he had, he imagined, entertained a devotion strong as death itself. Alas! his devotion had not survived a single year in any case.

When we arrived at the hotel, after a drive of eight miles from the railway station, we found Tom Singleton waiting for us rather impatiently, and in a quarter of an hour we were facing an excellent dinner. We were the only guests at the hotel, for though it was picturesquely situated on the high bank of the river, and was doubtless a delightful place for a sojourn in summer, yet in winter it possessed few attractions to casual visitors.

After dinner I strolled over the house, and found, to my surprise, that the old walls of the Priory were practically intact. The kitchen was also unchanged, but the great refectory was now divided into four rooms. The apartments upstairs had plainly been divided in the same way by brick partitions; but the outer walls, pierced with narrow windows, were those of the original Priory.

In the morning I made further explorations, only outside the building, and came upon the ruins of the old Priory tower; and then I perceived that only a small portion of the original building had been utilised for the hotel. The landlord, who accompanied me, was certainly no antiquarian. He told me that he had been 'let in' so far as the hotel was concerned. He had been given to understand that the receipts for the summer months were sufficiently great to compensate for the absence of visitors during the winter; but his experience of one year had not confirmed this statement, made by the people from whom he had bought the place, and he had come to the conclusion that, as he had been taken in in the transaction, it was his duty to try to take in some one else in the same way.

'I only hope that I may succeed, sir,' he said, 'but I'm doubtful about it. People are getting more suspicious every day.'

'You weren't suspicious, at any rate,' said I.

'That I weren't—more's the pity, sir,' said he. 'But it'll take me all my time to get the place off my hands, I know. Ah, yes; it's hard to get people to take your word for anything nowadays.'

For the next two days Tom Singleton and I were left a good deal together, the fact being that our friend Arthur parted from us after lunch and only returned in time for dinner, declaring upon each occasion that he had just passed the pleasantest day of his life. On Christmas Eve he came to us in high spirits, bearing with him an invitation from a lady who had attained distinction through being the mother of Miss St Leger, for us to spend Christmas Day at her house—it had already been pointed out to us by Arthur: it was a fine Georgian country house, named The Grange.

'I've accepted for you both,' said Arthur. 'Mrs St Leger is a most charming woman, and her daughter—I don't know if I mentioned that she had a daughter—well, if I omitted, I am now in a position to assure you that her daughter—her name is Sylvia—is possibly the most beautiful— But there's no use trying to describe her; you'll see her for yourselves to-morrow, and judge if I've exaggerated in the least when I say that the world does not contain a more exquisite creature.'

'Yes, one hour with her will be quite sufficient to enable us to pronounce an opinion on that point,' laughed Tom.

We remained smoking in front of the log fire that blazed in the great hearth, until about eleven o'clock, and then went to our rooms upstairs, after some horse-play in the hall.

My room was a small one at the beginning of the corridor, Arthur Jephson's was alongside it, and at the very end of the corridor was Tom Singleton's. All had at one time been one apartment.

Having walked a good deal during the day, I was very tired, and had scarcely got into bed before I fell asleep.

When I awoke it was with a start and a consciousness that something was burning. A curious red light streamed into the room from outside. I sprang from my bed in a moment and ran to the window. But before I had reached it the room was in darkness once more, and there came a yell of laughter, apparently from the next room.

For a moment I was paralysed. But the next instant I had recovered my presence of mind. I believed that Arthur and Tom had been playing some of their tricks upon me. They had burnt a red light outside my window, and were roaring with laughter as they heard me spring out of bed.

That was the explanation of what I had seen and heard which first suggested itself to me; and I was about to return to bed when my door was knocked at and then opened.

'What on earth have you been up to?' came the voice of Arthur Jephson. 'Have you set the bed-curtains on fire? If you have, that's nothing to laugh at.'

'Get out of this room with your larking,' said I. 'It's a very poor joke that of yours, Arthur. Go back to your bed.'

He struck a light—he had a match-box in his hand—and went to my candle without a word. In a moment the room was faintly illuminated.

'Do you mean to say that you hadn't a light here just now—a red light?' he cried.

'I had no light: a red light floated through the room, but it seemed to come from outside,' said I.

'And who was it laughed in that wild way?'

'I took it for granted that it was you and Tom who were about your usual larks.'

'Larks! No, I was about no larks, I can promise you. Good Lord! man, that laugh was something beyond a lark.' He seated himself on my bed. 'Do you fancy it may have been some of the servants going about the stables with a carriage-lamp?' he continued. 'There may have been a late arrival at the hotel, you know.'

'That's not at all unlikely,' said I. 'Yes, it may have been that, and the laughter may have been between the grooms.'

'I don't hear any sound of bustle through the house or outside,' said he.

'The stables are not at this angle of the building,' said I. 'We must merely have seen the light and heard that laughter as the carriage passed our angle. Anyhow, we'll only catch cold if we lounge about in our pyjamas like this. You'd best get back to bed and let me do the same.'

'I don't feel much inclined to sleep, but I'll not prevent your having your night's rest,' said he, rising. 'I wonder is it near morning?'

I held the candle before the dial of my watch that hung above my bed.

'It's exactly five minutes past twelve,' said I. 'We've slept barely an hour.'

'Then the sooner I clear out the better it will be for both of us,' said he.

He went away slowly, and I heard him strike a match in his own room. He evidently meant to light his candle.

Some hours had passed before I fell into an uneasy sleep, and once more I was awakened by Arthur Jephson, who stood by my bedside. The morning light was in the room.

'For God's sake, come into Tom's room!' he whispered. 'He's dead!—Tom is dead!'

I tried to realise his words. Some moments had elapsed before I succeeded in doing so. I sprang from my bed and ran down the corridor to the room occupied by Tom Singleton. The landlord and a couple of servants were already there. They had burst in the door.

It was but too true: our poor friend lay on his bed with his body bent and his arms twisted as though he had been struggling desperately with some one at his last moment. His face, too, was horribly contorted, and his eyes were wide open.

'A doctor,' I managed to say.

'He's already sent for, sir,' said the landlord.

In a few moments the doctor arrived.

'Cardiac attack,' said he. 'Was he alone in the room? No, he can't have been alone.'

'He was quite alone,' said Arthur. 'I knocked at the door a quarter of an hour ago, but getting no answer, I tried to force the lock. It was too strong for me; but the landlord and the man-servant who was bringing us our hot water burst in the door at my request.'

'And the window—was it fastened?' asked the doctor.

'It was secure, sir,' said the landlord.

'Ah, a sudden cardiac attack,' said the doctor.

There was, of course, an inquest, but as no evidence of foul play was forthcoming, the doctor's phrase 'cardiac attack' satisfied the jury, and a verdict of 'Death from natural causes' was returned.

Before I went back to town I examined the room in which our poor friend had died. On the side of one of the window-shutters there were four curious burnt marks. They gave one the impression that the shutter had at one time been grasped by a man wearing a red-hot gauntlet.

I started for India before the end of the year and remained there for eight months. Then I thought I would pay a visit to a sister of mine in Queensland. On my return at the end of the year I meant to stop at Cairo for a few weeks. On entering Shepheard's Hotel I found myself face to face with Arthur Jephson and his wife—he called her Sylvia. They had been married in August, but their honeymoon seemed still to be in its first quarter. It was after Mrs Jephson had retired, and when Arthur was sitting with me enjoying the cool of the night by the aid of a pretty strong cigar or two, that we ventured to allude to the tragic occurrence which marked our last time of meeting.

'I wish to beg of you not to make any allusion to that awful business in the hearing of my wife,' said Arthur. 'In fact I must ask you not to allude to that fearful room in the Priory in any way.'

[153]

'I will be careful not to do so,' said I. 'You have your own reasons, I suppose, for giving me this warning.'

'I have the best of reasons, Jim. She too had her experience of that room, and it was as terrible as ours.'

'Good heavens! I heard nothing of that. She did not sleep in that room?'

'Thank God, she didn't. I arrived in time to save her.'

I need scarcely say that my interest was now fully aroused.

'Tell me what happened—if you dare tell it,' I said.

'You were abroad, and so you wouldn't be likely to hear of the fire at The Grange,' said my friend, after a pause.

'I heard nothing of it.'

'It took place only two days before last Christmas. I had been in the south of France, where I had spent a month or two with my mother—she cannot stand a winter at home—and I had promised Sylvia to return to The Grange for Christmas. When I got to Northavon I found her and her mother and their servants at the Priory Hotel. The fire had taken place the previous night, and they found the hotel very handy when they hadn't a roof of their own over their heads. Well, we dined together, and were as jolly as was possible under the circumstances until bedtime. I had actually said "Good night" to Sylvia before I recollected what had taken place the previous Christmas Eve in the same house. I rushed upstairs, and found Sylvia in the act of entering the room—that fatal room. When I implored of her to choose some other apartment, she only laughed at first, and assured me that she wasn't superstitious; but when she saw that I was serious—I was deadly serious, as you can believe, Jim—'

'I can—I can.'

'Well, she agreed to sleep in her mother's room, and I went away relieved. So soon as I returned to the fire in the dining-room I began to think of poor Tom Singleton. I felt curiously excited, and I knew that it would be useless for me to go to bed—in fact, I made up my mind not to leave the dining-room for some hours, at any rate, and when the landlord came to turn out the lights I told him he might trust me to do that duty for him. He left me alone in the room about half-past eleven o'clock. When the sound of his feet upon the oaken stairs died away I felt as fearful as a child in the dark. I lit another cigar and walked about the room for some time. I went to the window that opened upon the old Priory ground, and, seeing that the night was a fine one, I opened the door and strolled out, hoping that the cool air would do me good. I had not gone many yards across the little patch of green before I turned and looked up at the house—at the last window, the window of that room. A fire had been lighted in the room early in the evening, and its glow shone through the white blind. Suddenly that faint glow increased to a terrific glare—a red glare, Jim—and then there came before my eyes for a moment the shadow of two figures upon the blind—one the figure of a woman, the other—God knows what it was. I rushed back to the room, but before I had reached the door I heard the horrible laughter once again. It seemed to come from that room and to pass on through the air into the distance across the river. I ran upstairs with a light, and found Sylvia and her mother standing together with wraps around them at the door of the room. "Thank God, you are safe!" I managed to cry. "I feared that you had returned to the room." "You heard it—that awful laughter?" she whispered. "You heard it, and you saw something— what was it?" I gently forced her and her mother back to their room, for the servants and the landlord's family were now crowding into the corridor. They, too, had heard enough to alarm them.'

'You went to the room?'

'The scene of that dreadful morning was repeated. The door was locked on the inside. We broke it in and found a girl lying dead on the floor, her face contorted just as poor Singleton's was. She was Sylvia's maid, and it was thought that, on hearing that her mistress was not going to occupy the room, she had gone into it herself on account of the fire which had been lighted there.'

'And the doctor said—?'

'Cardiac attack—the same as before—singular coincidence! I need scarcely say that we never slept again under that accursed roof. Poor Sylvia! She was overwhelmed at the thought of how narrow her escape had been.'

'Did you notice anything remarkable about the room—about the shutters of the window?' I asked.

He looked at me curiously for a moment. Then he bent forward and said—

'On the edge of the shutter there were some curious marks where the wood had been charred.'

'As if a hand with a red-hot gauntlet had been laid upon it?'

'There were the marks of two such hands,' said my friend slowly.

We remained for an hour in the garden; then we threw away the end of our cigars and went into the hotel without another word.

[155]

THE BLACK CAT
by W.J. Wintle

William James Wintle was a prolific journalist, and
contributor to the popular magazines, whose many
books include *Nights with an Old Lag*, *Continental
Dishes*, and *Armenia and its Sorrows*. While resident
at the Priory on Caldy Island, he told ghost stories
to the young novitiates, on Sunday nights over a
wood fire. 'They were so fortunate as to meet with
approval from their rather critical audience. Truth
to tell, the gruesome ones met with the best
reception. Boys like highly flavoured dishes.'
The stories were published in *Ghost Gleams* (1921).

I f there was one animal that Sydney disliked more than another it
was a cat. Not that he was not fond of animals in a general way—
for he had a distinct affection for an aged retriever that had
formerly been his—but somehow a cat seemed to arouse all that was
worst in him. It always appeared to him that if he had passed through
some previous stage of existence, he must have been a mouse or a bird
and thus have inherited—so to speak—an instinctive dread and
hatred for the enemy of his earlier days.

The presence of a cat affected him in a very curious fashion. There
was first of all a kind of repulsion. The idea of the eyes of the animal
being fixed on him; the thought of listening for a soundless tread; and
the imagined touch of the smooth fur; all this made him shudder
and shrink back. But this feeling quickly gave place to a still stranger
fascination. He felt drawn to the creature that he feared—much as
a bird is supposed, but quite erroneously, to be charmed by a snake.

He wanted to stroke the animal and to feel its head rubbing against his hand: and yet at the same time the idea of the animal doing so filled him with a dread passing description. It was something like that morbid state in which a person finds actual physical pleasure in inflicting pain on himself. And then there was sheer undisguised fear. Pretend as he might, Sydney was in deadly fear when a cat was in the room. He had tried and tried, time and again, to overcome it; but without success. He had argued from the well-known friendliness of the domestic cat; from its notorious timidity; and from its actual inability to do any very serious harm to a strong and active man. But it was all of no use. He was afraid of cats; and it was useless to deny it.

At the same time, Sydney was no enemy to cats. He was the last man in the world to hurt one. No matter how much his slumber might be disturbed by the vocal efforts of a love-sick marauder on the roof in the small hours of the morning, he would never think of hurling a missile at the offender. The sight of a half-starved cat left behind when its owner was away in the holiday season filled him with a pity near akin to pain. He was a generous subscriber to the Home for Lost Cats. In fact, his whole attitude was inconsistent and contradictory. But there was no escape from the truth—he disliked and feared cats.

Probably this obsession was to some extent fostered by the fact that Sydney was a man of leisure. With more urgent matters to occupy his thoughts, he might have outgrown these fancies with the advance of middle age. But the possession of ample means, an inherited dislike for any kind of work calling for energy, and two or three interesting hobbies which filled up his time in an easy and soothing fashion, left him free to indulge his fancies. And fancies, when indulged, are apt to become one's masters in the end; and so it proved with Sydney.

He was engaged in writing a book on some phase of Egyptian life in the olden days, which involved considerable study of the collections in the British Museum and elsewhere, as well as much search for rare books among the antiquarian bookshops. When not out on these pursuits, he occupied an old house which like most old and rambling places of its kind was the subject of various queer stories among the gossips of the neighbourhood. Some tragedy was supposed to have happened there at some date not defined, and in consequence something was supposed to haunt the place and to do something from time to time. Among local gossips there was much value in that nebulous term 'Something,' for it covered a multitude of inaccurate recollections and of foggy traditions. Probably Sydney had never heard the reputation of his house, for he led a retired life and had little to do with the neighbours. But if the tales had reached his ears, he gave no sign; nor was he likely to do so. Apart from the cat obsession, he was a man of eminently balanced mind. He was about the last person to imagine things or to be influenced by any but proved facts.

The mystery which surrounded his untimely end came therefore as a great surprise to his friends: and the horror that hung over his later days was only brought to partial light by the discovery of a diary and other papers which have provided the material for this history. Much still remains obscure, and cannot now be cleared up; for the only man who could perhaps throw further light on it is no longer with us. So we have to be content with such fragmentary records as are available.

It appears that some months before the end, Sydney was at home reading in the garden, when his eyes happened to rest upon a small heap of earth that the gardener had left beside the path. There was nothing remarkable about this; but somehow the heap seemed to fascinate him. He resumed his reading; but the heap of earth was insistent in demanding his attention. He could not keep his thoughts off it, and it was hard to keep his eyes off it as well. Sydney was not the man to give way to mental dissipation of this kind, and he resolutely kept his eyes fixed on the book. But it was a struggle; and in the end he gave in. He looked again at the heap; and this time with some curiosity as to the cause of so absurd an attraction.

Apparently there was no cause; and he smiled at the absurdity of the thing. Then he started up suddenly, for he saw the reason of it. The heap of earth was exactly like a black cat! And the cat was crouching as if to spring at him. The resemblance was really absurd, for there were a couple of yellow pebbles just where the eyes should have been. For the moment, Sydney felt all the repulsion and fear that the presence of an actual cat would have caused him. Then he rose from his chair, and kicked the heap out of any resemblance to his feline aversion. He sat down again and laughed at the absurdity of the affair—and yet it somehow left a sense of disquiet and of vague fear behind. He did not altogether like it.

It must have been about a fortnight later when he was inspecting some Egyptian antiquities that had recently reached the hands of a London dealer. Most of them were of the usual types and did not interest him. But a few were better worth attention; and he sat down to examine them carefully. He was specially attracted by some ivory tablets, on which he thought he could faintly trace the remains of handwriting. If so, this was a distinct find, for private memoranda of this sort are very rare and should throw light on some of the more intimate details of private life of the period, which were not usually recorded on the monuments. Absorbed in this study, a sense of undefined horror slowly grew upon him and he found himself in a kind of day dream presenting many of the uncanny qualities of nightmare. He thought himself stroking an immense black cat which grew and grew until it assumed gigantic proportions. Its soft fur thickened around his hands and entwined itself around his fingers like a mass of silky, living snakes; and his skin tingled with multitudinous tiny bites from fangs which were venomous; while the purring of the creature grew until it became a very roar like that of a cataract and overwhelmed all his senses. He was mentally drowning in a sea of impending catastrophe, when, by an expiring effort, he wrenched himself free from the obsession and sprang up. Then he discovered that his hand had been mechanically stroking a small unopened animal mummy, which proved on closer examination to be that of a cat.

The next incident that he seems to have thought worth recording happened a few nights later. He had retired to rest in his usual health and slept soundly. But towards morning his slumbers were disturbed by a dream that recalled the kind of nocturnal fear that is common in childhood. Two distant stars began to grow in size and brilliancy until he saw that they were advancing through space towards him with incredible speed. In a few moments they must overwhelm him in a sea of fire and flame. Onwards they came, bulging and unfolding like great flaming flowers, growing more dazzling and blinding at every moment; and then, just as they were upon him, they suddenly turned into two enormous cat's eyes, flaming green and yellow. He sprang up in bed with a cry, and found himself at once wide awake. And there on the window-sill lay a great black cat, glowering at him with lambent yellow eyes. A moment later the cat disappeared.

But the mysterious thing of it was that the window-sill was not accessible to anything that had not wings. There was no means by which a cat could have climbed to it. Nor was there any sign of a cat in the garden below.

The date of the next thing that happened is not clear, for it does not appear to have been recorded at the time. But it would seem to have been within a few days of the curious dream. Sydney had occasion to go to a cupboard which was kept locked. It contained manuscripts and other papers of value; and the key never left his possession. To his knowledge the cupboard had not been opened for at least a month past. He now had occasion to refer to a collection of notes in connection with his favourite study. On opening the cupboard, he was at once struck by a curious odour. It was not exactly musky, but could only be described as an animal odour, slightly suggestive of that of a cat. But what at once arrested Sydney's notice and caused him extreme annoyance was the fact that the papers had been disturbed. The loose papers contained in some pigeon-holes at the back had been drawn forwards into a loose heap on the shelf. They looked for all the world like a nest, for they had been loosely arranged in a round heap with a depression in the middle. It looked as if some animal had coiled itself up to sleep there; and the size of the depression was just such as would be made by a cat.

Sydney was too much annoyed by the disturbance of his papers to be greatly impressed at the moment by their curious arrangement; but it came home to him as a shock when he began to gather the papers together and set them in order. Some of them seemed to be slightly soiled, and on closer examination he found that they were besprinkled with short black hairs like those of a cat.

About a week afterwards he returned later in the evening than usual, after attending a meeting of a scientific society to which he belonged. He was taking his latch key from his pocket to open the door when he thought that something rubbed against his leg. Looking down, he saw nothing; but immediately afterwards he felt it again, and this time he thought he saw a black shadow beside his right foot. On looking more closely, nothing was to be seen; but as he went into the house he distinctly felt something soft brush against his leg. As he paused in the hall to remove his overcoat, he saw a faint shadow which seemed to go up the stairs. It was certainly only a shadow and nothing solid, for the light was good and he saw it clearly. But there was nothing in motion to account for the passing shadow. And the way the shadow moved was curiously suggestive of a cat.

The next notes in the book that Sydney seems to have devoted to this curious subject appear to be a series of mere coincidences: and the fact that he thought them worth recording shows only too clearly to what an extent his mind was now obsessed. He had taken the numerical value of the letters C, A, T, in the alphabet, 3, 1, and 20 respectively, and by adding them together had arrived at the total 24. He then proceeded to note the many ways in which this number had played its part in the events of his life. He was born on the 24th of the month, at a house whose number was 24; and his mother was 24 years old at the time. He was 24 years old when his father died and left him the master of a considerable fortune. That was just 24 years ago. The last time he had balanced his affairs, he found that he was worth in invested funds—apart from land and houses—just about 24 thousand pounds. At three different periods, and in different towns, he had chanced to live at houses numbered 24; and that was also the number of his present abode. Moreover the number of his ticket for the British Museum Reading Room ended with 24, and both his doctor and his solicitor were housed under that same persistent number. Several more of these coincidences had been noted by him; but they were rather far-fetched and are not worth recording here. But the memoranda conclude with the ominous question, 'Will it all end on the 24th?'

Soon after these notes were written, a much more serious affair had to be placed on record. Sydney was coming downstairs one evening, when he noticed in a badly lighted corner of the staircase something that he took to be a cat. He shrank back with his natural dislike for the animal; but on looking more closely he saw that it was nothing more than a shadow cast by some carving on the stair-head. He turned away with a laugh; but, as he turned, it certainly seemed that the shadow moved! As he went down the stairs he twice stumbled in trying to save himself from what he thought was a cat in danger of being trodden upon; and a moment later he seemed to tread on something soft that gave way and threw him down. He fell heavily and shook himself badly.

On picking himself up with the aid of his servant he limped into his library, and there found that his trousers were torn from a little above the ankle. But the curious thing was that there were three parallel vertical tears—just such as might be caused by the claws of a cat. A sharp smarting led to further investigation; and he then found that there were three deep scratches on the side of his leg, exactly corresponding with the tears in the trousers.

In the margin of the page on which he recorded this accident, he has added the words, 'This cat means mischief.' And the whole tone of the remaining entries and of the few letters that date from this time shows only too clearly that his mental outlook was more or less tinged and obscured by gloomy forebodings.

It would seem to have been on the following day that another disturbing trifle occurred. Sydney's leg still pained him, and he spent the day on a couch with one or two favourite books. Soon after two o'clock in the afternoon, he heard a soft thud, such as might be caused by a cat leaping down from a moderate height. He looked up, and there on the window-sill crouched a black cat with gleaming eyes; and a moment later it sprang into the room. But it never reached the floor—or, if it did, it must have passed through it! He saw it spring; he saw it for the moment in mid-air; he saw it about to alight on the floor; and then—it was not there!

He would have liked to believe that it was a mere optical delusion; but against that theory stood the awkward fact that the cat in springing down from the window knocked over a flower-pot; and there lay the broken pieces in evidence of the fact.

He was now seriously scared. It was bad enough to find himself seeing things that had no objective reality; but it was far worse to be faced by happenings that were certainly real, but not to be accounted for by the ordinary laws of nature. In this case the broken flower-pot showed that if the black cat was merely what we call a ghost for lack of any more convenient term, it was a ghost that was capable of producing physical effects. If it could knock a flower-pot over, it could presumably scratch and bite—and the prospect of being attacked by a cat from some other plane of existence will hardly bear being thought of.

Certainly it seemed that Sydney had now real ground for alarm. The spectre cat—or whatever one likes to call it—was in some way gaining power and was now able to manifest its presence and hostility in more open and practical fashion. That same night saw a proof of this. Sydney dreamed that he was visiting the Zoological Gardens when a black leopard of ferocious aspect escaped from its cage and sprang upon him. He was thrown backwards to the ground and pinned down by the heavy animal. He was half crushed by its weight; its claws were at his throat; its fierce yellow eyes were staring into his face; when the horror of the thing brought the dream to a sudden end and he awoke. As consciousness returned he was aware of an actual weight on his chest; and on opening his eyes he looked straight into the depths of two lambent yellow flames set in a face of velvet black. The cat sprang off the bed and leaped through the window. But the window was closed and there was no sound of breaking glass.

Sydney did not sleep much more that night. But a further shock awaited him on rising. He found some small blood stains on his pillow; and an inspection before the looking glass showed the presence of two groups of tiny wounds on his neck. They were little more than pin-pricks; but they were arranged in two semi-circular groups, one on either side of the neck and just such as might be caused by a cat trying to grasp the neck between its two forepaws.

This was the last incident recorded in Sydney's diary; and the serious view that he took of the situation is shown by certain letters that he wrote during the day, giving final instructions to his executors and settling various details of business—evidently in view of his approaching end.

What happened in the course of the final scene of the tragedy we can only guess from the traces left behind: but there is sufficient evidence to show that the horror was an appalling one.

The housekeeper seems to have been awakened once during the night by a strange noise which she could only describe as being like an angry cat snarling; while the parlour maid, whose room was immediately above that occupied by Sydney, says that she dreamt that she heard her master scream horribly once or twice.

In the morning, Sydney did not answer when called at his usual hour; and, as the door was found to be locked, the housekeeper presently procured assistance and had it broken open. He was found crouching on the floor and leaning against the wall opposite the window. The carpet was saturated with blood; and the cause was quickly evident. The unfortunate man's throat had been torn open on either side, both jugular veins being severed. So far as could be made out, he had retired to bed and had been attacked during sleep, for the sheets were bespattered with blood. He had apparently got out of bed in his struggles to overcome the Thing that had him fast in its fearful grip. The look of horror on his distorted face was said by the witnesses to be past description.

Both window and door were fastened, and there was nothing to show how the assailant entered. But there was something to show how it left. The bloodstains on the floor recorded the footprints of a gigantic cat. They led across the floor from the corpse to the opposite wall—and there they ceased. The cat never came back; but whether it passed through the solid wall or melted into thin air, no one knows. In some mysterious way it came and went; and in passing it did this deed of horror.

It was a curious coincidence that the tragedy took place on Christmas Eve—the 24th day of the month!

BACK FOR CHRISTMAS

by John Collier

John Collier (1901–80) is celebrated for his many
short stories and novels blending a light-hearted
style with bizarre fantasy and horror.
'Back for Christmas', taken from his greatest
collection *Fancies and Goodnight* (1951), is one of
his best short tales in the genre. Collier's best early
novels are the recently dramatized *His Monkey Wife*
(1930), *No Traveller Returns* (1931), and *Tom's-a-
Cold* (1933). Among his later collections are *Of
Demons and Darkness* (1965) and *The John Collier
Reader* (1976).

'**D**octor,' said Major Sinclair, 'we certainly must have you
with us for Christmas.' Tea was being poured, and the
Carpenters' living-room was filled with friends who had
come to say last-minute farewells to the Doctor and his wife.

'He shall be back,' said Mrs Carpenter. 'I promise you.'

'It's hardly certain,' said Dr Carpenter. 'I'd like nothing better, of
course.'

'After all,' said Mr Hewitt, 'you've contracted to lecture only for
three months.'

'Anything may happen,' said Dr Carpenter.

'Whatever happens,' said Mrs Carpenter, beaming at them, 'he
shall be back in England for Christmas. You may all believe me.'

They all believed her. The Doctor himself almost believed her. For
ten years she had been promising him for dinner parties, garden parties,
committees, heaven knows what, and the promises had always been kept.

The farewells began. There was a fluting of compliments on dear Hermione's marvellous arrangements. She and her husband would drive to Southampton that evening. They would embark the following day. No trains, no bustle, no last-minute worries. Certain the Doctor was marvellously looked after. He would be a great success in America. Especially with Hermione to see to everything. She would have a wonderful time, too. She would see the skyscrapers. Nothing like that in Little Godwearing. But she must be very sure to bring him back. 'Yes, I will bring him back. You may rely upon it.' He mustn't be persuaded. No extensions. No wonderful post at some super-American hospital. Our infirmary needs him. And he must be back by Christmas. 'Yes,' Mrs Carpenter called to the last departing guest, 'I shall see to it. He shall be back by Christmas.'

The final arrangements for closing the house were very well managed. The maids soon had the tea things washed up; they came in, said goodbye, and were in time to catch the afternoon bus to Devizes.

Nothing remained but odds and ends, locking doors, seeing that everything was tidy. 'Go upstairs,' said Hermione, 'and change into your brown tweeds. Empty the pockets of that suit before you put it in your bag. I'll see to everything else. All you have to do is not to get in the way.'

The Doctor went upstairs and took off the suit he was wearing, but instead of the brown tweeds, he put on an old, dirty bath gown, which he took from the back of his wardrobe. Then, after making one or two little arrangements, he leaned over the head of the stairs and called to his wife, 'Hermione! Have you a moment to spare?'

'Of course, dear. I'm just finished.'

'Just come up here for a moment. There's something rather extra-ordinary up here.'

Hermione immediately came up. 'Good heavens, my dear man!' she said when she saw her husband. 'What are you lounging about in that filthy old thing for? I told you to have it burned long ago.'

'Who in the world,' said the Doctor, 'has dropped a gold chain down the bathtub drain?'

'Nobody has, of course,' said Hermione. 'Nobody wears such a thing.'

'Then what is it doing there?' said the Doctor. 'Take this flashlight. If you lean right over, you can see it shining, deep down.'

'Some Woolworth's bangle off one of the maids,' said Hermione. 'It can be nothing else.' However, she took the flashlight and leaned over, squinting into the drain. The Doctor, raising a short length of lead pipe, struck two or three times with great force and precision, and tilting the body by the knees, tumbled it into the tub.

He then slipped off the bathrobe and, standing completely naked, unwrapped a towel full of implements and put them into the wash-basin. He spread several sheets of newspaper on the floor and turned once more to his victim.

She was dead, of course—horribly doubled up, like a somersaulter, at one end of the tub. He stood looking at her for a very long time, thinking of absolutely nothing at all. Then he saw how much blood there was and his mind began to move again.

First he pushed and pulled until she lay straight in the bath, then he removed her clothing. In a narrow bathtub this was an extremely clumsy business, but he managed it at last and then turned on the taps. The water rushed into the tub, then dwindled, then died away, and the last of it gurgled down the drain.

'Good God!' he said. 'She turned it off at the main.'

There was only one thing to do: the Doctor hastily wiped his hands on a towel, opened the bathroom door with a clean corner of the towel, threw it back onto the bath stool, and ran downstairs, barefoot, light as a cat. The cellar door was in a corner of the entrance hall, under the stairs. He knew just where the cut-off was. He had reason to: he had been pottering about down there for some time past—trying to scrape out a bin for wine, he had told Hermione. He pushed open the cellar door, went down the steep steps, and just before the closing door plunged the cellar into pitch darkness, he put his hand on the tap and turned it on. Then he felt his way back along the grimy wall till he came to the steps. He was about to ascend them when the bell rang.

The Doctor was scarcely aware of the ringing as a sound. It was like a spike of iron pushed slowly up through his stomach. It went on until it reached his brain. Then something broke. He threw himself down in the coal dust on the floor and said, 'I'm through. I'm through!

'They've got no *right* to come,' he said. Then he heard himself panting. 'None of this,' he said to himself. 'None of this.'

He began to revive. He got to his feet, and when the bell rang again the sound passed through him almost painlessly. 'Let them go away,' he said. Then he heard the front door open. He said, 'I don't care.' His shoulder came up, like that of a boxer, to shield his face. 'I give up,' he said.

He heard people calling. 'Herbert!' 'Hermione!' It was the Wallingfords. 'Damn them! They come butting in. People anxious to get
off. All naked! And blood and coal dust! I'm done! I'm through! I
can't do it.'

'Herbert!'

'Hermione!'

'Where the dickens can they be?'

'The car's there.'

'Maybe they've popped round to Mrs Liddell's.'

'We must see them.'

'Or to the shops, maybe. Something at the last minute.'

'Not Hermione. I say, listen! Isn't that someone having a bath?
Shall I shout? What about whanging on the door?'

'Sh-h-h! Don't. It might not be tactful.'

'No harm in a shout.'

'Look, dear. Let's come in on our way back. Hermione said they
wouldn't be leaving before seven. They're dining on the way, in
Salisbury.'

'Think so? All right. Only I want a last drink with old Herbert.
He'd be hurt.'

'Let's hurry. We can be back by half-past six.'

The Doctor heard them walk out and the front door close quietly
behind them. He thought, 'Half-past six. I can do it.'

He crossed the hall, sprang the latch of the front door, went
upstairs, and taking his instruments from the washbasin, finished what
he had to do. He came down again, clad in his bath gown, carrying
parcel after parcel of towelling or newspaper neatly secured with safety
pins. These he packed carefully into the narrow, deep hole he had
made in the corner of the cellar, shovelled in the soil, spread coal dust
over all, satisfied himself that everything was in order, and went
upstairs again. He then thoroughly cleansed the bath, and himself,
and the bath again, dressed, and took his wife's clothing and his bath
gown to the incinerator.

One or two more little touches and everything was in order. It was
only quarter past six. The Wallingfords were always late; he had only
to get into the car and drive off. It was a pity he couldn't wait till after
dusk, but he could make a detour to avoid passing through the main
street, and even if he was seen driving alone, people would only think
Hermione had gone on ahead for some reason and they would forget
about it.

Still, he was glad when he had finally got away, entirely unobserved, on the open road, driving into the gathering dusk. He had to drive very carefully; he found himself unable to judge distances, his reactions were abnormally delayed, but that was a detail. When it was quite dark he allowed himself to stop the car on the top of the downs, in order to think.

The stars were superb. He could see the lights of one or two little towns far away on the plain below him. He was exultant. Everything that was to follow was perfectly simple. Marion was waiting in Chicago. She already believed him to be a widower. The lecture people could be put off with a word. He had nothing to do but establish himself in some thriving out-of-the-way town in America and he was safe for ever. There were Hermione's clothes, of course, in the suitcases; they could be disposed of through the porthole. Thank heaven she wrote her letters on the typewriter—a little thing like handwriting might have prevented everything. 'But there you are,' he said. 'She was up-to-date, efficient all along the line. Managed everything. Managed herself to death, damn her!'

'There's no reason to get excited,' he thought. 'I'll write a few letters for her, then fewer and fewer. Write myself—always expecting to get back, never quite able to. Keep the house one year, then another, then another; they'll get used to it. Might even come back alone in a year or two and clear it up properly. Nothing easier. But not for Christmas!' He started up the engine and was off.

In New York he felt free at last, really free. He was safe. He could look back with pleasure—at least after a meal, lighting his cigarette, he could look back with a sort of pleasure—to the minute he had passed in the cellar listening to the bell, the door, and the voices. He could look forward to Marion.

As he strolled through the lobby of his hotel, the clerk, smiling, held up letters for him. It was the first batch from England. Well, what did that matter? It would be fun dashing off the typewritten sheets in Hermione's downright style, signing them with her squiggle, telling everyone what a success his first lecture had been, how thrilled he was with America but how certainly she'd bring him back for Christmas. Doubts could creep in later.

He glanced over the letters. Most were for Hermione. From the Sinclairs, the Wallingfords, the vicar, and a business letter from Holt & Sons, Builders and Decorators.

He stood in the lounge, people brushing by him. He opened the letters with his thumb, reading here and there, smiling. They all seemed very confident he would be back for Christmas. They relied on Hermione. 'That's where they make their big mistake,' said the Doctor, who had taken to American phrases. The builders' letter he kept to the last. Some bill, probably. It was:

Dear Madam,

We are in receipt of your kind acceptance of estimate as below and also of key.

We beg to repeat you may have every confidence in same being ready in ample time for Christmas present as stated. We are setting men to work this week.

We are, Madam,

Yours faithfully,

PAUL HOLT & SONS

To excavating, building up, suitably lining one sunken wine bin in cellar as indicated, using best materials, making good, etc.

...............£ 18/0/0

A CHRISTMAS
STORY

by 'Sarban'

'Sarban' was the pseudonym used by the British
diplomat John W. Wall (1910–1989) on three fine
books in the fantasy genre at the beginning of the
1950s. All are scarce collectors' items today :
Ringstones (1951), from which 'A Christmas Story'
is taken, and *The Doll Maker* (1953), were
collections of stories, and *The Sound of His Horn*
(1952) is an unforgettable novel, set in an
'alternate-world' England where the Nazis
won the war.

I will tell you a Christmas story. I will tell it as Alexander
Andreievitch Masseyev told it me in his little house outside the
walls of Jedda years ago one hot, damp Christmas Eve.

It was the custom among the few English people in Jedda in those
days to make up a carol-singing party on Christmas Eve. For a week
before, the three or four of us who had voices they were not ashamed
of, and the one or two who had neither voice nor shame, practised to
the accompaniment of an old piano in the one British mercantile
house in the place: an instrument whose vocal cords had not stood the
excessive humidity of that climate any better than those of some of
the singers. Then, on Christmas Eve, the party gathered at our house
where we dined and, with a lingering memory of Yuletide mummers in
England, arrayed ourselves in such bits of fancy dress or comic finery as
we could lay our hands on; made false whiskers out of cotton-wool or

a wisp of tow, blackened our faces, reddened our noses with lip-stick supplied by the Vice-Consul's wife, put our jackets on inside-out and sprinkled over our shoulders 'frost' out of a little packet bought by someone ages ago at home and kept by some miracle of sentimental pertinacity through years of exile on that desert shore.

I am no singer, but I always had a part in those proceedings. It was to carry the lantern.

Our Sudanese house-boys served us with more admiration than amusement on their faces, and the little knot of our Arab neighbours, who always gathered about our door to watch us set out, whatever the occasion, gave not the slightest sign of recognising anything more comic than usual in our appearance. We made our round of the European houses in our Ford station-wagon; I holding my lantern on its pole outside the vehicle and only by luck avoiding shattering it against the wall as the First Secretary cut the corners of the narrow lanes. Fortunately, except for our neighbours, who never seemed to go to bed at all (or, at least, didn't go to bed to sleep), the True-Believers of Jedda kept early hours, and by nine or ten at night the dark sandy lanes were deserted but for pariah dogs and families of goats settled with weary wheezings to doze the still, close night away. Poor Jedda goats! whose pasture and byre were the odorous alleys; pathetic mothers of frustrated offspring, with those brassières which seemed at first sight such an astonishing refinement of Grundyism, but which turned out to be merely an economic safeguard—girdles not of chastity but husbandry; with your frugal diet of old newspapers and ends of straw rope, to whom the finding of an unwanted (or unguarded) panama hat was like a breakfast of '*Id ul Fitr*; how many a curse and kick in the ribs have you earned from a night-ambling Frank for couching in that precise pit of darkness where the feeble rays of one paraffin lamp expire and those of the next are not yet born!

From the façades of the crazy, coral-built houses that hem the lanes project *roshans*—bow-windows of decaying wooden lattice-work—and on the plastered tops of these bow-windows the moonlight falls so clear and white this Christmas Eve that to the after-dinner eye it seems that snow has fallen.

Our first call was always at the Minister's. There, in the panelled hall which, but for its bareness, might have been in England, we used to range ourselves and, in comparatively good order, deliver our repertoire while the Minister, in his study above, turned down the wireless for a few minutes and his Lady and family listened from the staircase. We always gave the meteorological data of Good King Wenceslaus with feeling, perhaps more conscious than at other times of our prickly heat and the sweat trickling down inside our shirts. Then the Minister's Lady descended to congratulate us, kind-heartedly, on our singing and, spontaneously, on our disguises, while the mustachioed Sudani butler brought wassail on a tray. After our own Minister, we used to go to the American Legation and then to the Dutch Chargé d'Affaires where, also, loyalty to tradition had its traditional reward to the Red Sea equivalent of the wassail-bowl. That used to be about as far as our organisation was capable of maintaining a good custom with coherence. A touch of the strayed reveller used to creep in after that. But, while most of the party had still not lost their papers of words and while two or three were still agreed on the tune of any one carol, the Vice-Consul's wife used to insist on our going out to the Masseyev's. We were all always agreed that we wanted to go there; the argument used to be about the order it should take in our round of calls, for at this stage, the length of our stay at any particular house was unpredictable. However, the Vice-Consul's wife always won. So, letting in the clutch with a jerk, the First Secretary would roar round by the town wall and out of the Medina Gate and along the tyre-beaten track to the hut-suburb of Baghdadia.

Years and years ago, before even the Vice-Consul came to Jedda, Alexander Andreievitch Masseyev, sometime a lieutenant in the Tzarist Navy, exiled by the October Revolution, had ended a pilgrimage through the Middle East by accepting the post of instructor to the Arabian Air Force. When I knew him, he and his wife, Lydia, lived in a little white-walled house with a tiny courtyard before it between the straggling suburb and the sea a mile northwards from the Medina Gate.

There, then, we arrive this Christmas Eve. We are expected, but pretend not to be. We shush each other a good deal, and everybody shushes the Vice-Consul, and after the Vice-Consul's wife, being in conspiracy with Lydia, has caused the courtyard door to be opened we tip-toe in and range ourselves round, or some of us, upon a flower-bed the size of a pocket handkerchief, and let fly with 'Christians Awake'; then, after a lot of fierce 'all-togethering', render 'Hark the Herald Angels Sing', and, as a concession to the Vice-Consul, who thought that was what we were singing to begin with, 'Good King Wenceslaus' once more. Alexander Andreievitch and Lydia appear in their lighted doorway, smiling, not quite understanding, but smiling because this is something Christian with a faint affinity to white winters far away. With loud 'Merry Christmases' we crowd into their little sitting-room, while Lydia exclaims at our daubed visages and disarray, and chatters in a mixture of broken French and English, and Alexander Andreievitch, beaming all over his broad face, brings out bottles and glasses and tumbles his six words of English out at us. He and the Vice-Consul understand each other in what they call Arabic—but it would puzzle an Arab.

Lydia has made a cake. The Vice-Consul's wife has brought a bottle of wine for a present; we have produced a bottle of whisky, and the Vice-Consul is discovered to have brought a bottle of rum on general principles. There are little dishes of salted almonds and olives, slices of well-matured sausage, and even bits of ham procured from Yanni, the Cypriot grocer in the Suq (at a price that would make the Black Market look like a bargain counter). It is hot in the little room; burnt cork and lip-stick trickle down the plump face of Bartholomew, our sole representative of British Commerce; the First Secretary props open the door and fans himself; but Moslem Arabia is shut out beyond the courtyard walls: we are but fifty miles from Mecca and the desert between us and Bethlehem is ten times as wide, but we settle ourselves on the few chairs or the floor and, every Christian glass being filled, sing 'God rest you Merry, Gentlemen!'.

On the wall there is a faded photograph of some prospect in St Petersburg, and there hang from a nail a prismatic compass and an aneroid barometer in stout though worn leather cases, once the property of the Imperial Navy, which Alexander Andreievitch has saved from the wreck and managed to preserve through all these years. Alexander Andreievitch is a short, squarely built man with short, iron-grey hair and a broad, deeply-lined face that does not often smile. His heart is not so good now as it once was. He no longer flies in the two or three temperamental old Wapiti aircraft that constitute the Arabian Air Force. His job now consists mainly in trying to keep the saleable stores of the Air Force from seeping away into the Suq; in endeavouring to explain to the Nejdi camel-rider who commands the Force that the principles of aerial navigation are not explicit in the Quran, and in petitioning the Minister of War for arrears of pay. He has never announced any notable advance in any of these directions.

I sit near Alexander Andreievitch and pledge him in Russian, at which he smiles, then, with an exclamation as if suddenly remembering something, gets up and fumbles in a little cupboard in the wall. He brings out a strange-looking bottle which he proudly shows me. The label is one I have not seen within a thousand miles of Jedda. Then I remember that some months ago Alexander Andreievitch went to Baghdad. There, by a lucky chance, he has lighted on a bottle of Zubrovka, smuggled down, I expect, from Tehran or Tabriz. I am the only one in our party who knows what it is. The others prefer whisky or rum. Alexander Andreievitch sets out two little glasses and fills them. Back go our heads: *do dna!* We perform this exercise a good many times while the others are sipping at their longer glasses. Alexander Andreievitch smiles frequently now and talks all the time, in Russian.

The label of the bottle has always interested me. My Russian is not so copious that I can see the connection between the name Zubrovka and the picture of the European Bison which seems to be the Trade Mark. So Alexander Andreievitch explains and adds a word to my vocabulary. 'Da. . . .' he says, with a melancholy drawing-out of the syllable. 'They are all gone now. There were a few in the deep forest of Lithuania until the Revolution. The Tzar preserved them.' He sighs. I too remember, when I was a little boy, I saw an old, high-withered, ungainly beast with matted hair hanging on it like worn door-mats leaning against the rails of an enclosure in Regent's Park: a huge, tired, solitary beast hanging its heavy head with half-closed eyes, while a grubby fist thrust monkey-nuts under its muzzle and cockney voices wondered what it was.

'Did you ever see one?' I ask Alexander Andreievitch. He shakes his head so sadly and looks so full of the irrevocable past that I am led to see a symbolic correspondence between him and the Zubor, between them both and Imperial Russia, and the weight of what's gone beyond recall lies heavily on my spirit until we have lowered the level of the Zubrovka below the Bison's feet. Then we cheer up a little and I suggest: 'Perhaps. . . . Who knows? Russia is very wide. . . . There are untrodden forests still. . . .'

Very gravely Alexander Andreievitch nods his head. '*Da, v Rossii* . . . . Yes, there are rare things in Russia. I have seen—listen, Meester—, will you believe I have seen something, oh! far away beyond the forests, something that was not a Zubor?'

'No? What then?'

'No. Not a bison, not a reindeer, not an elk. I was a hunter when I was a boy. I know all those things. Once, it was in 1917, I was on board a cruiser, the *Knyaz Nicolai*, and we were ordered to Archangel.

From there we cruised eastward in the Arctic Ocean to the mouth of
the Yenessei River. It was summer, naturally. Why we went there no
one knew. It was 1917. Some of us thought our orders were to go
through the Behring Straits to Japan. We were young. We joked about
going ashore in Siberia to chop fire-wood when the coal ran out, the
same as the troops did on the railway. That shore in summer looks just
the same as these Hejaz mountains, brown and bare. The *Knyaz
Nicolai* carried a sea-plane, an English machine. That was a very new
idea, then. The English had thought of doing it. We Russians did it.
We made experimental flights in the fine weather up there in the
Arctic Ocean. The pilot was my old friend Igor Palyashkin. I was his
observer. It was a revolutionary idea. I think the Russians were the
first who practised it, though the English no doubt thought of it.

'Well, there was a little station near the mouth of the Yenessei
River, far, far away from anywhere. A few Russians kept the station
and collected furs from the natives; there was also an officer of the
Imperial Navy. He did not collect furs. He just drank. The *Knyaz
Nicolai* was ordered to call at this station—it was called Kamyenaya
Gora—and deliver some provisions. We approached, but the winter
that year began early. Already, when the sea should have been open
for another month, ice was forming. We met fields of ice that
stretched as far as the eye could see; thin ice, you understand, which
the cruiser could break through. But it was dangerous, for in one day
or so of sudden hard weather that thin ice will become solid and lock
you in immovably; then it begins to squeeze. The *Knyaz Nicolai* did
not reach Kamyenaya Gora. We returned to open water, but because
we were so near our captain decided to send the sea-plane with
a message. It was something that had never been done before. We
were to circle the station, drop our message and return and be picked
up on the open water.

'We made our calculations, Igor Palyashkin and I, and we took off.
It was very fine weather; the last, still, clear days of the Arctic
summer. We could not see far; the circle of our vision was bounded by
a blue wall, but beneath us we saw the sea quite clearly, without
waves, for it was covered with a thin skin of ice, but moving gently as
if it breathed; and a little further on we saw the land, brown with
streaks of snow. We flew a long way over the land. It is a mournful
land, and empty! Ah, emptier far than any you have seen even
between here and the Persian Gulf. We flew so far over the land that
I thought our calculations must be wrong, but we found that little

station, Igor Palyashkin and I! It was the first aeroplane they had ever seen, those people, I think. We saw them running out. We went very low and I waved and dropped the message, then we headed back for the cruiser again. We were the first men who had ever flown in the Arctic Circle, Igor Palyashkin and I.'

Alexander Andreievitch refills our little glasses. Bartholomew and the Vice-Consul are singing 'Good King Wenceslaus' again, but merely, I gather, to settle an argument about something. The Second Secretary is leaning against the wall behind the door. He appears to be asleep.

'*Da*,' says Alexander Andreievitch, as he sets down his glass on the tray, speaking softly to the Bison. 'They shot him afterwards, the Bolsheviki. But we were the first, Igor Palyashkin and I.' He shakes his head and I wait.

'You understand,' he says, 'our calculations were not quite right. We saw the land, oh! land on every side. Brown land with streaks of snow, and when we came low we saw the forests of little grey bushes and the mournful marshes, all the wide taiga on every side. But we did not see the sea. And then the blue wall which had been all round us between the sky and the sea turned grey and came very close, and soon we could see nothing at all but grey mist unless we flew very, very low. So we came down very close to the land, just over the tops of little fir trees and grey bushes and over the surface of desolate pools, black and glinting like steel. Up above there was no sun and no sky, and on every side there was only the mournful grey taiga.

'Then, soon, Igor Palyashkin turned and looked at me and I knew that we had no more petrol left. He signed with his arm that he was going to land, and we went down, swiftly, to the drab grey marsh; we touched the tops of the little bushes and then a blackness like steel spread before us and the floats of the machine sent up fountains of water and sheets of white ice. We came to a stop with the nose of our machine in the bushes at the edge of the marsh and we climbed out unhurt. He was a good pilot, Igor Palyashkin.

'We had our map and the compass and we made fresh calculations and set off to walk to Kamyenaya Gora. But the night came down, so we stopped and lit a fire. It took a long time to light that fire. The little willow bushes would not burn very well and before we had got it going well enough to put some moss on to make a smoke we were being tortured by millions of mosquitoes. We had our iron rations:

[176]

enough for one meal. We ate those, then wrapped our heads in our coats and lay on the wet ground in the smoke of the fire. But still the mosquitoes got at us. *Bozhe moi!* How they bit. "I wish it would freeze!" Igor Palyashkin said. "It would kill us but it would kill these damned mosquitoes first."

'When it was light we began to walk, but you cannot walk very well in the taiga. Everywhere in summer the ground is soft; the little bushes grow in the marsh and you cannot push your way through them when you are up to your waist in water and mud. And the mosquitoes never left off biting. We kept at it for two days. The second and third nights we could not even light a fire, because there was nowhere dry to light it and the matches had got wet, too. It was miserably cold and we had no food, but Igor Palyashkin was cheerful. He had his revolver. "I shall shoot a reindeer," he said. I said there were no reindeer in the marshes. "Well, then, a wolf. No? a fox, a hare, a rat. What matters it? I shall shoot the first thing I see and we shall eat it raw. And if God sends us nothing else to shoot I will shoot you and then myself, so we shall not die a hard death." "Igor Sergeievitch," I said, "shoot me now, for there is nothing alive in all this cursed taiga but the mosquitoes and we.'

'But I was wrong. On the third day we came to some dry ground where some fir-trees grew. Oh! little fir-trees like Christmas trees, but we were so glad to see them and to stop wading through the marsh that we clasped hands, Igor Palyashkin and I, and danced round one of them and sang the children's song about the Yolka.

'Beyond that dry ground was a broad river, so broad we could just see the other bank like a brown bar under the grey gloom of the sky. The river was full of spongy, water-logged ice so that it did not flow or ripple, but stood still while we, standing on the low bank by the little fir-trees, we, you understand, seemed to move backwards. It was so quiet! There was no bird or animal moving in all the world; even the mosquitoes had left us. It was so quiet that we could hear the sap creeping down the little fir-trees into the ground and we knew, Igor Palyashkin and I, that that night the Lord Frost would come to the taiga and bind the river and snap the boughs and freeze us like stones to the earth. It was so quiet that we could hear the Frost coming from far away and Igor Palyashkin pulled out his revolver and shot six times into the north. He was not afraid of God, Igor Palyashkin.

'Then, between the fir-trees, stepping softly in their skin boots and holding their bows in front of them, came six little men dressed all in skins; six Samoyed hunters. They took us to a little hut they had built among the fir-trees and gave us meat to eat. We ate and ate until we were sick. Then we lay down on some skins in the hut and heard the frost come walking through the dark, cracking the trees as he passed. It was too cold to sleep, but because they had a handful of fire in the middle of the hut and we cowered round it, eight men huddled close together, we did not freeze. They gave us some more meat and this time we kept it down and crouched over that little heap of embers all night, Igor Palyashkin and I and the six Samoyed hunters. Not a word of Russian had they and not a word of their tongue had we. Ah! If we had had a bottle of Zubrovka that night—one glass, even!'

The Vice-Consul's wife is on her feet, drawing out a long farewell to Lydia; the First Secretary is holding open the door, still fanning himself; the Second Secretary is on the floor behind the door leaning his back against the wall: he has been asleep for the last ten minutes. But the Vice-Consul has begun another argument with Bartholomew. 'What's your hurry?' he says. 'There's half a bottle of rum left yet. Time enough for the next folks!' So his wife and the First Secretary sit down again. 'Another little glass!' says Alexander Andreievitch to me. 'It's still early.' And he tilts the Bison.

'In the morning light we set out,' says Alexander Andreievitch. 'We said Kamyenaya Gora very loud to the Samoyeds to make them understand where we wanted to go. So they picked up their bows and arrows and one of them took up an old, old gun, so old and so heavy it had a fork attached to the barrel to support it by, and they beckoned to us to go with them. But Igor Palyashkin was eating some more of the meat, and in the morning light he was looking closely at what he was eating. It was a large piece of meat, purplish, like beef, you understand, but there was a piece of skin on it, and on the skin some hair, and that hair was long and woolly and reddish in colour, not like the hair of any cow or ox in Russia or Siberia. "What is this meat?" says Igor Palyashkin. I looked at it closely, too, and tasted it again, and because my hunger was appeased now I could taste it properly. Ah! it had a strong, high flavour; it was more than half rotten. I wondered how I could have brought my snout near it the night before. It was not cooked, you understand, just warmed in the ashes. It stank of age and the earth. I had heard that in summer when the Samoyeds kill a beast they bury what they cannot eat by digging down a little way until they come to the frozen earth which never thaws and there they lay their meat and cover it with earth and it will keep all summer through: or keep well enough for them. Dear God! It smelt like a grave-digger's boots!

' "This meat! This meat!" cries Igor Palyashkin, as he grips the oldest Samoyed by the stiff skin sleeve. "The Devil take you! Ot *kuda eto myaso?* From where, man where?"

' "*Myaso! myaso!*" bellows Igor Palyashkin, seeing they do not understand. He points to the rotten gobbet of flesh with the long red wool on it and roars "*Myaso!*" until the little old fellow looks frightened and they all put their heads together and mutter, and it seems they're wondering what to do to calm this ferocious Russian. Then they point away down the river and smile timidly and beckon to us to go with them again.

' "Kamyenaya Gora!" we said again and again to the little hunters as they led us through the brittle grey trees. They nodded their heads and smiled. God knows whether they understood that Russian name, but they knew that we were Russians and they would lead us to the nearest Christian men. It had grown bitter cold! The black sky was no higher than the fir-tree tops and so solid you bent your head, like going into a hut. An icy mist stood among the little trees like a palisade round us, not two arms' length from us. When we spoke our words rang sonorous as if they reverberated from solid walls all round us. They gave us the skins we had slept on to wrap round us, and we waddled among those little men, Igor Palyashkin and I, like bears on their hind legs.

'We walked all day in single file with the Samoyed hunters, and in the afternoon we came again to the wide marshes. But now the frost had bound them, and we walked over them, sometimes on black ice that bent like thin planks under us, sometimes on frozen mud that squeaked and whined when our boots pressed it, and we broke the brittle willow twigs like stubble on a reaped field. Not a living thing but ourselves did we see and not a sound of anything with a soul came through the cold mist to us.

'But towards evening, towards the early evening, a whisper woke far away on the marshes and came to us, and the mist thinned and a keen wind cut our cheeks. The Samoyeds stopped and looked at each other and snuffed the wind. We too knew what that wind was. It was the snow-wind.

'Far and wide we could see now over the immense, sad taiga: a level, lonely waste of drab brown and faded grey, every particle of life in it stilled by that one terrible grip of the Lord Frost and its dead body stabbed through and through by the bayonets of the snow-wind. When the wind ceased we knew that the winding-sheet would fall from the black sky. The mist, you understand, had not gone entirely, it had thinned to a ghost of mist that rode upon the wind and still half-veiled the lifeless world. There was neither light nor dark, but a mixture of both, as if the night to come were powder blown about us by the freezing wind. The wind cut us to the bone, but it did not rustle the bushes: they were frozen stiff as stone. We could see far and wide, we could see to the world's end, for there was nothing in all the world but that cancelled light, that drab brown earth and that drab grey scrub, as dead as a dead man's hair.

'We did not know, Igor Palyashkin and I, where we were going. We did not look at our compass or at our map. We bent our heads and stumbled through the dead world after the six little hunters. I did not think I should ever see Kamyenaya Gora; I did not think I should ever see Petersburg or any Christian house again. I thought I should die there where there was nothing but greyness and cold. I was young; I should have wept, but it was too cold to cry.

'But the little Samoyeds knew where we were going, and before the grey light was all gone they brought us where something with definite form was visible in that limitless murk. On one side we saw the broad river, immobile under its ice, but blinking pale and hard in that fugitive landscape; and before us, across the level of the marsh we saw a low dark brown cliff of earth caving above the river, its overhang that might have fallen in the brief thaw of summer arrested now and secured for all the long winter by the hand of the frost. About us on that immense and mournful level the thin grey bushes grew sparser but taller. They seemed like columns of smoke that had been drifting up to mingle with the low grey sky and had been frozen, they also, only a little more solid and more defined than the grey atmosphere. The brown mud that stretched so far on every side was wrinkled as it had shrunk in the grip of the frost and in all the wrinkles lay white veins and threads of ice.

'Just as we came in sight of the river and that low bank of earth, the snow-wind dropped. Igor Palyashkin and I, we looked at one another; our lips were so numb with cold we could not speak. The Samoyeds muttered together and their breath hung in little thick white clouds before them. In a few minutes it would begin to snow and not even a Samoyed hunter would then find his way across the waste when the white flurries filled all the air. The oldest hunter gazed round, up at the heavy sky, round at the spectral bushes, down at the glazed and shrunken earth and finally out at that distant low bank that just broke the endless level. Then he stared at us and his dark face, all seamed and wrinkled, was like the frozen mud of the taiga, and the moisture was frozen white in the wrinkles of his skin as it was in the furrows of the marsh. He smiled and the thick hoar-frost on his lip stirred and the skin of ice cracked over his cheeks. Then he pointed to the far-off bank by the river and in his thin, frozen voice croaked, "Myaso!"

'Igor Palyashkin struggled to shout and managed a hoarse whisper: "Devil take him! Tartar son of a bitch! What's he mean, meat?" I wanted to say, "He means we shall be meat if we don't get to some shelter before it snows," but I do not think my lips could follow my tongue.

'The Samoyeds led us off at a quicker pace towards the little cliff. Nearer the river the ground was not frozen so solid and sometimes it would not bear our weight, but wheezed and creaked and then gave way with a sucking sound. But the hunters glided over, picking out the harder places for us, and we, plunging and ploughing along, managed somehow to follow them. The sky hardened above us, the light thickened round us, the bushes seemed to thaw into smoke once more and waver and dissolve into the twilight. Then we reached the overhanging bank of earth and crouched under its frozen arch of clods. I squatted with my back to the bank, looking out into the dismal waste where all was now a dance of shadows with neither earth nor ice nor bushes any longer clearly to be distinguished from each other. Behind me I heard Igor Palyashkin making a strange noise: curses and laughter were clashing among the ice at his lips. I turned to look. He was kicking at the frozen earth. In the bank, sticking out where summer landslips had exposed them, and in the stiffened debris all round us, were huge yellow bones; whole mighty limbs, fleshy organs frozen hard as pottery, glassy hunks of purple flesh with the hide on them and rigid locks of wool like rusty iron.

'We asked with our eyes what devil's graveyard had we got into? Igor Palyashkin kicked at some of the carrion he had devoured with such appetite that morning. The little old hunter nodded: "Myaso, myaso!" he croaked, and champed his jaws and creased his stiff cheeks a little more. Igor Palyashkin wrenched at a long bone sticking up like a fence-post and I verily believe he would have clubbed the old fellow over the skull with it if he could have got it loose.

'Suddenly, one of them made a fierce hissing noise. The six Samoyeds all on the instant became as still as the frozen clods around us. Igor Palyashkin and I, we too shrank down against the earth; what we could hear then stilled us like an intenser frost, and I felt cold to the middle of my heart. Through the dead and awful silence of that pause before the snow we heard something coming across the blind waste towards us. All day in that dead world nothing had moved but ourselves; now, out there where the shadows advanced and retreated and the pallid gloom baffled our sight, something was coming with oh! such labour and such pain, foundering and fighting onwards through the half-solid marsh. In that absolute stillness of the frozen air we heard it when it was far away; it came so slowly and it took so long, and we dare not do anything but listen and strain our eyes into the darkening mist. In what shape of living beast could such purpose and such terrible strength be embodied? A creature mightier than any God has made to be seen by man was dragging itself through the morass. We heard the crunch of the surface ice, then the whining strain of frozen mud as the enormous bulk we could not picture bore slowly down on it; then a deep gasping sound as the marsh yielded beneath a weight its frost-bonds could not bear. Then plungings of such violence and such a sound of agonised straining and moaning as constricted my heart; and, after that awful struggle, a long sucking and loud explosion of release as the beast prevailed and the marsh gave up its hold. Battle after battle, each more desperate than the last, that dreadful fight went on; we listened with such intentness that we suffered the agony of every yard of the creature's struggle towards our little bank of earth. But as it drew nearer the pauses between its down-sinkings and its tremendous efforts to burst free grew longer, as if that inconceivable strength and tenacity of purpose were failing. In those pauses we heard the most dreadful sound of all: the beast crying with pain and the terror of death. Dear Lord God! I think no Christian men but we, Igor Palyashkin and I, have ever heard a voice like that. I know that no voice on all this earth could have answered that brute soul moaning in the mist of the lonely taiga that evening before the snow. That beast was alone in all the world.

'So near it came before it sank for ever! So near! Just beyond the baffling curtain of the gloom where the grey bushes were woven with the sullen twilight—even to there, where another last fearful effort would have brought it to the harder earth and to those gigantic bones about us, it struggled before it cried its last long cry. The Samoyeds cowered behind us and hid their heads in the flaps of their skin coats and tried to shrink into the bare earth. Igor Palyashkin felt his empty revolver, then folded his arms on his breast. He did not fear God, and he was prepared to face the Devil. As for me, what made my heart sink so was the pain in that wild voice; the pain, and the drear, drear loneliness. *Bozhe moi!* I am a christened man and that was a brute soul come out of the wild forest; but it was drowning there on the dead Arctic edge of the world where there was neither forest nor field, land nor water, sun nor snow, but only an interminable chaos of cold between day and night, and there was no ear in all the world or in all time to understand its pain. Something that time had forgotten was drowning there, alone, in the gulfs of the freezing dark.'

'Jimmy!' roars the First Secretary, exasperated by my failure to heed his repeated summonses. The Vice-Consul is on his feet at last; even Bartholomew is on his—though rocking slightly. I rise. Alexander Andreievitch inverts the Bison over my glass and picks up his own. '*Da* . . .' he says, emitting the word on a long sigh, and turning the glass slowly in his hand. 'I saw it. A moment only; but I saw it. A moment between the brown mud and the grey bushes. Then the snow came, sudden and thick, and nothing else was seen but the white swirls of the snow. Still the great head was above the morass, the head and the shoulders, robed with long red-brown wool; the great head and something upraised like a pliant arm and the long, long curling teeth sweeping out in front like sleigh-runners. Then the snow came.'

'Alexander!' cries Lydia. 'Open the yard door!'

We stumble and jostle out into the little courtyard. The Red Sea night wraps its damp heat round us like a wet sheet hot from the wash-copper. We trip over the sill of Alexander Andreievitch's narrow door; we block the entrance of the courtyard; we rouse the Masseyevs' turkeys to emulation with our clamorous good-nights. Alexander Andreievitch treads in a flower-pot and kicks the fragments with violence against the house wall. '*Chort vozmi!*' he swears at it, but comes back to shake my hand. '*Da* . . . We saw it, Igor Palyashkin and I. Afterwards it was the Revolution.'

Someone has started up the Ford station-wagon. I have lost my lantern. I invariably do at about this point in the proceedings. 'Jimmy!' squeaks the Vice-Consul's wife. 'What's that star up there?' The Second Secretary is surprisingly wide awake. He sings in basso profundo:

'They looked up and saw a bright star
Shining i-in the heavens beyo-ond them far . . .'

The moon is setting yellow in the sea haze; the whole Arabian firmament drips with stars: the clustered Pleiades, glowing Aldebaran, the Twins, straddling Orion, girt and jewelled. The Vice-Consul's wife cannot point straight. 'Canis Major,' I say brusquely, preparing to dive into the station-wagon, but tripping over my fancy dress—or perhaps someone else's. Three-quarters of a bottle of rum but makes the Vice-Consul more talkative.

'All the Latin I remember,' he remarks, 'is hic, haec, hoc.'

An all but forgotten love for the classics slides back this Christmas Eve into Bartholomew's susceptible heart. For a moment he ceases to sway, and with corroborative emphasis he ejaculates, 'Hic!' to the Arabian stars.

THE WAITS

by L. P. Hartley

Leslie Poles Hartley (1895–1972) is celebrated for
his novels of country life, notably *Eustace and Hilda*
and *The Go-Between*. He was also a highly regarded
writer of ghost stories, and a regular contributor to
the *Ghost Book* series for nearly forty years.
'The Waits' is taken from his collection *Two for
the River* (1961).

Christmas Eve had been for all the Marriners, except Mr
Marriner, a most exhausting day. The head of the house
usually got off lightly at the festive season, lightly that is as far
as personal effort went. Financially, no; Mr Marriner knew that
financially quite a heavy drain was being made on his resources. And
later in the evening when he got out his cheque-book to give his
customary presents to his family, his relations and the staff, the drain
would be heavier. But he could afford it, he could afford it better this
Christmas than at any other Christmas in the history of his steadily
increasing fortune. And he didn't have to think, he didn't have to
choose; he only had to consult a list and add one or two names, and
cross off one or two. There was quite a big item to cross off, quite a big
item, though it didn't figure on the list or on the counterfoil of his
cheque-book. If he saw fit he would add the sum so saved to his
children's cheques. Jeremy and Anne would then think him even
more generous than he was, and if his wife made any comment, which
she wouldn't, being a tactful woman, he would laugh and call it a
Capital Distribution — 'capital in every sense, my dear!'

But this could wait till after dinner.

So of the quartet who sat down to the meal, he was the only one who hadn't spent a laborious day. His wife and Anne had both worked hard decorating the house and making arrangements for the party on Boxing Day. They hadn't spent the time in getting presents, they hadn't had to. Anne, who was two years older than Jeremy, inherited her mother's gift for present-giving and had made her selections weeks ago; she had a sixth sense for knowing what people wanted. But Jeremy had left it all to the last moment. His method was the reverse of Anne's and much less successful; he thought of the present first and the recipient afterwards. Who would this little box do for? Who would this other little box do for? Who should be the fortunate possessor of this third little box? In present-giving his mind followed a one-way track; and this year it was little boxes. They were expensive and undiscriminating presents and he was secretly ashamed of them. Now it was too late to do anything more: but when he thought of the three or four friends who would remain un-boxed his conscience smote him.

Silent and self-reproachful, he was the first to hear the singing outside the window.

'Listen, there's some carol-singers!' His voice, which was breaking, plunged and croaked.

The others all stopped talking and smiles spread over their faces.

'Quite good, aren't they?'

'The first we've had this year,' said Mrs Marriner.

'Well, not the first, my dear; they started coming days ago, but I sent them away and said that waits must wait till Christmas Eve.'

'How many of them are there?'

'Two, I think,' said Jeremy.

'A man and a woman?'

Jeremy got up and drew the curtain. Pierced only by a single distant street-lamp, the darkness in the garden pressed against the window-pane.

'I can't quite see,' he said, coming back. 'But I think it's a man and a boy.'

'A man and a boy?' said Mr Marriner. 'That's rather unusual.'

'Perhaps they're choristers, Daddy. They do sing awfully well.'

At that moment the front-door bell rang. To preserve the character of the house, which was an old one, they had retained the original brass bell-pull. When it was pulled the whole house seemed to shudder audibly, with a strangely searching sound, as if its heart-strings had been plucked, while the bell itself gave out a high yell that split into a paroxysm of jangling. The Marriners were used to this phenomenon, and smiled when it made strangers jump: tonight it made them jump themselves. They listened for the sound of footsteps crossing the stone flags of the hall, but there was none.

'Mrs Parfitt doesn't come till washing-up time,' said Mrs Marriner. 'Who'll go and give them something?'

'I will,' Anne said, jumping up. 'What shall I give them, Daddy?'

'Oh, give them a bob,' said Mr Marriner, producing the coin from his pocket. However complicated the sum required he always had it.

Anne set off with the light step and glowing face of an eager benefactor; she came back after a minute or two at a much slower pace and looking puzzled and rather frightened. She didn't sit down but stood over her place with her hands on the chair-back.

'He said it wasn't enough,' she said.

'Wasn't enough?' her father repeated. 'Did he really say that?'

Anne nodded.

'Well, I like his cheek.' Even to his family Mr Marriner's moods were unforeseeable; by some chance the man's impudence had touched a sympathetic chord in him. 'Go back and say that if they sing another carol they shall have another bob.'

But Anne didn't move.

'If you don't mind, Daddy, I'd rather not.'

They all three raised questioning faces to hers.

'You'd rather not? Why?'

'I didn't like his manner.'

'Whose, the man's?'

'Yes. The boy—you were right, Jeremy, it is a boy, quite a small boy—didn't say anything.'

'What was wrong with the man's manner?' Mr Marriner, still genial, asked.

'Oh, I don't know!' Anne began to breathe quickly and her fingers tightened on the chair-back. 'And it wasn't only his manner.'

'Henry, I shouldn't—' began Mrs Marriner warningly, when suddenly Jeremy jumped up. He saw the chance to redeem himself in his own eyes from his ineffectiveness over the Christmas shopping—from the general ineffectiveness that he was conscious of whenever he compared himself with Anne.

'Here's the shilling,' Anne said, holding it out. 'He wouldn't take it.'

[187]

'This will make it two,' their father said, suiting the action to the word. 'But only if they sing again, mind you.'

While Jeremy was away, they all fell silent, Anne still trying to compose her features, Mr Marriner tapping on the table, his wife studying her rings. At last she said:

'They're all so class-conscious nowadays.'

'It wasn't that,' said Anne.

'What was it?'

Before she had time to answer—if she would have answered—the door opened and Jeremy came in, flushed and excited but also triumphant, with the triumph he had won over himself. He didn't go to his place but stood away from the table looking at his father.

'He wouldn't take it,' he said. 'He said it wasn't enough. He said you would know why.'

'I should know why?' Mr Marriner's frown was an effort to remember something. 'What sort of a man is he, Jeremy?'

'Tall and thin, with a pulled-in face.'

'And the boy?'

'He looked about seven. He was crying.'

'Is it anyone you know, Henry?' asked his wife.

'I was trying to think. Yes, no, well, yes, I might have known him.' Mr Marriner's agitation was now visible to them all, and even more felt than seen. 'What did you say, Jeremy?'

Jeremy's breast swelled.

'I told him to go away.'

'And has he gone?'

As though in answer the bell pealed again.

'I'll go this time,' said Mrs Marriner. 'Perhaps I can do something for the child.'

And she was gone before her husband's outstretched arm could stop her.

Again the trio sat in silence, the children less concerned with themselves than with the gleam that kept coming and going in their father's eyes like a dipping headlight.

Mrs Marriner came back much more self-possessed than either of her children had.

'I don't think he means any harm,' she said, 'he's a little cracked, that's all. We'd better humour him. He said he wanted to see you, Henry, but I told him you were out. He said that what we offered wasn't enough and that he wanted what you gave him last year, whatever that means. So I suggest we give him something that isn't money. Perhaps you could spare him one of your boxes, Jeremy. A Christmas box is quite a good idea.'

'He won't take it,' said Anne, before Jeremy could speak.

'Why not?'

'Because he can't,' said Anne.

'Can't? What do you mean?' Anne shook her head. Her mother didn't press her.

'Well, you are a funny girl,' she said. 'Anyhow, we can but try. Oh, and he said they'd sing us one more carol.'

They set themselves to listen, and in a moment the strains of 'God rest you merry, gentlemen' began.

Jeremy got up from the table.

'I don't believe they're singing the words right,' he said. He went to the window and opened it, letting in a puff of icy air.

'Oh, do shut it!'

'Just a moment, I want to make sure.'

They all listened, and this is what they heard:

> 'God blast the master of this house,
> Likewise the mistress too,
> And all the little children
> That round the table go.'

Jeremy shut the window. 'Did you hear?' he croaked.

'I thought I did,' said Mrs Marriner. 'But it might have been "bless", the words sound so much alike. Henry, dear, don't look so serious.'

The door-bell rang for the third time. Before the jangling died down, Mr Marriner rose shakily.

'No, no, Henry,' said his wife. 'Don't go, it'll only encourage them. Besides, I said you were out.' He looked at her doubtfully, and the bell rang again, louder than before. 'They'll soon get tired of it,' she said, 'if no one comes. Henry, I beg you not to go.' And when he still stared at her with groping eyes, she added:

'You can't remember how much you gave him last year?'

Her husband made an impatient gesture with his hand.

'But if you go take one of Jeremy's boxes.'

'It isn't a box they want,' he said, 'it's a bullet.'

He went to the sideboard and brought out a pistol. It was an old-fashioned saloon pistol, a relic from the days when Henry's father, in common with others of his generation, had practised pistol-shooting, and it had lain at the back of a drawer in the sideboard longer than any of them could remember.

'No, Henry, no! You mustn't get excited! And think of the child!'

She was on her feet now; they all were.

'Stay where you are!' he snarled.

'Anne! Jeremy! Tell him not to! Try to stop him.' But his children could not in a moment shake off the obedience of a lifetime, and helplessly they watched him go.

'But it isn't any good, it isn't any good!' Anne kept repeating.

'What isn't any good, darling?'

'The pistol. You see, I've seen through him!'

'How do you mean, seen through him? Do you mean he's an impostor?'

'No, no. I've really seen through him,' Anne's voice sank to a whisper. 'I saw the street lamp shining through a hole in his head.'

'Darling, darling!'

'Yes, and the boy, too—'

'Will you be quiet, Anne?' cried Jeremy from behind the window curtain. 'Will you be quiet? They're saying something. Now Daddy's pointing the gun at him—he's got him covered! His finger's on the trigger, he's going to shoot! No, he isn't. The man's come nearer— he's come right up to Daddy! Now he's showing him something, something on his forehead—oh, if I had a torch—and Daddy's dropped it, he's dropped the gun!'

As he spoke they heard the clatter; it was like the sound that gives confirmation to a wireless commentator's words. Jeremy's voice broke out again:

'He's going off with them—he's going off with them! They're leading him away!'

Before she or any of them could reach the door, Mrs Marriner had fainted.

The police didn't take long to come. On the grass near the garden gate they found the body. There were signs of a struggle—a slither, like a skid-mark, on the gravel, heel-marks dug deep into the turf. Later it was learnt that Mr Marriner had died of coronary thrombosis. Of his assailants not a trace was found. But the motive couldn't have been robbery, for all the money he had had in his pockets, and all the notes out of his wallet (a large sum), were scattered around him, as if he had made a last attempt to buy his captors off, but couldn't give them enough.

FLORINDA

by Shamus Frazer

'Shamus Frazer' was the pen-name used by James
Ian Arbuthnot Frazer (1912–1966) on several
unusual fantasy novels in the 1930s & 1940s.
During the early 1960s he wrote several fine horror
tales for magazines, one of the best being 'Florinda'.

'Did you and Miss Reeve have a lovely walk, darling?' Clare asked of the child in the tarnished depths of glass before her.

'Well, it was lovely for me but not for Miss Reeve, because she tore her stocking on a bramble, and it bled.'

'The stocking?'

'No, that ran a beautiful ladder,' said Jane very solemnly. 'But there were two long tears on her leg as if a cat had scratched her. We were going along by the path by the lake when the brambles caught her. She almost fell in. She *did* look funny, Mummy, hopping on the bank like a hen blackbird a cat's playing with—and squawking.'

'*Poor* Miss Reeve! . . . Your father's going to have that path cleared soon; it's quite overgrown.'

'Oh, I hope not soon, Mummy. I love the brambly places, and what the birds and rabbits'll do if they're cut down I can't imagine. The thickety bushes are all hopping and fluttering with them when you walk. And the path wriggles as if it were living, too—so you must lift your feet high and stamp on it, the way Florinda does . . .'

But Clare was not listening any more. She had withdrawn her glance from Jane's grave elfin features in the shadowed recesses of the glass to fix it on her own image, spread as elegantly upon its surface as a swan.

'And if Daddy has the bushes cut down,' Jane went on, 'what will poor Florinda do? Where will she play? There will be no place at all for the little traps and snares she sets; no place for her to creep and whistle in, and tinkle into laughter when something funny happens—like Miss Reeve caught by the leg and hopping.' This was the time, when her mother was not listening, that Jane could talk most easily about Florinda. She looked at her mother's image, wrapt in the dull mysteries of grown-up thought within the oval Chippendale glass— and thence to the rococo frame of gilded wood in whose interlacing design two birds of faded gilt, a bat with a chipped wing and flowers whose golden petals and leaves showed here and there little spots and tips of white plaster like a disease, were all caught for ever.

'That's how I met Florinda.' She was chattering quite confidently, now that she knew that it was only to herself. 'I had been down to the edge of the lake where there are no brambles—you know, the *lawn* side; and I knelt down to look at myself in the water, *and there were two of me*. That's what I thought at first—two of me. And then I saw one was someone else—it was Florinda, smiling at me; but I couldn't smile back, not for anything. There we were like you and me in the glass— one smiling and one very solemn. Then Miss Reeve called and Florinda just *went*— and my face was alone and astonished in the water. She's shy, Florinda is—and sly, too. Shy and sly—that's Florinda for you.'

The repeated named stirred Clare to a vague consciousness: she had heard it on Jane's lips before.

'Who is Florinda?' she asked.

'Mummy, I've told you. She's a doll, I think, only large, large as me. And she never talks—not with words, anyway. And her eyes can't shut even when she lies down.'

'I thought she was called Arabella.'

'That's the doll Uncle Richard gave me last Christmas. Arabella *does* close her eyes when *she* lies down, and she says 'Good night, Mamma,' too, because of the gramophone record inside her. But Florinda's different. She's not a house doll. She belongs outside— though I *have* asked her to come to tea on Christmas Eve.'

'Well, darling, I've lots of letters to write, so just you run along to the nursery and have a lovely tea.'

So Florinda was a doll—an ideal doll, it seemed, that Jane had invented in anticipation of Christmas. Nine in the New Year, Jane was growing perhaps a little old for dolls. A strange child, thought Clare, difficult to understand. In that she took after her mother—though in looks it was her father she resembled. With a sigh Clare slid out the drawer of the mahogany writing-desk. She distributed writing-paper and envelopes, the Christmas cards (reproductions of Alken prints), in neat piles over the red leather—and, opening her address-book, set herself to write.

Roger came in with the early December dusk. He had been tramping round the estate with Wakefield the agent, and the cold had painted his cheeks blue and nipped his nose red so that he looked like a large, clumsy gnome. He kissed Clare on the nape, and the icy touch of his nose spread gooseflesh over her shoulders.

'You go and pour yourself some whisky,' she said, 'and thaw yourself out by the fire. I'll be with you in a minute.' She addressed two more envelopes in her large clear hand, and then, without looking round, said: 'Have we bitten off rather more than we can chew?'

'There's an awful lot to be done,' said her husband from the fire, 'so much one hardly knows where to begin. The woods are a shambles— Nissen huts, nastiness and barbed wire. One would have thought Uncle Eustace would have made some effort to clear up the mess after the army moved out . . .'

'But, darling, he never came back to live here. He was too wise.'

'Too ill and too old—and he never gave a thought to those who'd inherit the place, I suppose.'

'He never thought we'd be foolish enough to come and live here, anyway.'

Roger's uncle had died in a nursing-home in Bournemouth earlier in the year, and Roger had come into these acres of Darkshire park and woodland, and the sombre peeling house, Fowling Hall, set among them. At Clare's urging he had tried to sell the place, but there were no offers. And now Roger had the obstinate notion of settling here, and trying to make pigs and chickens pay for the upkeep of the estate. Of course, Clare knew, there was something else behind this recent interest in the country life. Nothing had been said, but she knew what Roger wanted, and she knew, too, that he would hint at it again before long—the forbidden subject. She stacked her letters on the desk and went to join him by the fire.

'There's one thing you *can* do,' she said. 'Clear that path that goes round the lake. Poor Miss Reeve tore herself quite nastily on a bramble this afternoon, walking there.'

'I'll remind Wakefield to get the men on the job tomorrow. And what was Jane doing down by the lake just now as I came in? I called her and she ran off into the bushes.'

'My dear, Jane's been up in the nursery for the last hour or more. Miss Reeve's reading to her. You know, she's not allowed out this raw weather except when the sun's up. The doctor said—'

'Well, I wondered . . . I only glimpsed her—a little girl in the dusk. She ran off when I called.'

'One of the workmen's children, I expect.'

'Perhaps . . . Strange, I didn't think of that.'

He took a gulp of whisky, and changed the subject: 'Clare, it's going to cost the earth to put this place properly in order. It would be worth it if . . . if . . .' He added with an effort, 'I mean, if one thought it was leading anywhere . . .'

So it had come out, the first hint.

'You mean if we had a son, don't you? . . . Don't you, Roger?' She spoke accusingly.

'I merely meant . . . Well, yes—though, of course—'

She didn't let him finish. 'But you know what the doctor said after Jane. You know how delicate she is . . . You can't want—?'

'If she had a brother—' Roger began.

Clare laughed, a sudden shiver of laughter, and held her hands to the fire.

'Roger, what an open hypocrite you are! "If she had a brother," when all the time you mean "if I had a son". And how could you be certain it wouldn't be a sister? No. Roger, we've had this out a thousand times in the past. It can't be done.' She shook her head and blinked at the fire. 'It wouldn't work out.'

Roger went into the nursery, as was his too irregular custom, to say good night to Jane. She was in her pink fleecy dressing-gown, slippered toes resting on the wire fender, a bowl emptied of bread and milk on her knees. Miss Reeve was reading her a story about a princess who was turned by enchantment into a fox.

'Don't let me interrupt, Miss Reeve. I'll look in again later.'

'Oh, do come in, Mr Waley. We're almost ready for bed.'

'I was sorry to hear about your accident this afternoon.'

'It was such a silly thing, really. I caught my foot in a slipnoose of bramble. It was as if somebody had set it on the path on purpose, only that would be too ridiculous for words. But it was a shock—and I tore myself painfully, trying to get free.'

There was still the ghost of that panic, Roger noticed, in Miss Reeve's pasty, pudgy features, and signalling behind the round lenses of her spectacles. 'It's not a very nice path for a walk,' she added, 'but one can't keep Jane away from the lake.'

'I'm having all the undergrowth cleared away from the banks,' said Roger, 'that should make it easier walking.'

'Oh, that'll be ever so much nicer, Mr Waley.'

'Florinda won't like it,' thought Jane, sitting stiffly in her wicker chair by the fire. 'She won't like it at all. She'll be in a wicked temper will Florinda.' But she said aloud in a voice of small protest—for what was the use of speaking about Florinda to grown-ups—'It won't be nice at all. It will be quite horribly beastly.'

The men didn't care for the work they had been set to do. It was the skeletons, they said—and they prodded suspiciously with their implements at the little lumps of bone and feather and fur that their cutting and scything had revealed. There was a killer somewhere in the woods; owls said one, stoats said another, but old Renshawe said glumly it was neither bird nor beast, that it was Something-that-walked-that-shouldn't, and this infected the others with a derisive disquiet. All the same, fifty yards of path were cleared during the morning, which took them beyond the small Doric pavilion that once served as boathouse and was reflected by a stone twin housing the loch mechanism on the eastern side of the lake.

Miss Reeve took Jane out in the afternoon to watch the men's progress. Jane ran ahead down the cleared path; paused at the pavilion to hang over the flaking balustrade and gaze down into the water: whispered something, shook her head and ran on.

'Hullo, Mr Renshawe—*alone?*' she cried, as rounding a sudden twist in the path she came upon the old man hacking at the undergrowth. Renshawe started and cut short, and the blade bit into his foot. This accident stopped work for the day.

'It wasn't right, Miss Jane, to come on me like that,' he said, as they were helping him up to the house. 'You gave me a real turn. I thought—'

'I know,' said Jane, fixing him with her serious, puzzled eyes. 'And she *was* there, too, watching all the time.'

Whatever the killer was, it moved its hunting-ground that night. Two White Orpingtons were found dead beside the arks next morning, their feathers scattered like snow over the bare ground.

'And it's not an animal, neither,' said Ron, the boy who carried the mash into the runs and had discovered the kill.

'What do you mean, it's not an animal?' asked Wakefield.

'I mean that their necks is wrung, Mr Wakefield.'

'Oh, get away!' said Wakefield.

But the following morning another hen was found lying in a mess of feathers and blood, and Wakefield reported to his master.

'It can't be it's a fox, sir. That head's not been bitten off. It's been pulled off, sir . . . And there was this, sir, was found by the arks.' It was a child's bracelet of blackened silver.

The path was cleared, but on the farther side of the lake the shrubberies that melted imperceptibly into the tall woods bordered it closely. Here Jane dawdled on her afternoon walk. At the bend in the path near the boathouse she waited until her governess was out of sight—and then called softly into the gloom of yew and rhododendron and laurel, 'I think you're a beast, a *beast*! And I'm not going to be your friend any more, d'you hear? And you're *not* to come on Christmas Eve, even if you're starving.'

There was movement in the shadows, and she glimpsed the staring blue eyes and pinched face and the tattered satin finery. 'And it's no use following us, so there!' Jane stuck her tongue out as a gesture of defiance, and ran away along the path.

'Are you all right?' asked Miss Reeve, who had turned back to look for her. 'I thought I heard someone crying.'

'Oh, it's only Florinda,' said Jane, 'and she can sob her eyes out now for all I care.'

'Jane,' said Miss Reeve severely, 'how many more times have I to tell you Florinda is a naughty fib, and we shouldn't tell naughty fibs even in fun?'

'It's no fun,' said Jane, so low that Miss Reeve could hardly catch a word, 'no fun at all being Florinda.'

A hard frost set in overnight. It made a moon landscape of the park and woods, and engraved on the nursery window-panes, sharply as with a diamond, intricate traceries of silver fern. The bark of the trees was patterned with frost like chain-mail, and from the gaunt branches icicle daggers glinted in the sun. Each twig of the bare shrubs had budded its tear-drops of ice. The surface of the lake was wrinkled and grey like the face of an old woman. 'And Wakefield says if it keeps up we may be able to skate on it on Boxing Day . . .' But by mid-day the temperature rose and all out-of-doors was filled with a mournful pattering and dripping.

Towards evening a dirty yellow glow showed in the sky, and furry black clouds moved up over the woods, bringing snow. It snowed after that for two days, and then it was Christmas Eve.

'You *look* like the Snow Queen, but you *smell* like the Queen of Sheba. Must you go out tonight, Mummy?'

'Darling, it's a bore. We promised Lady Graves, so we have to.'

'You should have kept your fingers crossed. But you'll be back soon?'

'In time to catch Father Christmas climbing down the chimneys, I expect.'

'But earlier than that—promise . . . ?'

'Much earlier than that. Daddy wants to get back early, anyway. He and Wakefield had a tiring night sitting up with a gun to guard their precious hens . . .'

'But she . . . it never came, did it?'

'Not *last* night. And now you go to lovely sleeps, and when you wake perhaps Father Christmas will have brought you Florinda in his—'

'No,' cried the child, 'not Florinda, Mummy, *please.*'

'What a funny thing you are,' said Clare, stopping to kiss her; 'you were quite silly about her a few days ago . . .'

Jane shivered and snuggled down in the warm bed.

'I've changed,' she said. 'We're not friends any more.'

After the lights were out, Jane imagined she was walking in the snow. The snowflakes fell as lightly as kisses, and soon they had covered her with a white, soft down. Now she knew herself to be a swan, and she tucked her head under a wing and so fell asleep on the dark rocking water.

But in the next room Miss Reeve, who had gone to bed early, could not sleep because of the wind that sobbed so disquietingly around the angles of the house. At last she put out a hand to the bedside table, poured herself water, groped for the aspirin bottle and swallowed down three tablets at a gulp. It was as she rescrewed the top, she noticed that it was not the aspirin bottle she was holding. She could have sworn that the sleeping-tablets had been in her dressing-table drawer. Her first thought was that someone had changed the bottles on purpose, but that, she told herself, would be too absurd. There was nothing she could do about it. The crying of the wind mounted to shrill broken fluting that sounded oddly like children's laughter.

The first thing they noticed when the car drew up, its chained tyres grinding and clanking under the dark porch, was that the front door was ajar. 'Wait here,' said Roger to the chauffeur, 'there seem to have been visitors while we were away.'

Clare switched on the drawing-room lights, and screamed at the demoniac havoc they revealed, the chairs and tables overturned, the carpet a litter of broken porcelain, feathers from the torn cushions, and melting snow. Someone had thrown the heavy silver inkwell at the wall glass, which hung askew, its surface cracked and starred, and the delicate frame broken.

'No sane person —' Roger began.

But already Clare was running up the stairs to the nursery and screaming, 'Jane! . . . Jane!' as she ran.

The nursery was wrecked, too — the sheets clawed in strips, the floor a drift of feathers from the ripped pillows. Only the doll Arabella, with a shattered head, was propped up in the empty bed. When Clare touched her she fell backwards and began to repeat, 'Good night, Mamma!' as the mechanism inside her worked.

They found Jane's footsteps in the snow, leading over the lawn in the direction of the lake. Once they thought they saw her ahead of them, but it was only the snowman Roger had helped her to build during the afternoon. There was a misty moon, and by its light they followed the small naked footprints to the edge of the lake — but their eyes could make out nothing beyond the snow-fringed ice.

Roger had sent on the chauffeur to a bend in the drive where the car headlights could illuminate the farther bank. And now, in the sudden glare, they saw in the dark centre of ice the two small figures. Jane in her night-dress, and beside her a little girl in old-fashioned blue satin who walked oddly and jerkily, lifting her feet and stamping them on the ice.

They called together, 'Jane! . . . Jane! Come back!'

She seemed to have heard, and she turned, groping towards the light. The other caught at her arm, and the two struggled together on the black, glassy surface. Then from the stars it seemed, and into their cold hearts, fell a sound like the snapping of a giant lute-string. The two tiny interlocked figures had disappeared, and the ice moaned and tinkled at the edges of the lake.

THE HANGING TREE

by R. Chetwynd-Hayes

Ronald Chetwynd-Hayes (b. 1919), dubbed
'Britain's Prince of Chill', is one of this country's
most prolific writers of horror stories, with
paperback sales alone in excess of a million copies.
Two horror films, *From Beyond the Grave* (1973)
and *The Monster Club* (1980), have been based on
his collections. 'The Hanging Tree' is taken from
A Quiver of Ghosts (1984).

I am awake—*walking the haunting path that is terminated by that
damned tree and no matter how I try, there is no wandering so much as
an inch to either side. The grass on the green is frost-silver in the
moonlight, while the tree, which when I last walked still retained a rich
covering of brown leaves, now reaches up naked, skeletal branches against
the sky.*

*A narrow road is on my right and beyond the row of terrace houses; tall,
stately, not a whit different then in my day—the time when I breathed, ate
and did what so pleased me. The one in which I lived has a curtainless,
lighted window on the ground floor, and if I sit down on the bench opposite,
will myself to feel the wooden bars pressing into my back, then it is possible
to enjoy an illusion of sensory life, watch HER—the vessel which could feed
me with glorious, life-giving essence—if only she would come out and make
contact.*

*Cursed be those who still walk the earth with solid feet; may they be
doomed, even as I, to be confined to a narrow strip of grass, invisible to all*

but a select few, devoid of all emotion, save that to hate, permitted only to sit and stare into a lighted window, like a starving man tormented by a display of succulent food.

She's there! Coming to the window, pressing her lovely face against the glass—damn and blast her—why doesn't she come out?

'Movita,' Mrs Fortescue spoke from her chair by the roaring fire, 'for heaven's sake come away from that window. There's nothing more disconcerting than to see someone's face flattened against a window pane late at night.'

The girl did not look round, but raised her soft lilting voice.

'There's no one out there—much too cold. The moonlight gives the green a long-ago look and a long silver dress suddenly appeared. Papa says it was once a tilting yard, back in the days of Henry the Seventh. Perhaps knightly ghosts still go charging up the lists—or whatever it was they did.'

'You're in a nonsensical mood tonight, child. I'm certain those awful men who dressed up in a suit of hardware, did quite enough charging about during their lifetimes, to go on doing it now they are dead.'

Movita shifted her position and tried to peer round the window frame at the giant oak tree. A sudden gust of wind disturbed the gaunt branches.

'The hanging tree has just groaned.'

Mrs Fortescue shuddered and huddled closer to the fire.

'Don't use that expression. It sends a cold shiver down my spine.'

The girl turned and walked slowly towards the fire, her pale, oval face pensive, enhanced by dark, melancholy eyes. She sank into a chair opposite her mother and watched the orange flames consume a yule log.

'But everyone calls it the hanging tree. They say a century ago a young man murdered his sweetheart, then went out and hanged himself on that tree.'

'Good heavens, child, stop it. This is not the kind of talk I expect to hear, with Christmas but a few days away. I can't think what's got into you.'

Movita tossed her head and brushed back a strand of auburn hair.

'But isn't Christmastime the period for ghosts? I wonder if the young man lived in this house and maybe murdered his sweetheart in this very room?'

Mrs Fortescue banged a clenched fist down upon the arm of her chair and assumed as near stern expression as her normally placid features would allow.

'That's quite enough. Such morbid nonsense can only be the result of an unhealthy mind,. You will go to bed this instant and pray to God that you don't have horrid dreams.'

'I never dream. But I can't see what's so dreadful about having someone murdered in your house. It's only another way of dying . . .'

'Not another word. What Papa would say if he heard you talking like that, doesn't bear thinking about. Now—upstairs at once.'

'Very well. I'm tired and it's about time I went to bed anyway.' Movita got up and going over to her mother, kissed the smooth cheek. 'Good-night, Mama. I'm sorry if I frightened you.'

Mrs Fortescue clasped the young face between her two hands and sighed deeply.

'You're a strange child. So sweet one minute—so contrary the next. Goodnight, darling.'

She waited until her daughter had left the room, before rising and drawing the curtains. For some reason she was reluctant to look out over the moonlit green.

There was a fire in Movita's bedroom, lit by a maid some two hours before, and this had blunted the chill which haunted the upper rooms during the winter days. The girl put on a thick dressing gown before drawing a chair to the window and peering out through a six-inch gap in the curtains.

Now she could watch without fear of interruption and allow her thoughts to drift down enthralling lanes of conjecture; weave a web of fantasy and forget for a little while that she was an eighteen-year-old girl, trapped in a late nineteenth-century, middle-class household.

The green was a silver carpet that stretched out to the row of trees that reared up like giant sentinels on the far side, while over to the left stood the old gatehouse that had once been the entrance to a long ago destroyed palace.

Movita swung her gaze slowly round to the right.

The hanging tree stood stark and black under the frost-bright stars, its branches casting shadow replicas on the frozen ground; once in a while it groaned when tormented by the never resting wind and it was not difficult to imagine a dark figure that swung back and forth, then twisted round to reveal a distorted face.

Had he hanged himself in winter time? Climbed up into the cold maze of branches, tied the rope round his neck—then jumped? Or had it been on one glorious summer evening, while the tree was still clad in rustling green, with the birds singing a nocturne, that mingled with the happy laughter of children playing on the green?

A carriage drawn by two jet black horses rattled from round the corner, then came lumbering along the road. It passed the house, the coachman and footman bulky figures that were muffled in greatcoats and surmounted by funny bowler hats. The coach stopped in front of number 23 and instantly the footman climbed down from his lofty perch and hastened to open the near side door.

Movita giggled as Mr Davenport heaved his vast body through the narrow doorway, all the while wheezing and berating the unhappy footman, whose feeble efforts to extradite his master were more ludicrous than helpful. Then the big man was stamping his feet on the pavement, paying little heed to Mrs Davenport—in contrast to her spouse, a small extremely lean lady—who clambered down from the carriage unaided and loudly proclaimed that she was frozen to the bone.

'Mind you rub the horses down and give 'em plenty of hot bran,' he instructed the coachman. 'Why hasn't Travers opened the front door? Damn his hide.'

As though in answer to his question a slab of yellow light fell across the pavement, and Mr Davenport and his querulous lady mounted the three steps and disappeared from view. The footman climbed back on to his seat next to the coachman, the horses—which had been pawing the ground with impatience—broke into a quick trot and the carriage rumbled down the road, rounded a bend and became a fast receding blue and gold box on wheels.

Silence returned and Movita added another strand to her web of fantasy.

'Suppose,' she whispered, 'none of this is real, but a reflection of what used to be? Maybe Mama and Papa, fat Mr Davenport, awful thin Mrs Davenport—me—all are ghosts playing out a silly charade in a long dead world. If I closed my eyes just for a second, tilted my head in a certain way, said some strange words—then perhaps I would wake up in a strange world where no one would have time to dream.'

For one terrible moment Movita thought she heard a growling murmur of distant machinery and the faint sound of shouting voices, but when she again opened her eyes, the green still slept under a gleaming sheet of moonlight, the hanging tree was shaking its head as though in rebuke at such arrant nonsense—and the only person in sight was a young man seated on the bench opposite the front door, who was staring up at her window.

She had a fleeting impression that he was dressed in grey, with a white cravat at his throat, but he was so still, with not so much as a ripple of his fair hair, even though the wind continued to shake the old tree. Then she closed the curtains with a single, impulsive jerk and sat in near darkness, waiting for her thudding heart to regain its normal beat.

After a while she dared to part the curtains again and peer out at the moonlit scene. The bench was empty and nowhere was there the slightest sign of a young man dressed in grey.

A heavy fall of snow laid a thick white carpet over the green on Christmas Eve; made all the roof-tops look as if they had been decorated with cotton wool, and covered the hanging tree with a shimmering dress. But there seemed to be one place where snow either did not settle, or melted as it fell—and that was a long, narrow strip that ran from where the road curved, past the house and ended under the tree. An ugly black scar seared across a flawless white surface.

Mr Fortescue said it was much too cold for Movita to go out and she would be far better employed by helping her mother, who had much to do in preparing for the festivities which began that evening. So she spent the day in holding the ladder while Jane the parlourmaid put up paper chains, wrapping presents in holly-patterned paper, then as evening approached, supervising the elaborate laying of the dinner table, ensuring that every knife, fork and spoon was in its correct place and napkins were folded into neat pyramids.

Then fat, billowing clouds extinguished the pale rays of the dying sun and night stationed its first platoons on snow-clad green and ice-coated pavements; banished house-shadows into dank areas and transformed lighted windows into illuminated frames.

Occasionally Movita peered out into the spectral twilight, but could only make out the lamp post that was situated over to the far left and cast a flickering circle of yellow light that just managed to reveal one end of the wooden bench. She experienced a faint feeling of disappointment when no grey clad figure materialized to stare at her with disturbing intensity, although such an event would have unlocked the doors of fear.

The guests began to arrive and there was no more time for conjecture, toying with fearful possibilities, for now she had to smile, try not to mind if Mr Davenport retained her hand for longer than was strictly necessary, supply some suitable answer to Mrs Davenport's softly spoken remark: 'You're not looking well, child. Rather peaky, I think.'

Movita sensed the older woman's antagonism that stemmed possibly from an unconscious envy of unspent youth, the yet to be destroyed illusions, but above all the beauty which she never possessed. For Mrs Davenport was singularly unblessed with physical attraction, being small, bowed shouldered, lean to the point of emaciation—her sharp featured little face not enhanced by an extraordinarily large nose that on occasion was capable of emitting a loud, disapproving snort.

Scarcely had the Davenports been relieved of their outdoor clothes, seated and supplied with liquid refreshment, than Miss Mansfield— a sprightly spinster of some fifty years, who was suspected of having unconventional ideas—came tripping over the doorstep, loudly complaining that such weather was not good for her sciatica and she should have stayed at home.

'Snow,' Miss Mansfield said while being helped off with her coat, 'should be confined to Christmas cards. It has taken me half an hour to walk from Paradise Close.'

'Fortunately,' Mrs Davenport just succeeded in subduing a snort, 'we live but a few doors away. But had it been otherwise, we would have used the carriage.'

Miss Mansfield's voice sounded not unlike a knife being drawn across ice. 'How terrible for you. Being unable to walk any distance must be an awful liability.'

Mr Davenport exploded into a loud wheezy laugh, then pretended not to see his wife's reproving glare. Later, when they were all seated in large, over-stuffed armchairs, engaged in a hunt for polite conversation, Movita came to a shocking conclusion.

The Davenports disliked each other and Miss Mansfield was capable of murder. There was something about her bright, intelligent grey eyes, the way she watched her two fellow guests, the barely perceptible gesture of impatience when an opinion was uttered with which she disagreed; all combined to suggest that if provoked, given the opportunity, she would eliminate anyone who got in her way.

At the same time there was no reason to suppose the good lady would not walk her respectable, if erratic path to the grave, never suspecting that it might have taken a much more unconventional turning. On the other hand Mr and Mrs Davenport and Mama and Papa, could no more kill anyone than—Movita sought the right simile—walk naked in the snow. They were equipped with safety valves, mental ventilation holes through which the deadly fumes of boredom and hate could escape.

'And what of me?' Movita turned the spotlight of enquiry on to herself. 'I too could never kill anyone—but I might be a murderee. Or a potential suicide.'

I can see them sitting in that room . . . and She is facing me and damned if I can get through, make any kind of impression on that stupid brain . . . a life for a life . . . a soul for a soul . . . must I walk for so long as it takes for the sun to grow cold? She's got the right essence . . . I can feel it . . . I could lock on to her quivering white soul . . . if only she would come out . . . stand on the haunting path . . .

'Movita . . . Movita . . . stop day dreaming. We are about to go in to dinner.'

Mama was standing near the window, looking down at her with angry eyes, while from the sofa Papa was shaking his head in mock reproof. Mr Davenport was smiling, a kind of tolerant, little-girls-must-be-humoured smile, but his eyes were bright with tired lust. It was rather frightening to suddenly catch a glimpse of the real people who lurked behind carefully constructed masks. Then they all filed through the connecting doorway and into the dining-room beyond, where there seemed to be a great deal of unnecessary fuss as to where everyone should be seated, but inevitably Movita found herself next to Mr Davenport, who laid a moist hand on her arm and said:

'We will look after each other, eh, my dear?'

She murmured: 'Yes, I suppose so,' and stared with extravagated interest at the window, which was now transformed into a clouded mirror that reflected most of the room, including the six figures seated round the table. Heads bobbed up and down, hands raised spoons to gaping mouths, eyes were lost in black caverns—and it was as though she had been permitted to view a macabre feast; the dead dining in a fire-tinted chamber carved from the bedrock of hell.

But the mirror window was marred by the street lamp that created a bright splodge of light in the right hand bottom pane and even— when the eyes were adjusted to see beyond the reflection—revealed part of the seat back. A grey figure was standing in a network of shadows cast by the hanging tree—beckoning, a slow bending of the raised forefinger, a silent order to go out, join him under the tree. Then Miss Mansfield's voice shattered the cold band that paralysed her brain and the figure vanished, but still existed as a searing flame of memory.

'Murder is the most complex of human actions. But I am prepared to contend that it is rarely—if ever—a cold-blooded affair. And fear is the most prevalent emotion involved.'

Mr Davenport emitted a rumbling laugh and either by accident or intent, nudged Movita in the ribs with his elbow.

'Come, dear lady, are you saying a degenerate villain kills his victim because he's afraid of him? Surely it must be the other way round?'

'Fear is the governing factor in all of our lives and assumes many forms. Fear of poverty, exposure, ridicule, loss of livelihood, wife, husband, health—the list is endless. And anyone could drive a man or woman to murder.'

'I rather think . . .' Mrs Fortescue began a feeble protest, but was quickly interrupted by Mrs Davenport who regarded Miss Mansfield as rather common and therefore a person to be snubbed on every possible occasion.

'A civilized, rational being, with a shred of moral fibre would overcome any one of these misfortunes without resorting to killing a fellow creature.'

Miss Mansfield creased her face into a grim smile.

'What about the soldier on the battlefield?'

'That's a totally irrelevant question. He is defending himself.'

'Yes, because he's afraid of being killed.'

'I cannot imagine how we came to be engaged in such an unseemly conversation,' Mrs Davenport said after a particularly vicious snort. 'It is scarcely a fit subject for Christmas Eve, not to mention the presence of a young person of tender years.'

'Nonsense. What is Christmas but the birthday celebration of a man who was to be murdered in a most gruesome fashion?'

Mrs Davenport gasped and said: 'This is really too much!' and Movita could sense a probing spear of—something—that had possibly struck the wrong target. He—the man in grey—was trying to contact her brain, but instead had penetrated Miss Mansfield's mental storeroom and—assisted by hot punch and two glasses of the best Madeira—was forcing her to make statements she would later regret.

This terrifying assumption should have been dismissed as pure imaginative nonsense, but Movita knew with an unreasoning certainty that it contained at least an element of fact, although later—perhaps tomorrow when the sun shone down on a white world—she might be able to marshal a meagre force of disbelief.

'But I am special—special.' The silly phrase became a dull echo that bounced back and forth across her brain; created a nice superior feeling, sent fear scurrying before a warm glow of self-satisfaction. The knowledge had always been with her, only she had never been able to accept it before. No one else had seen the cringing shadow that sometimes came gliding down the stairs, or heard the faint sobbing that aroused her to instant wakefulness during the small hours.

'I hope the Christmas pudding is not too rich.' Mama was as usual walking a mundane path. 'Cook is inclined to be rather heavy-handed with the suet and one dare not offer a word of advice.'

'Delicious,' Mr Davenport wheezed his approval. 'Fit for the queen herself.'

'Excellent.' His wife gave the impression that her praise was not without certain reservations. 'I have tasted far worse.'

Miss Mansfield made no comment, but ate her portion in sullen silence as though fearful less her tongue again utter outrageous statements. Mr Davenport cast an enquiring glance to his right.

'Why, the little lady has eaten hardly anything at all! Come, my dear, this won't do. At your age I would have been asking for a third helping by now.'

Movita wished he would leave her alone, for now she was the centre of attention, with everyone making mock derogatory sounds that soon merged into fatuous remarks.

'Eating between meals always spoils the appetite,' Papa intoned.

'Perhaps she's in love,' Mrs Davenport suggested with something not far removed from a sneer.

'Or maybe she has something on her mind,' Miss Mansfield abandoned her self-imposed silence and watched the girl with bright, enquiring eyes.

'I would consider that to be most unlikely,' Mama commented dryly. 'But she has been looking off colour all day. Don't you feel well, dear?'

'Yes, Mama. I'm just not hungry, that's all.'

A welcome interruption came in the form of a chorus of childish voices that sent out a rather untuneful rendering of 'God Rest Ye

Merry Gentlemen' from just beyond the front door. Papa said heartily: 'Carol singers! We'd better have them in, my dear. A mince pie and a glass of wine for the older ones.'

'I'm surprised that you encourage them,' Mrs Davenport remarked. 'It's nothing more than begging.'

'Not at Christmastime.' He looked back over one shoulder and addressed the maid. 'Jane, let them in. Then ask cook to send up some more of her excellent mince pies.'

'Very well, sir.'

They entered the dining room, four boys and two girls, but it was the small lad who had yet to celebrate his eighth birthday that claimed Movita's full attention. While the others made appreciative noises when presented with a mince pie and a glass of diluted wine, he stared at her with wide open eyes, then, after a furtive glance at a tall girl who might have been his sister, edged his way round the table. Movita lowered her head until his mouth was an inch away from her left ear. The whispered words roared across her brain.

'Please, miss, the man on the seat says—he's waiting.'

'Charlie, come here this instant.' The tall girl raised a shrill voice, then blushed unbecomingly. 'Sorry, miss, but I don't know what's come over him. When we were singing he was sitting on that cold seat, pretending to talk to someone. He's usually so good and does what he's told.'

'Filled with Christmas spirit, I daresay,' Mr Davenport wheezed his amusement. 'You seem to have made another conquest, Movita. What was the young scallywag whispering in your ear?'

Movita did not answer, but looked fearfully at the window, which did no more than faithfully reflect the room and its occupants. Her father's voice broke the spell and restored a semblance of normality.

'Don't tease the girl, Davenport. We don't want a fit of sulks on Christmas Eve. Now,' he turned a beaming face to the line of carol singers. 'Do you all know "When Shepherds Watched Their Flocks By Night"?'

Some said: 'Yes, sir,' others just nodded and in no time at all the familiar words were being shouted, yelled and even sung by voices that made up in enthusiasm what they lacked in harmony. Mrs Davenport grimaced, Miss Mansfield shook her head, but Movita's parents at least pretended that the performance was quite up to their expectations. Then each child was given a shilling and escorted to the door by Jane, whose disapproving looks suggested that she was of the opinion they should never have been let in.

The small boy, just before he was pulled through the doorway by his tall sister, turned and uttered the fatal words with precision. It might have been assumed that he had been instructed by an assiduous parent always to speak up and the devil take the consequences.

'He'll be real angry, miss, if you don't go out.'

After the children had departed a kind of shocked silence hung over the room, like an ominous cloud that is the harbinger of a very violent storm. Then Mrs Fortescue spoke.

'What on earth did he mean? Movita, what have you been up to? Have you been making assignations with some man?'

'I knew she had something on her mind,' Mrs Davenport stated with obvious satisfaction. 'In my experience still tongue means active mind.'

Papa raised his voice, although he was clearly embarrassed that such a delicate matter had to be discussed in front of guests.

'Are we to understand, Movita, that there is a man outside who is expecting you to join him?'

To tell them the truth was an act of madness, but there was little alternative for silence would be interpreted as a confession of guilt.

'Not a man—I don't know—a ghost I suppose. He walks the green some nights—but not every night. At least I don't think so. I've sort of sensed him ever since I was a child, but only recently has he taken to—well—sort of calling me. I didn't think anyone else could see him, but that little boy must have.'

Her voice trailed off into silence and for a while no one spoke, until Mrs Davenport rose and motioned to her husband to do likewise.

'I think it's about time we went home. Christmas Eve you know, lots to do.'

'So soon!' Mrs Fortescue exclaimed, well aware that an embellished account of Movita's presumed insanity would be in full circulation before the night was out. 'I—we assumed you would stay for the entire evening.'

'Yes, well, now I've just remembered . . . Come, Harold.'

Mr Davenport heaved his vast bulk up from his chair with great reluctance, clearly enthralled by this splash of drama, which was even more intriguing than Miss Manfield's strange outburst. He oozed apologies, hinted at unexpected guests, a dire crisis that demanded immediate attention, then followed his wife out into the hall, leaving Movita alone with Miss Mansfield. She looked at the girl through narrowed eyes.

'Are you telling the truth? Not just covering up for a bit of nonsense with some boy?'

Movita shook her head, aware that she was very near tears.

'It's all true, but I can't expect anyone to believe me. For a long time I thought everyone knew about him, but was afraid to mention it.'

The woman nodded and cast a quick glance in the direction of the hall, where Mrs Fortescue could be heard still trying to detain her departing guests.

'Have you seen or heard anything else?'

'Sometimes. A shadow figure on the stairs, the sound of a lady sobbing. But I've never been frightened—up to now.'

The front door slammed and her parents re-entered the room both angry, possibly frightened, but it was her father who expressed his concern by words.

'Movita, aren't you ashamed of yourself? Making up such a childish and wicked story. What have you got to say?'

'It's all true. It is.'

'Perhaps she should see a doctor,' Mrs Fortescue suggested. 'She must be ill. There can be no other explanation.'

'The girl's psychic,' Miss Mansfield said quietly.

Mr Fortescue exploded into an uncharacteristic fit of rage.

'Nonsense, Miss Mansfield, and I'm surprised that a lady of your intelligence should encourage the girl in her—her madness. She's play acting, trying to put down a smoke screen for some misdemeanour—if not something far worse.'

'And I maintain,' the lady insisted, 'that she's a sensitive. Gifted with a perception that is fortunately denied to the rest of us. You may not be aware, but this house had a bad reputation long before you came to live in it. There was some talk of a murder committed here way back in the last century. Instead of ranting at the girl, you should be trying to help her.'

Mrs Fortescue gave the impression she might faint if given the least encouragement, while her husband sank into a chair and murmured:

'This is all beyond me. Are you saying my daughter can see spooks?'

'I'm saying she is aware of a phenomenon that cannot be explained in mundane terms. She has an affinity with the past and possibly an unconscious ability to give substance to—for want of a better expression—a personality extension. Something that is trapped in a haunting pattern.'

[211]

'Good God, woman, you must be mad!'

'Madness is the sanity shared by the select few. But I have read of similar cases and I know something must be done—and that quickly.'

'What do you suggest? Call in the vicar and get him to conduct an exercise service?'

'Exorcise,' Miss Mansfield corrected. 'But I doubt if you would welcome the kind of publicity such a proceeding would attract. My solution is much more simple. Let me take Movita out there and find out what he wants. If nothing happens, we'll know the child is living in a fantasy world and you can take other steps.'

'Great . . . ! Well, I suppose it can do no harm.'

'But it's so cold,' Mrs Fortescue protested. 'She'll catch her death out there.'

'It's only a few steps across the road and she can wrap up warm.'

Movita shook her head violently while tears ran down her white cheeks. 'I don't want to go. He'll do something awful to my mind. I know it. Please don't make me go.'

Miss Mansfield took one limp hand in hers and spoke with a gentle voice.

'Listen, my dear, and try to understand. He is already in your mind, because you believe in his existence. Do you want to be haunted all your life? The only way to dispel fear is to meet it face to face; look into its eyes and find out why it walks. You need only a spoonful of courage.'

'Something dreadful will happen.'

'It won't. Believe me.'

Parents watched with troubled eyes, the seductress slipped a coat around her shoulders and there seemed little point in further resistance; for was not this fate the reason she had been born?

Miss Mansfield opened the door and said: 'Come, my dear, it will soon be over,' and the wind drew her into its icy embrace, while over to the left the hanging tree groaned its perpetual lament. The seat loomed nearer; frozen snow hung like a bleached shroud over the back bars and formed glistening pendants that hung from the outstretched arms. And he was there—a shadow under the tree, a transparent column of mist that disappeared before it could take on a recognisable shape, a voice that spoke in her brain.

At last you have come out and now I can sip from the overflowing cup and free myself from the haunting path. Before the sun rises again, succulent fruits will dangle from the hanging tree and another earthbound soul will pace this narrow strip of grass, watch those who still eat, live and breathe through lighted windows.

Let me for a brief moment become a tiny spark of awareness that coils up in your brain, peers out through your eyes, feels the blood pulsing through your body . . . speaks with your tongue . . .

'You see, my dear, there's no one—nothing there. Together we have exorcised him. Two that walk together must prevail.'

Movita's head came slowly round, eyes bright, teeth bared in a grin of ferocious joy, twin rivulets of moisture seeped down over the lax lips. The slender throat contorted and presently a harsh, alien voice sent out a stream of tortured words.

'Thank . . . you . . . for . . . bringing . . . me . . . what . . . I . . . most . . . needed.'

Then the girl crumpled like a puppet when the invisible master drops the strings and lay on the ground, her face transformed by a peaceful smile. And Miss Mansfield, after giving vent to one long, drawn-out cry, ran round the seat, across the green and soon became a lurching, wildly gesturing figure that disappeared through the old castle gateway.

Fully dressed, wide awake, Movita lay on her bed and smiled gently in the moonlight. She had been wept over, cosseted, fed with any amount of nourishing liquids, then put to bed. Now had come the time for revelation, to go out fearlessly and face whatever the night had to offer. She got up and walked calmly to the door.

It was necessary to creep down the stairs, for her parents would soon be up and around if they heard the slightest sound and they must not view horror by moonlight; only very special people could do that and not lose their unique sanity. First a visit to the kitchen where a coil of clothes line was draped over a peg, then back to the hall, there to unbolt the front door, then . . . then out across the narrow road and on to that naked strip of grass.

The hanging tree groaned a mournful welcome, or perhaps an angry protest, for dangling on one of its lower branches was a dark-clad figure, that twisted gently from left to right, first presenting a mass of tangled hair, then an awful contorted face, with a purple tongue protruding from between blood-coated lips. Miss Mansfield had not been particularly pretty when alive, dead she was positively hideous.

[213]

The wind mischievously lifted her long skirts and revealed thin legs clad in black stockings, a liberty it would never have been permitted to take during the lady's lifetime. Movita uncoiled the clothes line and after pulling the skirts back to their rightful position, bound it tightly round the ankles. Then she stood back and smiled up a Miss Mansfield's grotesque face.

'I had what he needed to make you hang yourself. But you—you had the killing instinct. You were two of a kind.'

Presently she went back to bed and slept peacefully for the remainder of the night. Tomorrow promised to be an exciting day.

THE GROTTO

by Alexander Welch

Alexander Welch (who works in the television
industry) had his first story, 'The Eighth Day',
printed when he was eighteen. He has continued
to write short stories, and is now working on a
novel. Last year 'The Grotto' won the Christmas
ghost story competition in
Time Out magazine (December 1988).

S anta Claus stubbed out his cigarette, and took a swift gulp from
the hip-flask concealed under his costume. Thank God, he
thought, all over for another year.

The little sods seemed to get worse every day. Coming in with their
ridiculous Mothers or Sisters or Nannies (Say thank you to Santa,
there's a good boy) giggling and whispering and pulling his beard.
Give Santa a kiss. Sit on Santa's knee. Not bloody likely.

Another sip from the flask, and Santa shrugged off the padded
overcoat, flinging it carelessly over the antlers of a nearby Rudolph,
knocking off the hat of a Gnome in the process. Santa smirked. The
whisky was doing its job, thank the Heavens. He flopped back into his
chair, and surveyed his 'Kingdom'. God, what a dump. One of the
biggest stores in the city, and all they could manage was a few plastic
Gnomes, a stuffed reindeer, some fairy lights and about a ton of fake
snow. He scratched the back of his neck, the bloody snow stuff was
getting at his psoriasis again. Danger money, that's what was needed,
what with the bloody kids and the bloody snow.

The door swung open, and a head looked in. 'Don't be long Charlie,
we're shutting up'. The head disappeared. Could've fooled me, thought

Charlie, wincing as he peeled off the fake beard. Hell, Christmas Eve and still sober. Something must seriously be done about this.

'Goodnight boys. Don't do anything I wouldn't.' The Gnomes ignored him.

He switched out the lights, plunging the grotto into Stygian gloom, and made his way towards the exit.

Whether it was the whisky, or just the darkness, he stumbled and struck his shin sharply on a giant mushroom. 'Damn and blast,' he swore. That would be a real bruise by morning. He sat heavily on the offending fungus, and rubbed his leg.

Someone giggled in the darkness.

Charlie jumped to his feet. One of the little sods was still in here. 'Who's that?' he shouted.

Another giggle and the rustle of movement.

Eyes adapting to the blackness, Charlie saw a shadow dart from a corner into the sleigh. Very small, he thought, just a nipper. Must have been there for hours. 'I see you,' he said, rubbing his eyes. 'I'll leather your backside for you if you don't come out of there.'

Not the most convincing of threats, he thought, he'd be lucky to even catch the little bleeder. Another giggle, which this time made the hairs on the back of his neck stand on end.

Pull yourself together man, what's got into you, being spooked by a stupid kid. Gritting his teeth, he slowly made his way towards the sleigh. There was someone inside. Someone small.

Charlie waited for a second or two, and then pounced. He found himself grasping thin air. A chuckle from behind. Where had the kid got to so fast? He couldn't see more than a couple of yards ahead, but saw no way in which the child could have got past him without being seen.

Maybe he should call Security. They could deal with this. Not my job to chase kids, he thought. Besides, who wants to spend Christmas Day locked in one of the biggest stores in the city? He could think of quite a few who wouldn't mind, but he was not one of them. Not by a long chalk.

Charlie was just on the point of shouting for the guard when a movement caught his eye. There, in the corner behind the Seven Dwarves.

He shivered.

It certainly had got cooler since the store had emptied. There was a draught coming from somewhere. He could see the snow forming small drifts, just as if it were the real thing.

It was getting colder and colder.

The kid would freeze to death if he wasn't careful.

Charlie made his way back to the reindeer, to recover his coat. He reached out his hand, and drew it back sharply. The coat was freezing.

Carefully, he reached out again, and touched it. Damn it, it was like frost or something.

He then realised that his chair was covered in it as well. It was just like snow. The real sort. The stuff that falls from the sky. Ridiculous. Someone was playing a trick on him, and he knew who. He'd teach the little sod a lesson.

Charlie reached for the light switch, only to find that it too was covered with freezing ice. Bloody dangerous. Mucking about with water near electrics.

Charlie shuddered, not just with the cold. He was getting jumpy. He did not like being in this dark place on his own with a giggler who would not be caught. Another thought had crossed his mind. Rats!

The canteen had been buzzing for some weeks with the scandal in the food hall, where a two-foot rodent had been fished out of one of the deep freezers. The joke had gone round the store (until stopped) that the place was busier by night than by day. That was the last straw. He had seen enough rats in his time. Great black greasy-furred creatures, with red eyes and needle teeth. He wasn't going to hang around to be chewed by a rat. Not now or never. Trying to ignore the sense of panic which was rising in his throat he ran, slipping and sliding over the frozen floor towards the door into the main shop-floor. He flung the door open, and stopped dead in his tracks, his breath hanging in a freezing cloud before him. The store had gone. Well, not gone. Changed would be more like it. Instead of shining chrome and glass counters there were low counters of polished wood. Instead of piles of stuffed teddy bears, mechanical toys, computers and games, there were carved ships, china-faced dolls and rows of candy canes. Charlie's heart skipped a beat. What had happened to the prices? One Farthing, one Penny, Sixpence. What the hell was going on?

With a voice that trembled, he shouted for the guard. His voice echoed back. He rubbed his eyes. I know what's happened, he thought. I slipped on that snow stuff. I'm unconscious, that's what's happened. Then there was a chuckle to his left. He whirled, and from the corner of his eye caught sight of a small child, smaller than he would have believed, disappear around one of the counters. With his heart flapping in his chest like a stranded fish, he stumbled after. Only his feet dragged, and each step seemed to last an eternity. Ahead of him, he could hear the patter of small feet, and every now and then, the same giggle as before.

Charlie's breathing was coming in short gasps, and there was a pain shooting through his chest. He hardly cared anymore about the cold, which was biting at his fingers, or the glistening frost which covered all the ancient furnishings of the store. He had to follow the tiny creature, which he could now see scampering over the icy surface before him.

The child must have been deformed. It stood no more than two foot high, and yet moved with such speed. Long golden tresses, shimmering in the strange luminescence, flowed down the back of the dress which the child wore. Charlie tried to catch sight of its face, but the child was always ahead, giggling over its private joke. 'Come back,' he gasped, pain wracking his body. The freezing air pressed against him, and his face was turning blue with the cold. Still he followed, shaking with fatigue. He managed to find some extra speed, and rounded a corner. Too fast. His feet slid out from under him, and he fell heavily onto his face. Ahead of him, the child stood. At the opening of a lift entrance.

It was black and deep, and the iron gates were open.

The child stood, its back to Charlie, leaning over the edge. He raised a hand. 'Come back,' he wheezed. 'You'll fall.'

Still the child giggled. Then it raised a tiny hand, and pointed down the lift-shaft. Charlie felt a strand of dread steal into his heart. The child was turning. Charlie heard his own scream, for revealed before him was not the sweet face of a child, but a hideous parody of life, crawling with vermin and reeking of the grave. The thing turned back to the lift-shaft, and Charlie passed out.

He woke with a small cry. Something had touched him. His eyes, widened with terror, gazed up into the concerned face of Derek the Night Watchman.

'There now Santa,' he said, 'what are you doing here at this time of night?'

'God,' gasped Charlie, 'the lift-shaft, there's someone down there.'

The Watchman said nothing, but it was obvious from his face that he had caught a whiff of alcohol, and had put two and two together.

'Please,' said Charlie, almost with a sob, 'go and check in the basement. The old part at the back, where the lift used to be.'

With trembling hands, and sweat glistening on his brow, he followed the Night Watchman down the stairwell to the lowest level. The two of them made their way over to the oldest part of the foundations. Their footsteps echoed in the cavernous gloom as they searched for the old lift-shaft. The other found it, and with a shout announced this to Charlie. There was a pile of rubbish several feet high, which had apparently gone unnoticed for years. No one came down here if they could help it. With a grunt, the Night Watchman poked the pile with his foot. Something glistened white in the torchlight. Interested, he stooped to investigate, and recoiled sharply with a cry. In the feeble light from the torch, it was clearly a human bone. A leg bone, snapped cleanly below the knee. Pushing back the refuse, more of the skeleton came into view. A child, no more than four or five. But it was not this which set Charlie's mind screaming with horror. The corpse had a companion. A companion who had led him to this place of death on Christmas Eve. A companion who had never spoken and yet had found a voice. A companion who had never walked, and yet had sought him out.

A decayed dress covering its shattered limbs, skeletal hands gripping it tightly in a last embrace, the doll stared up at them for what seemed an eternity, and then slowly, as if in relief at its mistress having been found, closed its eyes in final rest.

JUST BEFORE DAWN

by Eugene Johnson

Eugene Johnson (b. 1930) has written several
poems and short stories. He contributed to the
nationally acclaimed anthology *In Praise of Slough*;
and his poem 'Beautiful Slough' was incorporated
in the Borough's Town Guide. His previously
unpublished story, 'Just Before Dawn', was
runner-up in the *Time Out* Christmas ghost story
competition last year.

Toby Bellman hunched his shoulders and pulled his grubby overcoat closer around his thin hungry body. His feet were cold and the Embankment air was moving in a cold draught over the bare part of his leg, exposed between the top of his short socks, and the bottom of his worn trouser leg.

The night was cold and damp, the moisture in the air causing the street lamps to glow through faint rainbow halos, unnoticed by the last few late night travellers making their way home in warm cosy cars.

Toby was crushed, his spirit had finally died, slowly strangled by years of continuous personal disasters that had finally washed him out of the sea of life, and deposited him here on the Embankment at Charing Cross, with other human derelicts and wrecks.

This night was to be his last. It was the only thing he had any control over; he was determined.

He wandered down from Trafalgar Square, where he had searched the waste bins for scraps of discarded food. The great Christmas tree

[220]

was in the square, and people had thronged around, some with excited children, even though the hour had been late.

As he had shuffled ashamedly around, seldom noticed, but given a wide berth by those who did, he prayed that someone, who may have been imbued with Christmas spirit, might have given him 30p or something, just to buy a hot drink. No one did.

Trafalgar Square had yielded him no food, so he shuffled off down Northumberland Avenue, towards the arches at the Embankment Underground station. Usually he would pick himself a spot amongst the other pitiful bodies crammed alongside each other on the pavement below the railway.

The overhead railway bridge and arches sheltered them from the rain, but nothing else. Collapsed cardboard boxes for mattresses, plastic bags and newspapers for blankets, they slept uncomfortably in the open street, many anaesthetised by some form of alcohol or methylated spirit.

Tonight Toby passed the miserable dormitory and shuffled on a short distance further to the Embankment and the river. As he sat on the Embankment bench, he became aware of the silence that had enveloped the great metropolis. No cars passing now, no swishing of tyres on the damp road. He looked left and then right, peering with red rimmed eyes, framed by crusted eye lashes.

He was alone, he had been alone for years. The weight of his despair was physically crushing him. For a moment his thoughts went back seven years, to the days when Toby Bellman was a successful ebullient man. A man with a thriving transport business, a fine detached house in Kingston, a beautiful wife. No, she had been pretty, but not beautiful. He had enjoyed life, nice holidays abroad, dining out with friends, entertaining at home. The children, oh God, the children.

His company had obtained some profitable contracts, hauling freight back and forth to Europe. Business was growing, and just as Toby was negotiating to buy some more container lorries, his partner killed the business stone dead.

Toby's partner, Richard Stillwell, had sold the contents of several valuable cargoes. He had got a good price for them, several hundred thousand pounds. The only trouble was that the cargoes did not belong to Richard Stillwell—or Toby, come to that.

Stillwell had always been a flash guy, but he had known his business, and had been liked by most. He had a rather risqué humour, and a never ending repertoire of stories which made him popular in the trade. He had also turned out to be a crook, and had been sought by the Fraud Squad for the past seven years.

As a result of Stillwell's fraud, the business had collapsed overnight. Toby had to face the investigations, as Stillwell had disappeared. Three drivers had been sent to prison, Toby was acquitted of any charges, but it was the beginning of Toby's destruction.

In the early days when he was building up his firm, Toby had, in order to protect his family against the vagaries of business, put his house, and several other costly items he possessed, into his wife's name.

His wife reminded him of this soon after the trial, and constantly blamed Toby for the collapse of the business. Finally, she threw him out and sued for a divorce, which she got two years later.

Toby had a nervous breakdown after the divorce, he went to pieces and spent several months in hospital. After leaving hospital he had found a low paid clerical job, but he had been unable to hold it down. His life spiraled downwards, he moved from the odd mediocre job now and then, to the abyss of unemployment. Simultaneously, his accommodation deteriorated from a small furnished flat, to a furnished room, to a hostel, to the pavements.

Once a decisive man, he now mustered just enough of his old will to put an end to his misery tonight.

He got up from the bench and shuffled towards Westminster Bridge. He looked at the lit face of Big Ben, it was nearly 3 a.m. No wonder he was cold to his very core, he had been sitting still for hours. As he approached the bridge he heard a car approaching from Parliament Square. Toby shielded his eyes as the headlamps swept across him when the car turned down Embankment Road.

The brief flood of light had illuminated the embankment parapet, and Toby glimpsed a small packet on the broad ledge. He walked to the parapet and picked up the packet. It was a neatly folded brown paper bag. Toby opened the bag and found two cheese sandwiches nestling inside, wrapped in plastic film.

His crusty eyes opened wide, he was starving and here was a feast. Hunger displaced his thoughts of self destruction, he forced his numb fingers to tear away the plastic wrapping from one sandwich, peering around nervously as if afraid someone would rush up and snatch his prize away. He stumbled forward and round the corner to the bridge, and as he lifted the sandwich to his mouth and took a bite at the delicious food, he saw a movement in the shadows of the bridge.

The remnants of his heart missed a beat, surely he wouldn't have to lose the first meal he had found for days. Toby knew he was too weak to fight off a determined assault by a brother dosser, and he knew the assault would be ferocious.

The shadow moved nearer and Toby saw the dark bundle was small and hunched. His cracked lips curled back over his yellow teeth, he believed he could retain his sandwiches from this night prowler.

The bundle halted a few feet from him. Toby stood still on his dead feet and watched carefully. He focused his eyes on his hungry competitor. He saw a broken hag of a woman before him. She was dressed in a bundle of jumble clothes. The street lamps showed she was wearing a man's overcoat that hung open, because it had no buttons to do it up—it's original owner having removed them, before donating the coat to the local vicar.

The frayed ends of a long woolly sleeve protruded from the arms of the overcoat, and wisped over her crumpled arthritic hands. She looked at him expressionlessly with black limpid eyes. Toby saw the street lamps reflected in those eyes. The two dossers stood like stone unmoving in the dark morning, as the smooth river flowed silently below.

Toby really did need to eat those sandwiches, he was starving. The old woman moved and startled Toby, as she lifted those poor old useless hands, reaching toward him.

Deep inside the human wreck that was Toby, an emotion flickered, in the depths of his despair he felt pity for the old woman. He gave her the sandwiches and shuffled down the bridge.

At the middle of the bridge he stopped and hauled himself up onto the rail, and simply toppled over. He fell, a ragged bundle, down into the river. His falling seemed an age, he had time to see the lights illuminating the buildings on the South Bank, illuminated ships moored down towards Blackfriars. Then suddenly the black smooth oily surface of the Thames rushed to claim him.

He was surprised how soft the water was. He had expected a felling blow on impact, but it was soft and warm as he plunged into the depths.

At about the same time Toby Bellman was creeping painfully along the embankment in London, Richard Stillwell, the crooked partner of yesteryear was creeping his cabin cruiser out of the tiny harbour of Giens in the South of France.

Stillwell had been living in a holiday apartment, in the village of Giens, for the past ten months. He had pretended he was a writer, and from time to time posted bulky envelopes containing blank sheets of paper to fictitious publishers in England. Now the local gendarmes, who were very friendly, were becoming very curious. He decided it was time to move on.

He had stayed on his boat all day, studying the inshore charts; should he go east or west? Finally he settled for Spain. It would be a short trip, just down the coast to the west.

It was a calm night, the air was a little chilled, but not so cold that a light pullover couldn't handle it. Earlier, Stillwell had dined at a harbourside cafe, topping himself up liberally with drink. He felt comfortable, self satisfied and fulfilled. No one would be concerned at his departure in the small hours; the locals had become accustomed to him coming and going at odd times.

Probably this is what made the gendarmes curious. Anyway he was on his way now. Cruising quietly and steadily on a mirror glass sea towards Spain.

Stillwell went down to his cabin for a cup of coffee. He looked around as he sat on his bunk: it was a very cosy little cabin, he thought to himself. Cosy wasn't the word for it, the cabin was a treasure house. It was full of currency, French, German, Spanish, Swiss, if you knew where to look for it.

A thought suddenly came to his mind—Toby Bellman! Stillwell laughed out loud, what a wally old Toby turned out to be. He had ignored all the hints and nods and winks, the wally just had to be straight. Tough for wally Toby Bellman.

Just then his outboard motors faltered, started, faltered again and stopped. Stillwell sat listening, puzzled and cursing. He got up off his bunk, climbed out of the cabin and went aft to look at the outboards. As he leaned out over the stern and peered down, both motors suddenly roared into life. The gleaming white boat leapt forward and Stillwell was flung over the stern into the sea.

As Toby Bellman felt himself rising to the surface of the river, somewhere in the recesses of his mind he remembered he would have to descend for two more times, before the river claimed him.

His head broke the surface, and the sky seemed lighter than it had been a few seconds ago when he leapt from the bridge. For some reason he began treading water and looked around. The South Bank had gone! Big Ben, Westminster Bridge, gone!

The sound of purring engines made him turn again, as a white cabin cruiser pulled alongside. It had fat white pudding fenders dangling from its side. Toby caught hold of a rope holding one of the fenders and somehow found the strength to haul himself aboard. He fell into the cosy cabin; there was no one there, just some hot coffee percolating.

The night editor of a popular London newspaper put down his telephone, turned to a colleague and told him of the puzzling call he had just received. The editor's contact at Cannon Row police station reported that a beat policeman on patrol at Westminster Bridge had seen what appeared to be a male dosser jump from the bridge in the early hours of the morning.

The policeman had radioed his base immediately, and a river police patrol boat in the area was on the scene in minutes. There was no sign of the dosser, but they recovered a sun-tanned man wearing expensive lightweight boating gear.

They had tried to resuscitate him and thought they had succeeded, when he simply gasped something that sounded like, 'To be hell man', and died!

BUGGANE

by Peter Tremayne

'Peter Tremayne' (b. 1943) is one of Britain's
most successful writers of horror fiction, with
several novels to his credit including *Kiss of the
Cobra, Nicor!, The Ants, The Morgow Rises!*
and *Bloodmist.*
Under his own name, Peter Berresford Ellis is an
expert on Celtic culture, and has written several
authoritative books on the subject (*The Cornish
Language and Its Literature*; *A Dictionary of Irish
Mythology*, etc.), as well as biographies of Captain
W.E. Johns, Rider Haggard and Talbot Mundy.

It started with the scent of violets. Wild violets at Christmas time;
the perfume of violets permeating the crisp frosty air of December.
And there was the sound of the fiddle, its music rising and falling
in mocking cadences somewhere far, far away across the mountains.

Or perhaps it started earlier; perhaps it started with my great-
grandfather over 125 years ago. Ah, if only my mind would clear; if
only I were not so confused . . . and frightened. When did it start? If I
wrote a story in which the entire action depended on an implausible
coincidence, my editor would throw it back at me for ignoring the
prime rule of fiction—credibility! Surely someone has written a little
book of rules about writing fiction? If so, credibility must be a cardinal
rule. Coincidence is only something which happens in reality, not in
fiction. People never believe in coincidence in fiction. Well, what
matters? It is reality that I am concerned with. And perhaps my
beginning was some ghastly, terrible coincidence. If I had not come to

the Isle of Man to research the scripts; if I had not hired this particular cottage at Rhullick by Lag-ny-Cailleeyn; and if my great-grandfather . . .

Let me begin at my beginning.

I was scripting for a television soap-opera, a fairly successful series set against big-business and jet-setters. There was a new series due for shooting in the summer and Grant, the director, wanted to locate it outside the claustrophobic environs of the City of London, away from the usual locations, where the first episodes had been set. It was Grant who came up with the idea of setting the next series in the Isle of Man. Grant always had a keen eye for up-to-date financial developments. The Isle of Man was evolving into the fastest growing offshore financial centre in the world. I hadn't even known that the Island was not part of the United Kingdom. It was a self-governing Crown Dependency outside UK jurisdiction except for matters of foreign policy and defence. Fiscally, the Island was fully independent with its own laws on companies, trusts, banks, insurance, investment management and ship-owning. Wealthy financiers from all corners of the globe were going to the Island to establish headquarters, attracted by an income tax of a standard 20 p.c. and no other direct taxes; attracted also by the fact there was a range of tax exemptions for international operations. That, in a nutshell, was why Grant despatched me to the Island early in December with the brief to spend a few months there and return with drafts of six connecting story-lines for the next series.

To be truthful, Douglas, the Island capital, with its Atholl Street as the equivalent of Wall Street, was a disappointment. It reminded me of a typical northern English seaside town in spite of the bilingual street-signs in Manx and English. I hadn't even known that the Manx had their own language, a branch of Gaelic. Everything seemed dead; the shuttered amusement arcades, the closed hamburger joints, even the still-open Chinese take-away food emporiums seemed . . . well, dead is the only descriptive word. A few days in Douglas was all I could stand. I hired a car and set off to tour the Island. The Island is only 33 miles from north to south and 13 miles from east to west at its widest point. Nevertheless there is space enough for its 65,000 inhabitants to lose themselves in the splendid country behind Douglas, in the rugged mountains and glens.

It was during this brief tour that I decided to hire a cottage for a couple of months and approached an estate agent outside Douglas, thinking a small rural agent would be able to come up with something more in my line than one of the big Douglas agents. Sure enough, it was the third place I saw that I fell in love with. As soon as I saw the whitewashed walls of the thatched cottage, the tiny building sheltering under the shoulder of one of the larger Island mountains, I felt a sense of familiarity, of 'coming home'. I had always had a hankering to exchange my London Victorian terraced house for a rural croft in the wilds. This was it.

There was only one road into the glen in which it stood. You travelled south from Cronkgarroo, away from the lowland areas of population, and climbed over the dark brown and russet winter slopes of Slieau Managh into the narrow glen called Lag-ny-Cailleeyn. The cottage stood on a shelf of the mountain which moved upwards before coming to an abrupt halt where a precipice dropped back one hundred feet down a sheer granite wall into the glen. It was isolated enough and yet, by car, within fifteen minutes of the nearby town of Ramsey.

I put down rent for three months and moved in twelve days before Christmas. I set up my word-processor, stacked the bookshelves with guides, pamphlets and materials on the Island and its business life and was fully confident that by the end of February I would be able to produce the story-lines required of me.

I luxuriated that first day in the cottage. I lit the big open fire, stacking it with turf, with its bitter-sweet perfume, and found myself warm and comfortable before its glow. Even the small bedroom was warm when I slid between the sheets which smelled faintly of the scent of wild violets as a result, I presumed, of being stored in some preservative to keep moths at bay.

The day following my move into the cottage, I decided to take advantage of the crisp December sunshine and go for a walk to get the juices stirring and ease my mind into a working attitude. I left the cottage and set off at a steady pace over the broad shoulder of Slieau Managh which, the estate agent had informed me, meant 'mountain of the monks'. It was part of the range which included Snaefell, the highest mountain on the Island, across whose broad slopes the Isle of Man Tourist Trophy, the famous T.T. motorcycle race, is held annually. It was chilly but I was well protected from the elements and the pale watery sunshine gave one the impression that the cold was not as bad as it actually was. A steady pace soon dispelled any feeling of chill as I climbed the steep brush covered slopes of the mountain.

I think I felt her coming before I heard her. The gentle trembling of the ground made me pause and turn a split second before I heard the thunder of hooves. A large roan mare was coming along the path which I was following. Astride it sat a girl, rather a young woman. Her slim figure was clad in a rather old fashioned riding habit of a vivid green. Her hair was a blaze of red while her skin was almost translucent in its paleness. The eyes that peered down at me were like rounds of cold, polished steel.

'Good morning,' I called as she rode abreast.

She inclined her head and would have moved on but I said: 'It's a grand day, isn't it?'

Her brows drew together in a frown and she hesitated, then drew rein.

'Nice enough,' she replied, almost distantly. 'You're a stranger here.' It was a statement.

'I've just moved into the cottage in Lag-ny-Cailleeyn.'

Her eyebrows arched for a moment although the surprise did not seem to register on her face or in those curiously cold eyes.

'You are living in Rhullick?'

'Yes. My name is Jon Jameson.'

Actually 'Jon Jameson' was only my writing name but I had been using it for so long that few people used my real name.

'Why have you taken the cottage at Rhullick?' she demanded abruptly. The voice was cold, abrasive. I was a little surprised but I was determined to coax some friendly response from her. I must admit I was fairly attracted by her Celtic beauty. I told her of my job. It usually impressed most women. I had an ego to feed as well. She seemed neither impressed nor interested.

'Rhullick is usually rented only during the summer months,' she said. 'It is not a nice place to be in winter. Do you intend spending Christmas Eve there?'

I was somewhat abashed.

'Yes. Why?'

'It is not a nice place to be.'

Then she was nudging her horse along the path.

I was slightly dumbfounded as I watched her disappear down the slopes.

That evening I decided to make myself known in the local public house. It turned out to be over a mile away in a little hamlet that had obviously seen better days. The tavern was called 'Thie-ny-Cailleeyn', according to the signboard on which were three crones and a cauldron looking like the characters from Shakespeare's *Macbeth*. The landlord was a fleshy, red faced man, and garrulous. The first question I asked him was the meaning of the name.

'Well, now, it would mean the hags' tavern. I suppose that would be the right rendering of the Manx, eh, Juan?'

He glanced across to where the only other occupant of the hostelry was sitting sipping his beer. He was an old man, clearly a local. He nodded in affirmative.

'That would be the meaning,' he said in a curiously singsong accent.

'I'm renting a cottage in a place called Lag-ny-Cailleeyn, so I was wondering about the name.'

The landlord stared for a moment.

'That wouldn't be Rhullick?'

'Yes.'

'Rhullick—the cemetery.'

I turned to stare at the old local who had spoken.

'I beg your pardon?'

'That's what Rhullick means,' interrupted the landlord. 'A grave-yard. Not that it was a proper graveyard. It was called that on account of some people being killed there. You wouldn't be a nervous type, would you?'

He grinned at me.

I laughed.

'I don't believe in ghosties, ghoulies or long legged beasties and things that go bump in the night.'

'That's good,' the landlord turned with a wink to the old local. 'Because they do say that the *buggane* haunts Rhullick.'

'The *buggane*? That sounds more like a disease than a ghost,' I quipped.

'The *buggane* is an evil spirit which seeks vengeance, a spirit of retribution for an unpunished wrong.' It was the old local who spoke.

I chuckled.

The old man stared at me sourly.

'It doesn't do to mock such things, mister,' he said. 'The story is true enough.'

'Then tell me about it?' I invited, my grin broadening.

The old man shook his head, put down his empty beer glass and left without another word.

The landlord looked unhappy.

'Old Juan Qualtrough there doesn't take kindly to strangers who mock at local belief and custom.'

'I didn't mean to insult him,' I replied, 'but I can't take stories of weird ghosties and ghoulies seriously.'

Ah well, I thought, if the locals were so touchy then I'd better shut up. Change the subject.

'By the way, I saw a young girl out riding today. Maybe you can tell me who she is.'

I described to the landlord the girl that I had met on the mountain that morning. He shrugged. 'Can't say I recognise her from your description, mister. Might be one of the Carroon girls, though. They have a farm the other side of Slieau Managh.'

I returned to the cottage. The stew I had left simmering on the turf fire was excellent. I worked for a few hours on the basic idea for the series and then went to bed. I lay there snug, turning things over in my mind before sleep overtook me. It was in those last few moments before I plunged into the arms of Morpheus that the scent of wild violets registered in my mind. I recalled that I noticed the smell on the previous night but it seemed stronger than before. Much stronger.

I worked very well the next day. I started the day with a walk across the mountains and looked for signs of the girl. But I looked in vain. I returned to my script and before I knew it, it was evening again. I went off to 'Thie-ny-Cailleeyn' for a drink, leaving the rest of the stew simmering on the fire.

The old man, Juan Qualtrough, was sitting next to the fire as I entered the pub. I offered to buy him a pint and expressed my apologies for being flippant on the previous evening.

'It is not right to mock at the spirits of the dead,' he said in his soft Manx accent.

'I did not mean to,' I replied, hoping that I wasn't sounding too patronising. I was hoping that he would go on to tell me the story about the spirit of Rhullick, the *buggane* as he called it. But the door was thrust open and a half-a-dozen local men came in, strong, burly, rug-headed Celts they were. Brawny mountainy men whose complexions spoke of a life outdoors amidst the elements. One of them, spotting old Juan Qualtrough, came across and clapped him on the shoulder.

'*Cre 'n-ash ta shiu? Ta mee treishteil dy vel shiu ayns slaynt vie.*'

I had never heard Manx spoken before. Indeed, in spite of the street names set up in Manx and English, I had thought the old language dead.

'*Cha nel veg aym dy hrughaney mysh,*' replied the old man. Then he glanced at me. '*She Sostnagh eh.*'

At once the man began to speak in English and I was sure that this was for my benefit for the Manx are a courteous people and usually hospitable to strangers. They invited me to drink with them and one of them started up a song. Then old Juan Qualtrough was asked to sing. He sang a song in Manx which the landlord told me was called '*Kirree fo Niaghtey*' or 'The Sheep Under the Snow', a ballad of a shepherd looking for his lost sheep in winter. I went home humming the song.

As I drove up to the cottage my headlights caught a glimpse of a shadow by the door.

'Who's there?' I called as I climbed out.

There was no answer and I called again before I turned to the door, opened it and switched on the light so that it fell across the porchway from the open door.

It was the girl whom I had met on the previous day.

'Why, hello!' I gaped in surprise.

She stared at me with her pale, emotionless face.

'Why are you still here?'

I smiled jovially. 'I've rented the cottage for a few months. You don't appear friendly.'

'You must be warned.' The voice was a monotone.

I frowned.

'I beg your pardon?'

'This cottage is not the place to be at this time of year. You must leave.'

I blinked.

'I think that you had better come in, have a drink, and explain.'

She jerked her head violently.

'No, no. I cannot . . .'

She took a step backwards and disappeared from the pool of light.

I moved forward.

'Hey!' I called.

There was no answer.

I reached for the torch which I kept inside the door and shone it into the blackness. There was no sign of her, though I thought I heard the soft beat of hooves on the springy turf of the glen.

Shaking my head, I went inside and decided the stew was overdone and settled for a cold supper of bread, cheese and pickle. I had drunk a little too much to work that evening and so I went up to bed and read for a while.

I must have dropped asleep reading for I awoke with the bedside light still on and my watch showing it to be one o'clock. I lay for a moment feeling the rasping taste of alcohol dehydrating my mouth and wondering whether to foresake my warm bed and go down to make a cup of coffee. It was then that I became aware of the scent of violets again. Violets in winter. I sighed. I would have to find the moth-balls or the sachet of scent and get rid of it. The smell was beginning to irritate me.

As I rose to make my coffee I heard a faint sound. The sound of music. It was coming as if from far away, outside the cottage, from the mountain slopes. A soft air played on a fiddle. I shook my head in amazement. Who in their right mind would be playing a fiddle at one o'clock in the morning?

I went to the window and drew back the curtain. The moon was up, bright and full, shining down in the crisp clear air of the winter night. I could see no sign of anyone. But the music was clear enough now. I thought I recognised the tune. *Kirree fo Niaghtey*—The Sheep Under the Snow.

Then I could hear it no longer.

I went down to make the coffee.

The next day I went into Douglas and did a lot of shopping in preparation for Christmas. I have never been a celebrant of that particular festival—probably that's why Grant knew it would not be interrupting my domestic life to send me off to the Island in December. I have never celebrated Christmas since my ex-wife Pamela left taking our two children seven years ago. Christmas was a time to be ignored, not indulged in.

Afterwards, I went into a working phase which lasted until a couple of days before Christmas Eve. I saw no one nor did I even go down to 'Thie-ny-Cailleeyn' for an evening drink. Nor did I catch a glimpse of the strange red haired girl again. The only thing that disturbed my piece was that damned fiddler who played across the mountains, and always the same tune and shortly after midnight. I had reasoned that it must be some lonely shepherd on the hills comforting himself on the winter nights.

There was one thing which annoyed me. I searched high and low for the moth-balls or perfumed sachet but could not find them anywhere. The bedclothes must have been impregnated with the scent to produce such a pungent odour.

Two days before Christmas Eve I entered 'Thie-ny-Cailleeyn'. The landlord looked surprised to see me.

'Why, bless me, we thought you must have moved on. Is it a pint?'

I nodded.

Juan Qualtrough was in his usual seat by the turf fire, an empty glass near his hand. I ordered one for him.

He raised the pint. '*Shoh slaynt!*' he grinned.

'Cheers!' I replied solemnly.

'Are you still living in Rhullick?' he asked.

I nodded.

'And still don't believe in ghosts?'

'Not even your friend, the *buggane*,' I assured him. 'But you were going to tell me the story about this *buggane* creature.'

He turned a troubled eye on me.

'Best you didn't know if you are still living at Rhullick.'

'Oh, come on,' I cajoled.

'Well,' he said, after a moment or two's hesitation, 'it's a simple story. It took place in the days of Governor Loch.'

The landlord, leaning across the bar, intervened.

'The Island is ruled by a Lieutenant-Governor on behalf of the King or Queen of England. Since the mid-18th Century the monarchs of England have been Lords of Man. Governor Loch was here during the 1860s.'

Juan Qualtrough ignored the landlord's explanatory interruption.

'It was in the days of Governor Loch,' he repeated firmly, 'a harsh, military man. The Governor ignored our ancient customs and laws, even ignored our ancient parliament, the Tynwald. He welcomed in a lot of English settlers to the Island who, with their wealth, soon bought large estates. And Governor Loch allowed them to make these estates even bigger by setting our laws of common land at nothing and allowing them to raise fences where no fence should have been. Naturally, the Islanders did not stand meekly by. Some of our young men, hot blood coursing through their veins, went out at night and threw down the fences. They were nicknamed 'Cossacks'. Loch issued rewards to any who would betray them but none did.

'Up at Rhullick . . . mind you, it was not called Rhullick then . . . up at Rhullick there lived a man named Callan Kissack. He was a farm labourer and a widower. He lived there with his daughter, Calyhony. Aye, Calyhony Kissack. She was a beautiful girl by all accounts. Seventeen years old and engaged to be married to a shepherd named

Kerron Moughty. It is said that Kerron was a man of great girth and bold spirit and he could play a fiddle to charm the angels. He could make people laugh or cry just by the way he drew a bow across the strings of his little instrument. No wake, wedding or *giense* . . .'

'A sort of party,' interrupted the landlord by way of explanation.

'. . . could be held without inviting Kerron Moughty and his fiddle. Well, what was known among the people was that Kerron Moughty was a leader of the "Cossacks".'

Juan Qualtrough paused and sipped his beer.

'It happened that Governor Loch, in an attempt to stamp out the "Cossacks", sent English soldiers into the country. A company was stationed in the village and their officer, a young lieutenant, quartered himself at Kissack's cottage. He was young and handsome, grandly dressed in his red coat and white breeches and representing a world that was alien yet withal curious and exciting. Is it a wonder that young Calyhony Kissack became infatuated with him? Aye, and more than infatuated. She lost her heart and soul to the man.

'Calyhony became with child . . . the child of the handsome English lieutenant. When Kerron Moughty heard this he fell into such a rage that his friends feared for his sanity. Calyhony, young, innocently petulant about the passion she stirred in men, told her father that she wanted no more to do with Kerron Moughty. She told Callan Kissack that her heart was for the young lieutenant and that the English soldier loved her.

'Alas, Callan Kissack thought he was doing right for his daughter. He knew Kerron Moughty would kill the young lieutenant at the first opportunity. So, thinking to keep the lieutenant safe and his daughter happy, the poor, confused man betrayed Kerron Moughty to the soldiers. Some say it was murder, others that it was self-defence. But one night the lieutenant and his men came upon Kerron Moughty, shots rang out and the parish lost its best fiddler. Kerron Moughty was killed.'

'So it is the ghost of Kerron Moughty who haunts Rhullick?' I asked.

Juan Qualtrough shook his head.

'There is more.'

'More?'

'A few days after the killing of Kerron Moughty, the lieutenant was recalled to Douglas for an inquiry into the shooting. He left promising to return for Calyhony. Even though the lieutenant had slain her former lover, she cared not a whit. Heart and soul had she given to the lieutenant.'

'What happened?'

'Time went by and there came no word from Douglas. Callan Kissack rode into the town to make enquiries and found that the lieutenant had left the Island. He had been posted to India, having been cleared by the court of inquiry of any misconduct in Moughty's death. And he had left the Island without a word to Calyhony. All along, he had been using her. And now he left her without support and with a child on the way.'

'Sounds a bit of a bastard,' I observed.

'When Callan Kissack returned and broke the news to his daughter, she ran out into the night. It was Christmas Eve, as I recall. She was found the next morning at the foot of the precipice beyond the cottage at Rhullick. She had plunged over the granite fall into Lag-ny-Cailleeyn. It was agreed that she had thrown herself over, killing herself.'

'And the baby, I suppose? It's a sad story.'

'Sadder still,' observed the landlord and Juan Qualtrough continued.

'Some of Kerron Moughty's friends, men of the "Cossacks", came for Callan Kissack that same night and threw him over the precipice after his daughter. That's why the place is called Rhullick—the cemetery. And that's why they say that the *buggane* haunts Rhullick now. A frightful spirit seeking vengeance for a crime unpunished.'

'Ah,' I smiled, 'but according to your story, the friends of Kerron Moughty took their vengeance.'

'Aye, but vengeance did not come to the man who started the actions which resulted so tragically.'

'The English lieutenant, you mean?'

'The same.'

That night I started from my bed hearing the strains of the fiddle across the mountain—the sad strains of *Kirree fo Niaghtey*.

And the smell of violets was almost overpowering.

I could not work all the next day. I wandered the cottage in an irritable mood. I wondered why I, I who did not believe in ghosts, *bugganes* or otherwise, was made to feel so uncomfortable by the story. Was it because I had heard fiddle music? That was so easily explained. And why was I troubled by the scent of wild violets? And what of the red haired girl . . . the girl whose name I did not know?

I was unable to settle to anything. I tried tidying up some papers. Searching for a place to store them I came on a cupboard. There was a lot of bric-a-brac inside and I began clearing it out to make some room to store my own junk. I was shifting out some old musty Victorian books when an old photograph fell to the floor. It was so old that the sepia tint had almost faded into nothing. I picked it up and stared hard at it, my blood growing cold. The picture was familiar to me. I had grown up with it hanging in a gilt frame on the wall in my father's study.

The photograph showed a young officer, an officer in full regimentals; young, handsome, dashing. The writing across the bottom of the picture was near fading but showed a strong handed calligraphy. 'To my darling Cal—my love for always, Jonathan'.

A sound behind me caused me to start. I wheeled around and saw the girl standing behind me.

'So,' she said after a long pause, the cold steel eyes staring into mine, 'so now you know.'

I swallowed hard, trying to keep my senses.

'Know, know what?'

'You know the story of poor Calyhony Kissack and Kerron Moughty.'

The cold steel eyes went to the photograph in my hand.

'The lieutenant was young and handsome, wasn't he? You favour him, you know, Jon . . . Jon Jameson, or should it be Jonathan . . .?'

'What of it?' I demanded petulantly. 'Jonathan Lambert is my real name. I only write as Jon Jameson.'

Her mouth parodied a smile.

'That was his name, wasn't it? Lieutenant Jonathan Lambert.'

¬I suddenly noticed the overpowering scent of wild violets.

'Violets,' whispered the girl. Her lips were still smiling, though the eyes were still as cold as steel. 'They were her favourite scent.'

'Her . . . ? Who do you mean?'

'Why, Calyhony Kissack, of course. And Jonathan Lambert said they were his favourite scent as well.'

I drew myself up.

'Look here, I don't understand. This is a picture of my great-grandfather, Jonathan Lambert. He was a Major-General in the Indian Army but he . . .'

'We have been waiting many lifetimes for your return, Jonathan Lambert.'

Her voice was soft, deadly. The eyes held mine.

'What the hell do you mean?' My voice was harsh, unnerved by the odour of violets.

'Can't you guess, Jonathan Lambert?'

'Guess what?'

'My name is Calyhony.'

I forced myself to laugh outright.

'Are you trying to kid me that you are Calyhony Kissack?'

She smiled.

'You are round the twist!' I snarled, trying to control the hysteria I was feeling.

The girl gave an odd chuckling sound.

'We have all been waiting for your return, Jonathan Lambert.'

'I am not Lieutenant Jonathan Lambert, ' I protested. 'My great-grandfather was killed in the Boer War in 1901. He was the lieutenant. Not me! Not me!'

The perfume of violets had increased until it was a choking stench. I felt unable to breathe.

I became aware of a fiddle playing. It must have been playing for some time and its rhythms were harsh on my ears. I raised my hands to shut out the sound.

Suddenly, I was pushing by the girl, running out of the cottage into the dark night. In the light which shone from the door I saw a man seated on the old stone wall outside. He was a big, tough looking working man in corduroys and a waistcoat and a cloth cap. He held a fiddle under his chin and a bow in his hand. He bared his teeth in silent laughter at me and went on playing. *Kirree fo Niaghtey!* The Sheep Under the Snow!

I let loose an inarticulate sound. Then I was running. I had no idea where I was running to. I knew that I had to escape from this madness. From the overpowering smell of violets and the sound of the fiddle music. I raced up behind the cottage across the slope of Slieau Managh. Then I knew where I was going. I was heading for the top of the small precipice over which Calyhony Kissack had jumped to her death over a century before; jumped to her death because of the betrayal of my great-grandfather! I tried to halt myself but my legs seemed to have a will of their own.

Then I fell sprawling. I hit a boulder and heard something crack in my leg. I was sent crashing forward on my face and a dark pool seemed to open up before me. I dived in. It seemed to have no bottom.

I came to in bed in the cottage. There was a bandage around my head and my leg was strapped between hard supports. A jovial, red faced man was bending over me.

'Hello, young feller,' he greeted. 'How do you feel?'

My only answer was a groan.

'You've had a nasty tumble. Lucky I happened by. There's a fracture in your lower leg. I set it. I'm a good bone-setter. It will mend soon enough.'

I blinked and stared around me.

'What day is it?'

The man chuckled.

'Why, Christmas Eve, my boy. You were lucky. It was a harsh night last night. Some of the sheep across the mountain were buried under the snow. You could have died of exposure had I not happened by. This is not the countryside to go roaming around at night in.'

I leant back on the pillows with a sigh of relief.

'My daughter is downstairs making you some soup. You'll have to relax for a few days.'

Relax? I felt relaxed already. Safe and relaxed as if I had come through some ghastly nightmare.

A few moments later the door was pushed open.

'Ah, here is my daughter now,' smiled the man, turning.

Almost at once I breathed in the perfume of wild violets and heard, far off, the sound of a fiddle playing.

The girl stood framed in the doorway smiling at me. A smile with her lips only for the eyes were still cold, as cold as polished steel.

'Come in, Calyhony,' said the man at the side of the bed.

THE UNINVITED

by John Glasby

John Stephen Glasby (b. 1928) is one of Britain's
most prolific writers, with over 500 stories to his
credit in various genres—horror, crime, war,
adventure, and even a few hospital romances. In
spite of this vast output, he always maintained a far
higher standard than many of his contemporaries
in the 1950s. His profession is Research Chemist
(with ICI), and he has written a four-volume
Encyclopaedia of Chemistry. He is also the author
of several reference books on astronomy, including
Variable Stars (1968), *Dwarf Novae* (1970),
and *Boundaries of the Universe* (1971). The best
known of his many fiction pseudonyms is
'A.J. Merak', named after the bright star in the
Great Bear constellation.
These two new stories show that Glasby has lost
none of his storytelling gifts, and we look forward
to reading many more tales by him in the future.

'Surely you're not thinking of spending Christmas all alone in
that big house, Mrs Forester?'
Doctor Gledden folded his stethoscope and went back to
his chair. He lowered himself into it and eyed her over the top of his
steel-rimmed spectacles.

'And where else would I spend Christmas, doctor?' Celia Forester
buttoned up her blouse. She was a tall, slim woman in her late forties,
still attractive, although the last year seemed to have hardened her,
deepened the lines across her forehead and tightened the curves of her
mouth.

Gledden saw her look of half-sullen indignation and pushed his point.

'Don't you have any relatives or friends you could visit for a couple of weeks? Believe me, that would help your nervous condition far more than any pills I can give you. It wouldn't be so bad if you lived in the village. But High Towers is so isolated.'

He was going to add that the situation this year was very different to that of only the year before. Then, he knew, she had had plenty of company during the festive season.

Her husband, Stephen, had been around then, he recalled. But he had gone off shortly before the New Year and village gossip had it that there was another woman involved. Certainly there had been talk that after only four years of married life, relations between Celia Forester and her husband had degenerated into a round of almost daily quarrels.

Her father had also been alive then and her brother and his wife had spent Christmas at High Towers, perched up there on the hill five miles outside the village.

'There's no one now, doctor,' she said grimly.

'What about your brother? Couldn't you stay with him for a little while?'

'Him!' There was undisguised scorn in Celia Forester's voice. 'He and that wife of his only stayed around to get their hands on our father's money. When everything was left to me he emigrated. The last I heard of them they were somewhere in Australia.'

Gledden sighed. He took out his handkerchief and wiped his glasses. 'Well, that's none of my business, I suppose. But as your doctor, I don't think staying alone as you do is helping these nervous symptoms. You need a complete rest and change of scenery.'

'All I need is something to calm my nerves and let me sleep at night.'

'Very well.' Gledden threw up his hands in exasperation. 'But it's only fair to warn you, these tablets will only alleviate these symptoms. They won't cure you. You'll only really get better if you leave that place and make a fresh start somewhere else. At least think over what I've said.'

He scribbled the prescription and handed it to her, watching as she folded it with an exaggerated care and placed it in her handbag.

'Will you?' he insisted.

'I'll bear in mind what you say, doctor. Maybe next year.'

Leaving the small surgery, Celia crossed the street to the chemist on the corner. It was now snowing thickly, huge white flakes that had already formed a blanket over the hard, frosty ground. It was almost half past three and already getting dark. By morning, if the snow kept up, it would be so deep the road back into the village would be virtually impassable.

Fortunately, she had sufficient food in the house to last for three or four weeks so that would present no problem. But it might make it difficult for Mrs Clements to get through to help her with the housework.

Picking up the tablets, she walked back to where she had left her car outside the doctor's surgery and settled herself behind the wheel. There were few people about. The few lamps along the street cast small, isolated pools of yellow light on the snow which were almost lost in the darkness. She switched on the headlights and drove slowly out of the village.

The night was completely black now and there was an absolute stillness that seemed to wrap itself around the car, insulating it from the outside world. Her fingers gripped the wheel until her hands ached with the strain. Peering ahead, she found it difficult to make out the narrow road. The headlights probed into the thickly falling snow for ten feet or so, but went no further.

She knew she ought not to have left things so late. The snow had been forecast and she really should have gone into the village before noon. Her mind was beginning to play strange tricks again. She had the odd idea that there was something lurking in the black shadows of the hedges, just out of sight, waiting with a patient stillness, ready to leap out at her if she relaxed her guard.

The sensation of restless apprehension had been growing stronger in her mind all day and now it was solidifying into something more definite, more imminent. The dimly-seen fields, white with their covering of snow, seemed to be peopled with soundless, half-noticed shadows that flitted on the edge of her vision as she tried to keep her gaze fixed on the road. Suddenly, she found herself sweating in spite of the chill inside the car.

For an instant, the sense of impending disaster was so powerful that she almost stopped the car. Desperately, she nerved herself to follow the winding curves of the road, struggling to ignore the feeling that there was *something* out there, waiting for her with a patience that was not of this earth, hiding in the darkness, knowing by some strange instinct that she was now on her way back to the house, preparing for her when she arrived.

The thought made her subconsciously grip the wheel even more tightly, convulsively, and her muscles tautened of their own volition. After a moment, she caught herself at it and forced herself to relax. There was nothing to be afraid of. Nothing at all. Just because it was almost Christmas. It was simply that her nerves were in a bad way, that was all. Living alone in the big house with only Mrs Clements coming in four days a week to help with the cleaning.

During the summer it hadn't been too bad. The nights were short and there was very little real darkness. No sooner had the sun set than the dawn began to brighten. Now it was different. There were noises in the house which she couldn't pin down and identify. Strange creaks and rattles that were not simply due to the wind moaning around the ancient eaves or the shutters banging on hinges that urgently needed repair.

Maybe the tablets in her bag would help her to relax and get some sleep at night. Once the winter was over she would seriously consider selling the place and moving elsewhere, possibly even go abroad. After all, she now had plenty of money to do with as she wished. She was a free woman. She could go anywhere she liked.

Leaning forward tensely, she peered hard through the windscreen, searching the darkness for the small signpost which pointed the way up the hill to the house. In this abominable weather, it would be easy to miss it altogether.

The windscreen wiper was a thick black finger, sweeping away snow and piling it thickly on either side of the glass. It seemed she must have been driving for miles with only the hedges on either side. Surely she hadn't driven past it.

Then it appeared without warning and she was forced to brake hard, the wheels skidding in the soft snow. Reversing a few yards, she turned off the main road, put the car into second gear and began the slow, difficult climb up the hillside. The bad thing about driving, especially at night, was that it gave her time to think, to remember. To remember the previous Christmas when there had been the five of them in the house.

She pulled hard on the wheel as the headlights picked out the tall stone pillars flanking the entrance to the drive. The house lay brooding behind the wide lawns where the gnarled shapes of stunted bushes, their branches bare of leaves, struggled towards the sky. To her overwrought imagination the trees and plants peopled the night with fearsome, scurrying shapes and flitting phantoms.

She was glad when she pulled up outside the front door and switched off the engine. In the darkness she fumbled with the key. Her fingers were numbed with the cold and it was several moments before she managed to open the thick oaken door. Closing it behind her, she switched on the lights and listened to the silence.

Going into the parlour, a long, wooden-beamed room with low rafters, she noticed with satisfaction that the fire was still burning in the wide grate. Logs spluttered and threw a warm glow into the room. Pulling off her heavy coat and gloves, she held her hands out to the flames. She could feel the heat seeping into her chilled bones.

She piled more logs onto the fire before making herself something to eat, sitting in front of the fire with the plate balanced on her knees. Her entire body was tired and aching and her eyelids were sore and tender from staring into the darkness in front of the car for so long.

Afterwards, she tried to read for a little while but her mind wasn't on the printed pages. Inwardly, she knew she was waiting for the noises to start. She wasn't sure when they had first begun, although she had a vague feeling she had not really noticed them until the nights had started drawing in towards the winter solstice. But certainly over the past couple of weeks they had become more pronounced, making it impossible for her to sleep.

She suddenly tensed and sat up straight, rigid. Her heart was palpitating in her chest and her whole being twitched with a strange mixture of fear and expectation as though she had just woken from some terrible, half-forgotten nightmare. The sound came from below her, from the cellar.

She had heard it several times before but this time it seemed louder; a rumbling, sliding noise as if something heavy were being moved. Her hand fluttered to her mouth. Every night for the past month it had been the same. First the noise in the cellar and then, a little later, the faint intermittent tapping at the window.

She had tried to tell herself that the former was nothing more than the old house settling on its foundations and the latter just a branch blown by the wind. Yet this explanation no longer satisfied her. Desperately, she clamped her lips tightly together and forced herself to breathe deeply.

Getting to her feet, she took the lantern from the corner, lit it, and made her way down the stone steps into the cellar. It was the first time she had been down there for almost a year, ever since last Christmas Day. Now that she was there, the noise had stopped. The thick stone walls shone with moisture in the yellow lamplight and huge cobwebs festooned the corners. The fear which had come with a rush when she had first heard the sound began to subside a little. The damp, earthen floor was undisturbed.

Thoughts formed hazily in her mind as she remembered that previous Christmas Day. The five of them sitting round the long table in the candlelight, the meal just finished. Then, one by one, the others slumping forward in their chairs as the poison had done its work.

She had planned everything meticulously, down to the last detail. Her father had been ill for some months with his heart and old Doctor Mellow had warned her he could go at any time. She had forseen no difficulty in getting him to sign the death certificate. But her husband and her brother and his wife were a different matter. She had already decided how to explain their disappearance. But the bodies had to be disposed of. Fortunately, Mrs Clements would not be back for a couple of days and there had been plenty of time to carry through her plans.

With an effort, she had forced Stephen halfway out of his chair so that he was leaning partly across the table. Then she had thrust her head beneath his chest and taken his weight across her shoulders. Straightening up, she had been able to carry the heavy weight in a fireman's lift, his arms and legs hanging limply on either side. In this manner, she had carried him across the room and down the wine cellar steps. At the bottom, she had dropped him like an ungainly sack.

The pickaxe and shovel she had taken down into the cellar two days earlier and working by the light of the lantern she had dug into the hard-packed earth of the floor. By the time she had opened up the deep hole and thrust the body into it the sweat on her body was icy cold in the chill air. It had taken her more than two hours to bury Stephen and pack the earth back into place.

Returning to the dining room she had left the two remaining bodies in their chairs until darkness had fallen. So far, everything had gone very satisfactorily. There had not been sufficient room in the cellar for Peter and Marjorie to join her husband. But she had made provisions for that. The weather had been unseasonably mild for several days and the ground outside was relatively soft.

Digging the hole for them had been easier than that in the cellar and there had been no chance of being observed. Her nearest neighbours lived more than three miles away and it was unlikely anyone would be abroad at that time of night.

She had been forced to work in total darkness, however. She hadn't wanted a light to be spotted by some late-night motorist on the road at the bottom of the hill. Furthermore, she'd had to carry them, one at a time, out of the house and across the soft, slippery earth. Marjorie hadn't been too difficult. She was a small woman, intent on keeping her figure in trim. But Peter had let himself go in middle age, running to fat. She had had to pause several times, and once or twice doubt had overwhelmed her, in case her well-laid plans should fail for lack of bodily strength.

But she had forced herself to go on, staggering under her inert burden. Finally, she had slept exhausted in her bed, waking only a quarter of an hour before ten o'clock. It had snowed through the night and all traces of her work lay buried under a thick blanket of white.

After that, it had been comparatively easy. Doctor Mellow had certified a heart attack for her father and he had been buried in the family vault near the little church a mile along the road towards the village. Where Stephen had been concerned, she had put on the act of the woman abandoned by her husband. She had suffered the looks given her by some of the women in the village, known of the talk that went on behind her back. She had waited anxiously for several weeks, wondering if anyone would come inquiring about Peter and Marjorie. But the months passed and nothing had happened so that by the summer she had felt reasonably secure.

So why this apprehension and dread? She pulled her thoughts back to the present and lifted the lantern high over her head to survey the cellar thoroughly. There was nothing out of place, certainly nothing to account for that queer noise. She searched every corner meticulously, peering behind the large cases which had been stacked down there since she and Stephen had moved in with her father.

Nothing.

She shook herself mentally. What the devil was wrong with her? Maybe it was because she was allowing her thoughts to dwell on the past. That was all gone and should be forgotten. She had planned everything perfectly, no suspicion was attached to her. All she had to do was keep her nerves under control and once the spring came she would get out, go away and get on with her life.

She went back into the parlour and glanced at the tall grandfather clock in the corner. It was almost eight o'clock. Perhaps if she got a good night's sleep things would be better in the morning. Switching off the lights, she went upstairs to her room. After swallowing a couple of the sleeping tablets, she undressed quickly, feeling the chill of the room in her bones.

The last thing she heard before she fell asleep was a faint, insistent tapping on one of the windows downstairs.

Celia woke with a splitting headache. She lay there, unmoving, scarcely breathing while she listened to the sounds of the old house. There was a pulse at her temples, hammering away from the adrenaline that had been pumped into her system. She knew she'd been wakened by some foreign sound and a second later it was repeated. It was the whirring of the vacuum cleaner downstairs.

Mrs Clements must have let herself in with her key. Rolling over, she threw a glance at the bedside clock. It was a little after ten. Pulling herself from the warm bed, Celia padded into the bathroom, splashed warm water onto her face and rubbed it dry with the towel. She dressed quickly, her fingers shaking a little as she fumbled with the buttons of her dress.

Going downstairs, she found Mrs Clements in the parlour. The other woman looked up as she entered.

Mrs Clements switched off the vacuum cleaner. She looked at Celia concernedly. 'Are you all right, Mrs Forester?' she asked. 'I must say you don't look too well.'

Celia felt her tongue move around her dry lips. Somehow, she forced evenness into her voice. 'Yes, I'm fine. It's just that I must have overslept. I didn't expect you to get here today through the snow.'

'Oh, it's not too bad. Besides, Dan brought me to the top of the hill and he'll pick me up when I'm finished. Seeing as it's Christmas Day tomorrow, I thought I'd better come and not leave things until after Boxing Day.'

She eyed Celia closely. 'I'll make you a cup of coffee. You look as though you could do with one.'

'Thanks. Make one for yourself.'

Celia seated herself in front of the blazing fire and held out her hands to it. The tension and the sensation of dread were beginning to grow within her again. She had the unshakable conviction that something terrible was going to happen. How she knew it so definitely, she couldn't tell.

There was the sound of dishes being moved around in the kitchen.

Then Mrs Clements came back with two mugs of hot coffee. She handed one to Celia before seating herself in the other chair.

Looking at Celia over the rim of her mug, she said, 'I know this is really none of my business, but I do think you shouldn't stay here alone over Christmas. Why don't you come back with me and Dan. You'd be more than welcome.'

For an instant, Celia was tempted to accept, then she shook her head. 'Thanks for the offer, but I'd rather stay here. Don't worry, I'll be all right.'

'Well, as long as you're sure.' Mrs Clements sounded dubious. 'It's just that . . .' she paused, uncertain how to put her thoughts into words that would not offend, '. . . I know it sounds odd but sometimes I've had the feeling there's someone else here, watching me.'

Celia forced a shaky laugh. 'Well, I can assure you the house isn't haunted. I'd be the first to know if it was.'

She finished her coffee and got up. While Mrs Clements got on with her work she put on her heavy coat and went out into the garden. The sky was still overcast but the snow had stopped and her thick boots crunched on the frosty ground. The countryside lay still under its blanket of white and there was scarcely any sound apart from the dry, eerie rustle of the bare branches.

Somehow, she felt herself drawn towards the small copse on the brow of the hill about fifty yards from the rear of the house, recalling that seemingly endless staggering walk of a year ago when she had carried the bodies of Peter and Marjorie to their last resting place. Dead weeds tangled over the spot now and the place held a peculiar, deserted appearance. But in spite of the fact that the dead were buried deep beneath the surface, there was a little flutter of panic stirring in her mind and she searched the snow-covered ground intently as if expecting to find some sign that their existence might be visible to anyone who happened this way.

The impulse to get away from this place, to run down the hill and keep on running until she was miles away, exploded in her. But the house was there; it was what she had always wanted for herself. She had killed to get it and, deep inside, she knew she would never go away in spite of her words to the doctor and Mrs Clements. Drawing herself up to her full height, she told herself she was acting like a stupid fool, feeling this way. With a conscious effort of will, she pushed the thoughts away and walked slowly back to the house, shivering a little in the biting wind.

That night, after Mrs Clements had gone, she put on all the lights in the house. From the parlour window, she could just make out the lights in the village, five miles away. Down there, she thought, there would be carol singers going around the doors, children being put to bed early, preparations being made for Christmas Day. It was the first time for several years there had been a white Christmas; a perfect setting for the forthcoming festivities. A time of joy and thanksgiving.

She shivered and pressed her thin lips together into a hard line. Suddenly, there was something chill and empty and dead about the house in sharp contrast to the scene in the distance. She knew she was letting her nerves and imagination get the better of her again and the sick sensation of impending disaster began to take a firm hold on her, stirring in the depths of her mind. With a savage twist of her hand she pulled the heavy drapes across the window, shutting out the sight of the nearby trees which flung a black tracery of forlorn branches against the moonlit sky.

The wind had got up, whistling around the eaves. Standing there, Celia thought she heard faint voices in the sound, rising and falling in a ghastly cacophony of inarticulate words. The monotonous ticking of the grandfather clock was like a heart beating against the silence. The house seemed full of unexplainable noises. Something scraped along the wainscot like bony fingers scratching at the wood. Far off, near the top of the house, there began a regular, insistent banging as if one of the shutters was hammering against a window. But Celia knew for certain that none of the shutters were loose. She had checked all of them with Mrs Clements only two hours earlier.

Fear threatened to pull her mind apart, to rip it into a thousand screaming fragments. The sudden chill that seized her made it difficult for her to breathe properly. Desperately, she edged closer to the fire for warmth. But the flames that still leapt high around the spluttering logs seemed to give out no heat.

After a while, she forced herself to go around the doors and all of the windows, ensuring they were locked and securely bolted. Once she had made sure nothing could get in, she went into the kitchen, boiled a kettle, and made herself a hot drink, sipping it slowly, both hands around the cup.

It was still quite early but she recalled how well the sleeping tablets had acted the previous night, putting her to sleep almost at once. If she could get the night over, things would not be so bad in the daylight.

Taking a glass of water with her she went up to her room. She felt drained physically, but her senses were curiously sharp and alert, her ears straining to catch every sound, her eyes watching each corner.

She swallowed two of her tablets before going to bed and lay for a while, keeping the bedside light on. The mere thought of the darkness started the little germ of panic screaming in her brain. Finally, she fell into a drugged sleep but this time, when she woke, it was still dark outside. The white moonlight threw long shadows across the floor.

As on the previous night, she knew that something had awakened her and she jerked upright in her bed, tensed and rigid. From down below, the grandfather clock chimed midnight. Had she only slept for three hours?

Steeling herself, she peered around the bedroom. Everything seemed normal. She realized she was gripping the edge of the coverlet so tightly that her fingers were numb with the pressure. Slowly, she released her hold. Whatever had brought her out of the drug-induced sleep it must have been something grossly abnormal.

It was then that she recognized that now the sound of the chimes had died away, everything was absolutely still and silent. The wind no longer made its eerie moaning around the house. Even the normal creaks and groans of the old building were absent. It was as if the entire place was holding its breath, waiting for something to happen.

Marshalling her courage, she moved silently to the door and opened it a crack, peering out, glad now that she had left on all the lights. The long landing and stairs were empty, the doors to all of the other rooms were shut. For a long moment she stood there, listening, scarcely daring to breathe, unable to move.

At that instant, a sound broke the clinging stillness; a muffled rumbling from somewhere beneath the house. Startled by the noise, her nerves already drawn out to a razor's edge, she panicked and tried to scream. But the yell refused to come past the constricted muscles of her throat. In that split second, she realized it was the same noise she had heard on those previous occasions over the past few weeks but now it was louder, echoing through the downstairs floor and up the stairs.

Instinctively, she drew back into the bedroom, shivering involuntarily. All of the fear and dread of the past few days came back with a rush, overwhelming her.

She thought frenziedly: *This isn't really happening. I'm just imagining it all. Something to do with those pills the doctor gave me.*

Her thoughts stopped suddenly, gelling in her brain. There came a sharp knocking at the front door. The muscles of her stomach contracted into a tight knot of terror. She tried to think coherently. Perhaps one of the villagers had seen all of the lights on and had come to check that everything was all right.

She spun frantically on her heel, her heart racing, the blood pounding through her head. She knew instinctively she had been stupid to turn down Mrs Clements's offer. There was something terrible in the house, something malignant that was determined to get her. Wildly, she ran down the stairs, her trembling hand trailing along the banister. The knocking came again at the door and she thought she heard a woman's voice call her name.

It was Mrs Clements, after all. There was now one thought uppermost in her mind. No matter what they thought of her dishevelled and wild-eyed appearance, she had to get them to take her away from this place. Running through the parlour, she reached the front door and pulled back the two steel bolts before turning the key in the lock.

A blast of icily cold air swirled about her as she pulled the door open.

Marjorie stood there with Peter immediately behind her. Their hideous, deformed faces leered at her, much of the flesh already rotted away. Bony fingers lifted towards her. Marjorie's lipless mouth gaped wide, teeth showing whitely in a grisly smile.

'Merry Christmas, Celia,' she hissed sibilantly.

Celia recoiled, a thin scream bursting from her shaking lips. For a wild second, she stood rooted to the spot, unable to move an inch as the two ghastly apparitions shambled forward. There was a horrible clicking of bones as they moved, skeletal hands outstretched towards her.

Then, suddenly, she found herself able to move. With a thin, high-pitched shriek of terror she turned and ran for the large dining room, hoping to reach the back door and get away. A low, bubbling moan escaped from her lips as she staggered across the hall with the stairs leading up to the upper floor and saw that the thick oaken door to the cellar was no longer shut. It was opening slowly and something was coming through.

When she saw what was coming through the dark opening, Celia Forester felt sure she would faint. Her heart literally stopped beating for perceptible seconds. The dry earth of the house's foundations had preserved Stephen's body a little more than those of her brother and his wife. The decaying fragments of clothing still clung around his body and dirt covered the face so that it was almost unrecognizable.

Wisps of dark hair sprouted out of the ghastly grey-white skull. White ribs gleamed spectrally beneath the shredded coat.

The grinning mouth opened wide. 'Happy Christmas, darling,' Stephen said hollowly.

At this point, Celia began to scream. Her shrill, hysterical cries filled the house, terror-filled and nerve-shaking. For moments, the corpse-thing stood beside the stairs. Then it lumbered towards her with a low chuckle. There was a kind of hellish glee in that hideous laugh.

Wildly, Celia pushed out her hands as if to fend him off. The action broke the paralysis which held her rigid. A swift glance over her shoulder told her that Marjorie and Peter were almost upon her from behind. Her shrieking mind told her she had to flee for the sake of her own life and sanity. Somehow, she forced her legs to move, rushing for the dining room door.

A foetid odour washed around her in a nauseating wave as she ran past Stephen into the long dining room, slamming the door behind her. If only she could unlock the back door and get out, she had a chance. Even in her terrified, demented state she felt sure she could outrun these creatures.

She fell against the edge of the table, hitting her leg hard, but scarcely feeling the pain. A little part of her whirling mind told her that this wasn't really happening; that it was some strange and frightening hallucination induced by the drug. But those horrible figures had been real enough and, as she lurched around the table, she heard the handle of the door being turned behind her.

Somehow, she gained the back door, her shaking fingers scrabbling wildly with the thick bolts. She could feel the horror closing in around her, encircling her in its nightmarish embrace. She got the top bolt out of its sockets and bent swiftly to grasp the bottom one, babbling incoherently as it stubbornly resisted her efforts.

The dining room door burst open. Without looking round, she redoubled her efforts, putting all her strength into forcing the bolt back. It suddenly gave a screech of metal on metal. Straightening, she grabbed the key and turned it savagely in the lock, pulling the door open in the same frenzied movement.

The chill, icy air seemed to pierce her bones through the thin nightdress as she made to run out into the night. If she could only reach the main road at the bottom of the hill there was just the chance she might be able to stop a car, even at this late hour. Once she was in the village, she would be safe.

Her heart thudding madly against her ribs, aware that those dead, but animated, things were close behind her, she threw herself headlong through the door, gasping as the night air bit savagely at the back of her throat.

Madness and insanity lay in the house behind her but if she could only—

The blood left her face and she reeled with a sudden dizziness, wanting to cry out but her throat would not open. A tall, dark figure was shuffling through the snow towards her. Even in the pale wash of moonlight she recognized the travesty of a face.

'Father!' The single word burst unbidden from her lips as she fell against the wall.

Merciless bony fingers seized her by the arms and hauled her upright. Remorselessly, she was dragged back into the house. Celia must have fainted for when she once more grew aware of her surroundings, she was sitting in the high-backed chair at the head of the long table, her arms and legs bound so that she was unable to move.

The others sat around her, their hideous faces turned in her direction, eyeless sockets fixed on her and in her terrified, bemused state she thought she saw tiny hellish flames burning malevolently where their eyes should have been.

'It was good of you to let us in.' Marjorie's sibilant voice burned through Celia's brain.

'We thought it would be nice to spend Christmas with you, Celia,' hissed Stephen. 'And what would Christmas be without a present from all of us.'

Celia cringed immovably as she saw the eager, skeletal faces around her, leaning forward over the table. She could smell the rotten odour of earth and long-decayed flesh. All of her senses were keyed to screaming pitch, but she couldn't scream, could find no way of relieving her fear in that way.

'Only, as you know, we've all been away where it was impossible to get you a present,' whispered Peter. 'So all we can do is give you the one you gave us last Christmas.'

Celia wanted to scream; *But I didn't give you anything last Christmas.*

But the thought was abruptly choked off in her mind as the sudden, awful realization came to her. Her head seemed to be locked rigidly on her shoulders, but out of the corner of her eye she saw Stephen thrust himself awkwardly to his feet, the dried earth from his cadaverous body dropping onto the table top.

The harsh glare of the electric light glinted brilliantly off the blade of the long carving knife held in his bony fingers.

A PRESENT FOR CHRISTMAS

A.J. Merak

Another story by John S. Glasby, see page 240.

I t is, of course, impossible for me to prove that my story is true. It certainly was not a dream, for something of the horror that happened on Christmas Eve is known to some of the people in the village. But the hideous reality is known only to me—and Doctor Morton, the only other witness to the grotesque happenings of that night, is dead and cannot testify to the truth.

But if there is any sane explanation, I pray to God I may be told of it for I begin to fear for my sanity. Certainly my actions on that Christmas morning cannot be construed as those of a man in full possession of his senses. But there still exist things on this earth which give the lie to our fond belief that all is rational and explainable by science and logic.

That morning I took my old Service revolver from the locked drawer in my room, checked that it was loaded, then thrust it into my overcoat pocket and walked up to the Manor. It was cold and frosty and the snow which covered the whole countryside sparkled in the wintry sunlight. There were few of the villagers abroad; most of them were indoors getting ready to attend the Christmas service in the small church.

At the manor, I asked to speak to Anne Kirby, telling the butler it was important I should see her before she left for church. Waiting

[255]

there while she came, I knew exactly what I had to do. When she appeared a few moments later, looking down at me with a faint smile on her lips, I took out my revolver and put a bullet through her brain.

After that, things got a little hazy and confused. I remember the gun being snatched from my hand, the screams of Anne's mother, the police arriving and bundling me roughly into the car with an officer on either side of me.

There was a short drive to Exeter where I faced a barrage of questions from grim-faced men who were not prepared to believe my story.

Now I am in this place which I know is an institution for the criminally insane and gradually my memory has returned so that I can vividly recall every detail of that Christmas Eve. The doctors tell me I must remain calm and they have finally allowed me pen and paper so that I might record everything that happened. This I shall do in an attempt to preserve my sanity and to convince them that what I did was not murder.

I had lived in Redforde all of my life and when the small subsidiary telephone exchange was opened three years before I had taken the job as telephonist on permanent night duty. Living alone and a bachelor, such nocturnal work was ideal. There were very few calls through the night; an occasional villager wanting Doctor Morton in a hurry and the odd visitor from Exeter needing a taxi to take him home. But most of the villagers tended to go to bed at sunset and begin their morning chores at sunrise whatever the season of the year.

Being Christmas Eve I expected a little more activity in the village and more late night calls than usual. For some weeks the village had been preparing, not only for Christmas, but for the engagement party of Anne Kirby, Sir John's only daughter, and Jonathan Weatherby whose father owned Deepdale Farm some four miles away. The couple had known each other all their lives and had set their engagement for Christmas Day. Everyone was more than pleased when the snow came giving just the right touch to the scene.

By ten thirty I had made myself the first of several mugs of hot coffee and settled myself at the small switchboard with only a dim red light burning near the ceiling. A couple of late-night revellers made their noisy way along the street beneath the window and I listened to the sound of their voices until it faded into the distance. After that the night was very calm and still.

I sipped my coffee slowly, lit a cigarette, and was on the point of opening the novel I had brought with me when the buzzer sounded on the switchboard.

'Number please,' I said automatically.

I recognized the Vicar's voice at once.

'Good evening, Charles, and a Merry Christmas,' he said, his tone sounding slightly apologetic as usual. 'Would you put me through to the Manor, please. I know it's a little late but there are a few things I'd like to discuss with Lady Kirby.'

'Certainly, Vicar, I'm putting you through now. Just hold the line.'

I connected him with the Manor, waited until his call was answered and then sat back in my chair, keeping the headphones on and listening in to the conversation.

It was strictly against the rules, of course. But I never divulged a word of anything I overheard and saw no harm in it. Just an innocent habit that helped to pass the long hours. The call lasted for five minutes with the Vicar suggesting the hymns he thought would be appropriate for the service the following day and thanking Lady Kirby for the flower arrangement on the altar.

When he had finished his call I unplugged the connection and walked over to the window, staring out into the night. It was very quiet and there was a moon, almost full, shining brilliantly in the south-east. Snow lay thickly over the fields and on the branches of the trees. I noticed, too, that there were still lights burning in one or two of the nearer cottages and still more gleamed in the windows of the Manor where it stood among the distant elms.

There was bound to be a lot still going on there, I reflected; last-minute preparations for the engagement reception. I wondered where young Jonathan was and whether I could expect a call from him within the next half hour.

A little later, however, I saw the headlights of a car swing across a space between the trees and watched it head away from the Manor along the wide drive towards the road. It passed through the village five minutes later and I recognized Jonathan's red sports car. Obviously, I wouldn't be receiving any calls from him during the night. In that surmise, however, I was mistaken for the full horror was just about to begin.

I rinsed out my mug and refilled the electric kettle in preparation for brewing up a second time which I usually did around midnight. Scarcely had I sat down in my chair than the buzzer sounded again. I ran my glance along the switchboard wondering who could be calling me at that moment. It came from the phone box five miles away along the back road beside the cemetery. Probably some motorist who had broken down along that narrow stretch of country road and needed help, I told myself.

Yet somehow, an eerie feeling came over me as I answered the call. Almost at once a man's voice began babbling incoherently at the other end of the line. I broke in hurriedly, unable to make head or tail of what he was trying to say. The words were all running into each other.

'What number do you want?' I realized I was speaking a trifle more loudly than I had intended.

'Listen. There's some maniac of a woman wandering around here. I just came round the corner. I swear I was only doing thirty and there she was, standing in the middle of the road. I jammed on the brakes but I must have hit her.'

I felt a little shiver at his words but I couldn't for the life of me pinpoint why.

'Do you want the police or an ambulance?'

'Yes—I mean no. That's the scary part of it. I stopped and walked back but there's no sign of her. I've even looked in the ditch along both sides and—'

'Just try to calm yourself,' I broke in, speaking patiently. 'Is your car damaged?'

'No, it seems to be all right, but—'

'Then take it from me, there was no one there. I know that stretch of road. The moonlight can play funny tricks with you. It would have been nothing more than a branch across the road.'

'But I did see her, as clear as day, standing there right in the headlights. A young woman, red hair, dressed in white as if she was sleep walking.'

'Listen to me,' I said quietly, forcing evenness into my voice. 'Are you absolutely certain there's no one there now?'

There was a long pause and I knew he was staring through the glass of the telephone box, looking along the road in both directions.

Then he said shakily, 'Yes, I'm sure.'

'Then if I were you, I wouldn't bring the police into it.' I felt sure he had been drinking. 'Just get back into your car and drive straight home. You can take it from me there would be no one walking along that road at this time of night.'

'But I tell you I saw her!'

'You saw something. But whether it was a branch waving in the moonlight or just some trick of the light on the snow, I don't know. But if it had been a woman you'd have felt it when you hit her and there would be a body lying in the road. Now wouldn't there?'

I was beginning to feel a little shaky myself but I did my best not to let anything show in my voice.

'Well, yes . . . I suppose so.'

'Very well then. If it will make you feel any better, give me your name and address and if anything does come up during the night I can let the police know. But I'm sure it won't.'

'That's very good of you.'

'Don't mention it.' He gave me his name and an address in Exeter and then rang off. I made myself the second mug of coffee even though it was only eleven-fifteen. I needed it at that moment. Whether the caller had been drunk or not, he had certainly sounded scared and something must have happened along that lonely stretch of road to have sent him running for the telephone.

As I gulped my coffee I visualized that winding stretch of road. Even though it lay close to the cemetery there had never been any talk of it being haunted. Out there in the country, men were much closer to the earth and nature than in the big cities. Such things as ghosts were not laughed at or dismissed out of hand. If there had been any hint of a haunting in that area I would have heard about it.

Nevertheless I had an odd feeling in my bones that I had not heard the last of this incident and although the room was warm and stuffy I felt a chill spread over me as I stood by the window and watched the yellow lights in the village go out one by one as the folk settled down for the night.

Very soon, the only lights showing were at the Manor. Anne Kirby would be asleep by now, I thought. But clearly her parents were still awake.

There were no further calls until five minutes before midnight and in spite of the tight grip I had forced on my emotions, the strident sound of the buzzer brought me bolt upright in my chair.

Now what? I wondered as I made the connection.

'Charles?'

'Yes,' I said, 'what number do you want?'

'This is Jonathan Weatherby. I wonder if you'd do me a favour and check that Anne is still at the Manor.'

'Still at the Manor!' I realized I was repeating his words. 'But why on earth shouldn't she be there? Surely she was there when you left a little while ago. I spotted your car leaving.'

'Yes, she was. And I know this may sound odd, Charles, and I don't quite know how to put it. Maybe it was just my imagination, all the excitement of tomorrow, but I swear I just saw Anne walking along the road outside the house.'

'But that's not possible,' I said. 'You live on the other side of the village more than four miles from the Manor. She couldn't possibly have walked all that way in so short a time.'

I paused and then went on quickly, giving him no time to reply, trying to reassure him. 'Besides, what would she be doing out at this time of night?'

'I honestly don't know. The only thing I can think of is that she's walking in her sleep. Now I come to think of it, she did look strange. She was staring straight ahead as if she didn't know where she was. And if she'd come to see me for some reason, why didn't she come in instead of walking straight past without even a glance at the window?'

'Then you must realize it was nothing more than your imagination,' I told him. I tried to make it sound convincing but deep down I was becoming really scared. First that motorist on the road outside the village and now this. What in God's name was going on?

'Maybe you're right, Charles.'

'I know I am.'

'But just to set my mind at rest, would you call the Manor and make sure Anne is still there? I don't care what excuse you give for asking but I'd be glad if you didn't mention what I've just told you.'

'All right. I'll call you back in a couple of minutes.'

I didn't relish the idea of calling the Manor at that time of night to ask such a foolish question. I could imagine the kind of reception I'd get. But I knew this might be the only way of getting answers to some of the questions that were beginning to nag me.

It was Anne's mother who answered the phone two minutes later. After apologising for the lateness of the call I asked if Anne was there, explaining that I had caught sight of someone resembling her walking along the street a few moments earlier.

'Then you must have been mistaken, Charles,' she retorted testily. 'Anne went to bed almost an hour ago and she hasn't left her room.'

'I see. Perhaps it was a trick of the moonlight. I'm sorry to have troubled you, Lady Kirby.'

I rang Jonathan and told him what Anne's mother had said. He accepted it but somehow he didn't sound as though he was really convinced.

'Better get yourself some sleep, Jonathan,' I told him. 'You've a big day in front of you tomorrow.'

'I guess you're right, Charles. And thanks for checking for me. I must say it gave me quite a nasty turn at the time.'

'Nothing to worry about,' I said, trying to force a laugh. 'I reckon you've got Anne on your mind. It's quite natural you should imagine you saw her.'

He hung up at that and I sat in the silence of the little room and tried to put my chaotic thoughts into some kind of order. But it was far from easy. I couldn't shake off the feeling that there was something out there in the snow which had no right to be.

I got up and walked over to where the map of the village and the surrounding countryside hung on the wall. The room seemed strangely cold and there was a chill on my body where the sweat had congealed.

In the dim red light I managed to trace the winding line of the road where it ran through the village, past Deepdale Farm, and then north past the cemetery and on towards Exeter. I located the spot near the bend where the telephone box stood and then moved my finger slowly on until it reached Deepdale Farm.

It was then that something clicked in my mind. I put two and two together and came up with . . . well, almost four. Because I suddenly realized that the distance between these two points was such that someone could walk it comfortably in the time between those two odd telephone calls!

And whoever—or whatever—it was, was heading now in the direction of the village. I don't know why I was suddenly so convinced that both the motorist and Jonathan had been telling the truth. But a moment later I had switched off the light and was standing just beside the window in the cold darkness, staring down into the village street, waiting with a kind of dazed anticipation that was frightening.

The ticking of the clock on the wall was loud in the utter stillness. Down below me, in the flooding white moonlight, the snow glistened brilliantly. It covered the roofs and chimneypots, lay thickly along the outstretched branches of the trees. From where I stood, it looked a perfect Christmas card setting. Yet instead of the peace and joy of Christmas, there was something evil abroad.

When the sudden movement came near the St Margaret's Cross in the middle of the tiny square, I was almost expecting it. I pressed myself close against the cold hardness of the wall and screwed up my eyes against the snowglare in an attempt to identify the white-clad figure that moved slowly along the opposite side of the street. Even from that distance I would have sworn it was Anne Kirby down there. Yet commonsense told me it could not possibly be her; that at that very moment she was lying asleep in her bed at the Manor.

Was I having hallucinations too? Just like that half-drunken driver and Jonathan Weatherby? For a moment I was considering opening the window and calling down to her as she drew level with the building. But there was something oddly frightening and sinister about the slow, purposeful way she walked that kept me silent and drew me further into the room so that I might not be seen.

I knew that if it was really Anne down there, wandering around like this in the middle of the night, almost certainly sleep-walking, I ought to ring the Manor again and let her parents know.

I stood trembling as I watched the slim figure turn off the main street and head along the narrow path which eventually led across the fields and through the trees to the Manor.

My hands and legs were oddly numb and I was aware of my heart beating loudly, pumping the blood through my veins. There was a strange malevolent pressure all around me which remained all the time that figure was visible. And when I opened my mouth to suck in a shuddering gasp, the air seemed to be filled with the taste of evil.

Somehow, I got back to my chair in front of the switchboard and sank into it. I felt I ought to do something. But what? Ring Anne's mother and tell her what I had just seen? On the face of it that seemed the logical thing to do. But I'd already claimed to have seen her once and Lady Kirby's attitude had not been too friendly. And if Anne really was asleep — as by rights she should be — I felt reluctant to make an even bigger fool of myself.

I could phone the police, of course. But I could imagine what they would say. They would undoubtedly treat my story with the same scepticism as I had that of the motorist. Moonlight and shadows, sir. Nothing more. You must have imagined it.

It was then I thought of Doctor Morton. As well as being a personal friend of mine he had also known the Kirbys for more years than either of us cared to remember. Indeed, he had delivered Anne twenty years before and watched her grow into the beautiful young woman she was today. I also knew he was a late bird like myself, seldom going to bed before one or two in the morning. So there was no question of waking him from a deep sleep.

Now I had reached a decision to take someone else into my confidence I felt a little better. I picked up the connection, ready to dial his number. But before I could do so another call came through. Somehow, the sound of the buzzer and the red light on the switchboard sent a thrill of horror through me. Whether my nerves had become so taut at the events of the night, or whether some strange sense of presentiment told me this was no ordinary call, I could not say. But I hesitated for several moments before making the connection and my voice sounded oddly hoarse and unlike my own as I said, 'Number, please.'

For a moment I could hear nothing beyond a faint burring crackle on the line and I was on the point of repeating my question when a woman's voice, curiously faint and far-away, said, 'I'd like to speak to Anne Kirby.'

'Anne Kirby,' I said. The chill of horror settled deeper within me and I could feel the sweat damp on my palms and forehead. 'But it's well after midnight. She'll be asleep now. Can't this wait until morning?'

'No. It can't wait. This is important.'

'Very well. Just hold the line and I'll put you through to the Manor.'

I dialled the Manor and waited for several moments hoping inwardly there would be no reply. Then Lady Kirby came on the line.

'I've a call for you, Lady Kirby,' I said, forcing myself to speak evenly. 'The party says it's important.'

'Oh, all right, Charles. I'll take it.'

I made the connection and for the first time since I'd taken the job, I wished I had never got into the habit of listening in on the conversations.

'Lady Kirby?' said the woman.

'Yes. Who is this?'

'I'd like to speak to Anne.'

There was a brief pause and then Lady Kirby said, half-angrily, 'I'm sorry but my daughter is asleep. It's her engagement party tomorrow and I don't intend to wake her at this time of the morning. If it's important you can tell me and I'll see she gets the message first thing tomorrow.'

'No.' The woman was adamant. 'This is something strictly between Anne and myself. It's vitally important I speak to her now.'

[263]

There was a much longer pause this time. I could visualize Lady Kirby standing at the phone, asking herself who could possibly be phoning at that hour and what was so important she had to waken Anne to hear it.

'Very well,' she said finally. 'I'll put you through to the extension.'

I sat quite still in my chair, totally enmeshed in an atmosphere of rising terror. For more than a minute there had been a nagging thought at the back of my mind, something about the other woman's voice which touched my nerves with an icy finger. Now I recognized what it was. It was oddly faint and far away as if the owner's lips were some distance from the mouthpiece of the phone. But it was undeniably Anne's voice. Yet how could that possibly be?

I tried desperately to suppress the shivers that went through me as I sat there in the dim light, struggling to find a logical answer to what was happening.

Then Anne Kirby's sleepy voice came on the other end of the line. 'Who is that?'

For a second there was silence. It was then that something very terrible happened. There is a point when human credulity is stretched to its maximum limit and what happens afterwards cannot be explained in any rational manner.

There came a faint, evil chuckle that made me grip the edge of the switchboard in white-knuckled hands and brought a cold, clammy sweat out afresh on my body.

Then the sibilant, whispering voice came again cutting through the silence. 'You don't know who I am, Anne. But I know you. I've known everything about you ever since you were born. For twenty years you've had what was rightfully mine. But not any longer. You thought this was to be your best and happiest Christmas ever. But I'm here now and I'm coming to claim what's mine.'

'What are you talking about?' Obviously jerked out of her sleep and quite possibly just as frightened as I was, Anne's voice suddenly lifted slightly in pitch. 'I don't know what you're talking about and if this is a joke, it's in very poor taste.'

'It's no joke, Anne. I just wanted to tell you that I'm coming. It won't be long now.'

There was a sharp click and the line went dead. I heard Anne calling frenziedly on the Manor end of the line and cut in quickly.

'This is Charles at the exchange, Miss Kirby. The caller has rung off.' I knew my voice was quavering but there was nothing I could do to control it.

'Who was that, Charles?' Anne sounded really scared.

'I'm afraid I don't know. She didn't give any name.'

I heard Anne's quick gasp of breath. Then she said, 'Do you know where she was calling from?'

'Just a minute,' I said. I lifted my head and glanced along the rows of connections, picking out the one which had glowed red a few moments before. Even before I checked it, I knew which it had been.

Before I could stop the words, they came tumbling from my lips. 'It came from the call box just along the lane leading to the Manor.'

'I see,' she said in a strangely hushed tone. 'Thank you.'

After the line had gone dead, I sat shivering in a web of numbed horror. I felt terrified. There was no other word to describe my emotional state. I was wholly convinced my fears were founded on some hideous reality which I could not understand. For as I had listened to that hateful, whispering voice, a mental picture of that white shape drifting along the narrow, empty street towards the Manor kept popping into my mind and I knew, without any shadow of doubt, that something unutterably evil had come into the village.

Several minutes passed with just the wild thumping of my heart and the loud ticking of the wall clock breaking the unbearable stillness. Just when the wild idea came into my mind it was impossible to tell. At first, I rejected it utterly because it seemed too absurd, too fantastic, even to contemplate. But it refused to go away and the more I thought about it, the more I knew I had to pursue it.

I rang Doctor Morton. He answered almost at once and I knew from his voice he had not been asleep.

'Doctor. This is Charles at the switchboard.'

'Oh, hello Charles,' he said genially. 'What's wrong? Getting lonely out there and wanting someone to talk to for a while?'

'I only wish it was just that, Doc. But something's happened tonight and I need your help.'

'Fire away then.'

As best I could, I told him all that had happened, starting with the frightened motorist and finishing with the conversation I had just overheard. I half expected him to suggest I had imagined most of it and was making a mountain out of a molehill. But he remained silent for several moments.

Then he said quietly, 'You're absolutely certain of all this, Charles?'

'Do you honestly think I could make up a story like that if it wasn't the truth?'

'No, I reckon not. And I think there must be some reason why you rang me. Do you have some theory as to what's going on?'

'God, I'm not sure. It's just a funny idea that came to me and I had to talk to you about it. Now it all seems so utterly insane I don't know how to put it into words.'

'Let's have it, Charles. What's on your mind?'

I hesitated. I knew I was still shaking and the silence in the room had grown more oppressive, charged with evil.

'I was just thinking, Doc. You delivered Anne Kirby twenty years ago, didn't you?'

'Yes.'

'Tell me; was Anne an only child or . . . or was there a twin born?'

There—it was out now and I expected him to laugh at me. But he didn't.

Instead, he said softly, 'Yes, there was. Another baby girl was born first. But she died within half an hour. There was never any chance of her surviving and both Sir John and Lady Kirby begged me not to breathe a word of it to a single soul. Not even Anne knows.'

'Oh, my God!' Seized with a great loathing and sense of horror, I struggled desperately to keep a tight rein on my whirling thoughts. I didn't want to acknowledge the ideas that were coming, unbidden, into my mind. The thought of that white figure moving with an evil purpose along that lonely country road where the cemetery lay, past Deepdale Farm and through the village, and on up to the Manor, was something I found difficult to accept. But, quite suddenly, it was impossible not to believe that something foul and corrupt had walked through the snow on this Christmas Eve.

Morton's voice snapped my thoughts back to the present. 'Listen, Charles. We've got to get to the bottom of this. It's just possible it's a hoax although I doubt it. But until we're certain of what we're dealing with I don't want to unduly worry anyone at the Manor. You understand?'

'Of course. But what can we do?'

'There's only one thing to do. I'm going out to the cemetery to take a look at that grave for myself. Depending on what I find there I'll phone you from the call box along the road. It'll probably take me about an hour. Just sit tight and wait for my call.'

'Don't you think it would be better to wait until morning, when it's light?' I said harshly.

'No. This is something that has to be done right away. If we're right, there's something evil and grotesque abroad and the sooner we know about it, the better.'

I knew from the tone of his voice how he felt and that nothing I could say would deter him. 'All right, Doc. I'll be here waiting.'

I wanted to add a warning to him to be careful. But he rang off before I could say anything further.

There was nothing for me to do then but wait for his call. I knew it was going to be the longest hour of my life. I made myself more coffee and drank it standing in front of the window.

There was a solitary light shining in one of the windows of the Manor. But it went out as I watched and then there was only the bright moonlight and a multitude of moving, flitting shadows. The stars were jewel-hard in the frosty heavens. Down below, in the street, the snow was criss-crossed with tyre marks and footprints. But everywhere else it lay deep and unsullied.

I tried to picture the doctor making his way along that lonely moonlit road, parking his car near the cemetery gates and walking inside to where the headstones jutted out of the snow-covered earth like rows of gaping teeth. But the mental image refused to come. Instead, I saw only that moving white shape drifting through the moonlight on an errand of horror.

I smoked one cigarette after another, something I had never done before, feeling the tension mounting inside me like a coiled spring growing tighter with every passing second. In my mentally confused state it was difficult to assess what frightened me most; what was happening at the Manor, or what Doctor Morton might find among those shadowy tombstones at the cemetery.

When the buzzer sounded on the switchboard, I almost jumped clean out of my skin. Even though I had been expecting the call, it still took a supreme effort of will to answer it.

'Charles, is that you?'

'Yes. What have you found?' I could tell at once by the curious quaver and timbre of his voice, even though it sounded oddly distorted over the line, that something terrible had happened.

'It's horrible, Charles. Truly horrible. I've run here all the way from that accursed spot in the cemetery. The grave . . . all dug up and opened. *But from the inside!*'

He was shouting the words, trying desperately to get them out. He must have known that what he had discovered made no sense as far as this sane, everyday world was concerned.

I must have hesitated for quite a long while although I was scarcely aware of it.

Then I picked out his voice again. But this time it was much fainter and the words seemed oddly slurred. 'Charles. I think I'm . . . get an ambulance. Please hurry.'

'Doc! What is it?' I was yelling myself now, thoroughly alarmed.

There was no answer although the phone had not been replaced. Almost without thinking, I broke the connection and dialled for an ambulance and doctor from Exeter, giving them the necessary directions.

It was some hours later, just as dawn was breaking, that I learned what the ambulance man had found. Doctor Morton's body was in the phone box with the phone still off the hook. He had obviously died of a heart attack brought on by the exertion of running more than a quarter of a mile from the cemetery.

With Morton dead, I knew no one would believe my story. The opened grave would be considered nothing more than an act of deliberate vandalism. Nobody in authority would even consider the near impossibility of digging through the iron-hard ground. But that explanation would be much more acceptable than what I knew to be the truth.

It was dreadful to think that such a nightmare-spawned horror as that which came to Redforde on Christmas Eve should be allowed to exist, unguessed by everyone but myself.

Accordingly, that crisp, clear Christmas morning, I left my home and walked through the deep snow to the Manor. Significantly the only tracks visible along that narrow lane were my own.

When Anne Kirby came to the door she looked exactly the same as the girl I had known all her life—except for the eyes. Cold and evil, they stared directly at me and I felt a sharp chill of fear and utter revulsion, for I knew it was not Anne who stood there and that she knew I was aware of her true identity. Which is why I took out my old revolver and put a bullet through that monster's head.

Ironically, it was the best Christmas present I could give to Anne Kirby.

THE DELIVERER

by Simon MacCulloch

Simon MacCulloch (b. 1960) is a civil servant
who has recently applied his life-long interest in
supernatural fiction to the writing of tales of dark
fantasy. He is a regular contributor to the British
Fantasy Newsletter, and his non-fiction work has also
appeared in the genre magazines Fear and Dagon.

'And that concludes this morning's service.' These words, uttered in the Reverend Piper's customarily soft yet somehow vibrant rasp, emerged raw and steaming into the chill air of the little church. To Tim, at seven years old the youngest member of the sparse congregation, they were the most welcome he had heard that morning. It was unlikely that he was alone in this, for the Vicar was not popular among the inhabitants of the village in which he had taken up residence less than a year before. He lived alone, having dispensed with the services of the housekeeper, a fiercely voluble widow by the name of Mrs Atterby, with quite remarkable ease shortly after his arrival. He took no part in the village's admittedly limited social life; if he was seen at all on weekdays it would be only on a visit to the butcher or greengrocer, where those who served him proved notably unsuccessful in drawing him into conversation. It was hardly surprising that attendance at the church, patchy at the best of times, had dwindled. The combination of the Vicar's aloofness with a predilection in his homilies for esoteric topics, abstruse arguments and dubious conclusions had seriously eroded what little loyalty to the Sabbath tradition had existed among his spiritual charges. By Christmas, it was generally predicted, he would perform his offices alone.

Yet interest in the Reverend Piper himself had increased even as the attraction of his liturgies diminished. Thus it was that, when Tim and his elder brother Robert were released after that Sunday's lunch from the confines of their terraced cottage in the upper part of the village into silvery ineffectual late autumn sunshine, their talk and their footsteps turned simultaneously towards the church again.

'Mum's decided we're not going to church any more,' declared Robert.

'Why?'

' 's obvious. She doesn't like the Vicar, and Dad doesn't neither. No-one can stand him. He's so boring. Ol' Thomas used to come round visiting all the time. And he had that tea party in the summer. Piper just doesn't do *anything*. And the way he always *stares* at you . . .'

'But what does he *do* all the time?' prompted Tim.

'Don't know. P'rhaps he just sits and reads books. Must be really boring. I'll bet that's why he goes on so much on Sunday mornings. He just reads all these books all week and *gurgitates* them.'

'Ol' Mrs Atterby sneaked back into the vicarage, didn't she, with her spare key. And Piper scared her off. She said . . .'

'That silly ol' baggage is scared of her own shadow. I'll bet ol' Thomas didn't really like her either. I'll bet he was glad to get away from her.'

'Why'd he have to go, anyway?'

'Cause the Bishop told him to of course, dummy.'

'Why?'

'Stop asking stupid questions.'

Tim contented himself with contemplation of the view from the end of a row of cottages at a sharp bend in the lane. From here he could look down over the major part of the village, a small grid of one- and two-storeyed grey stone terraces that looked as if it had been assembled elsewhere and dropped in one piece on the side of the valley it occupied. He could see the slate-roofed schoolhouse perched halfway up, wearing its weekend aspect of dormant foreboding. Moorland and white sky above made everything seem puny.

Soon the two boys had reached the place where the church, a building remarkable for its lack of interesting architectural features, squatted despondently on the valley floor. The sides of the valley outreached the stub of a tower with indifferent ease, excluding most of the daylight long before evening. But the glass of the windows was stained only with dust, enabling Tim and Robert to peer into the dim interior when they had scrambled up to a flaky stone sill.

They had doubtless expected no more than the fleeting satisfaction that a valedictory survey of a place of former incarceration may yield. It was with surprised delight that they discerned the tall, dark-clad figure of the Reverend Piper before the altar-stone, which was situated on a small platform at the end of the church farthest from their vantage point.

'What's he doing?' asked Tim, whispering although there seemed little likelihood of their being heard from within the church.

'Don't know.' Robert's voice was uncomfortably strident in its determination not to whisper. He licked his fingers and began to rub dirt from the window. Tim strained to see through the clear patch with him. The Vicar was addressing the deserted nave as if in continuation of the morning's service, although they could not tell whether or not he was speaking. His form was indistinct in the murk. Tim squinted in an attempt to distinguish the movement of lips. The Vicar's head bent forward as if to look upon an invisible congregation. But Tim saw only featureless black where the staring eyes should have been. The blind head lacked even a mouth with which to pronounce its cryptic discourse.

Tim cried out and tugged at his brother's arm. Robert stared uncomprehendingly at him for a moment, then glanced once more towards the figure in front of the altar. When he turned back to Tim there was a certain familiar glint in his eyes, one which promised an interlude of prolonged and merciless teasing.

'He's standing with his back to you, stupid! You *stupid* idiot. "Where's his face gone?"' (This last with devastatingly accurate mimicry.) 'Can't you see what he's doing? I don't know how someone of your age can be so stupid . . .' And so forth. When Tim looked at the altar again he saw that, rather than facing the body of the church as he had supposed, the Vicar had his back turned to the dusty pews and was gazing into what appeared to be a full-length mirror, mounted where the lectern was usually placed. It was impossible to see what the mirror was reflecting, but it appeared from the man's stance before it and occasional movement of the hands and arms that he must be practising the delivery of a sermon. This amusing inference was confirmed for the boys when, presumably as a result of the Vicar's rising enthusiasm for his text, they began to catch brief phrases and, shortly, what sounded like whole sentences, echoing strangely and disjointedly in the emptiness within.

'What language is that he's talking?'

'Must be Latin. They used to talk that all the time in church.'

'How can he give his sermon in Latin, stupid,' retorted Tim, trying by his scornful tone to regain some lost dignity. 'It doesn't sound anything like Latin to me.'

'Well, I don't know. Who cares?' Robert's lack of a knowledgeable rejoinder was the signal for the end of the conversation, and of their inconclusive eavesdropping. The pair slipped off their ledge and began to dawdle homeward. Tim wanted to mention that his final glimpse of the Reverend Piper had caught him in the act of kneeling down before his mirror, but as Robert's scathing commentary upon the Man With No Face incident extended itself he began to wish the subject closed, so held his peace.

It must have been about the beginning of Advent that services at the Reverend Piper's church ceased, although no-one could be certain about this afterwards. The few in whom force of habit had proved equal to the increasingly bitter weather did not protest very strongly when they found the church door locked one Sunday morning, and as far as anyone knew it remained so until the following summer, when the building was reopened and reconsecrated by a new minister. That the vicarage was still inhabited was evident only from the fact that the groceries, which were by then being delivered to its door, continued to be paid for and, presumably, consumed. The local doctor had earlier exerted his strength of personality long enough to confirm that the Vicar was probably not ill, although undoubtedly very rude, and the village settled down thereafter to a seasonal feast of speculation.

If the various hypotheses that were aired in adult circles were improbable, their translation to the realm of juvenile theorization rendered them entirely fantastic. An eyewitness report of the arrival by van at the vicarage during the preceding summer of some unidentifiable item of furniture came to be viewed by Robert and certain of his acquaintances as the most trifling in an endless series of clandestine deliveries, and the incontrovertible evidence of the Vicar's involvement in criminal activities on the grandest scale imaginable. Schemes were devised whereby unlawful entry to the church or the vicarage might be obtained, and the Reverend Piper's booty brought to light by heroically public-spirited investigators. This would all be of little interest, save that one of the proposed methods of secret ingress to the church turned out to be feasible, and Tim felt that his status among his peers had yet to recover from the blow dealt it by his brother's widespread publication of the earlier adventure and Tim's less than impressive contribution to it. Even so, it seems unlikely that matters would have progressed as they did had not Tim committed another embarrassing indiscretion by letting slip to Robert something of his long-standing ambition to 'stay awake and see Santa Claus' on Christmas Eve. Perhaps it was the added humiliation resulting from this that finally propelled Tim in the direction of the church again and, more specifically, towards a broken window in the vestry that the boys had noted on a previous expedition.

It was with a sense of unreality that Tim found himself crouching alone on the stone floor of the deserted vestry to recover his breath, the window having proved unexpectedly amenable to his half-hearted attempt to open it. It was not quite full night outside, and once he could identify the furnishings of the meagre antechamber with reasonable confidence, he forced himself to move towards its door to commence the brief circumnavigation of the building that he intended should restore his prestige among his schoolfellows.

The vestry door opened into the chancel behind the altar. The scuff of Tim's shoes was amplified as he stepped out into the larger space. The interior of the church had expanded since he had last been there, its sides visible solely on account of the dead grey oblongs of the windows, its roof a vault of darkness that sucked echoes from the slightest sound. Tim became conscious of his breathing, of the faint rustling of his clothes. It seemed as if even the contact of his eyelashes each time he blinked must be audible in the depthless hush. But the gaunt, cloaked figure that waited by the altar-stone made no sound at all, and Tim was almost upon it before he saw it. Terror held him immobile just long enough to enable him to recognize the oval outline of the Reverend Piper's mirror, now covered with a dust sheet. He turned away from it hastily and began to pace stiffly down the centre aisle, determined to go at least as far as the main door at its other end before the inclination to flee from the whispering shadows became irresistible.

He had almost reached his destination when something slithered behind him. He turned. Disturbed, presumably, by a draught from the open window in the vestry, the sheet that had veiled the mirror now lay in a heap at its base. The mirror's frame held only a clot of thick darkness. Tim's nerve had all but gone. He began the walk back to the altar, this being the sole route by which he could regain the vestry door; only his reluctance to pass by the mirror again prevented him from running. The echoes of his footsteps became louder than ever, and the aisle now seemed like a long dim tunnel, with the mirror forming a patch of inky black instead of light at its end. As he drew nearer, the patch took on a dull sheen and he began to make out his dark twin emerging from the oily deep of its own tunnel. He was still trying to recognize his own features on the rapidly distending silhouette when his foot struck the first of the steps leading up to the altar, and he began to topple forward. One knee cracked painfully against the third step up, but then he had regained his balance and was running for the door, overwhelmed by panic. Half a minute later he was out of the church.

He told no-one of the incident. Indeed, he found difficulty in remembering afterwards exactly what had happened. His breathless race home proved sufficient to relegate to his sub-conscious the realization that, as he had raised himself from his involuntary genuflection before the abandoned altar-stone, the echo of his footsteps had continued with purposeful regularity, and the shadow in the mirror had not stopped growing.

The expected snow did not come that year, although the sky looked heavy with it, and perhaps it was this that produced a sense of imminence in the village during the fortnight preceding Christmas. Such an atmosphere was unusual, for the villagers never displayed much fervour in their celebration of the midwinter festival, anticipation of the event usually being confined to the youngest among them, for whom the promise of midnight-delivered bounty still held magic. Otherwise the season was marked by the odd sprig of holly on doors that closed earlier than usual, or a candle faint behind a window's winter grime, and each slow dawn found the streets as uninviting as the frostbound fields beyond, and as desolate.

The school holiday began a week before Christmas. The light was already poor when Robert made his typically erratic way home on the last day of term, so he had scarcely noticed the hunched shape that waited in a doorway, its face engulfed in a dark shawl, before it stepped forward to block his path. It was Mrs Atterby, who it seemed had observed Robert in the vicinity of the church (over which she still liked to 'keep watch', as she put it) and was intent upon the dispensation of appropriate admonitions. Familiar as he was with the format of such reprimands, Robert could not help noticing as he waited for the old woman to finish that hers contained an element of the uncommon. References to 'the book' and 'the arched portal' occurred frequently, intermingled with phrases such as 'the word made flesh and the flesh made word', 'the black despoiler', and 'the tenth plague of Egypt'. The Biblical overtones were vaguely apparent to Robert; perhaps it was the fog that puffed from Mrs Atterby's lips that shrouded their sense. Her disapproval of the new Vicar was the most clearly expressed part of her monologue—'Ought to have defrocked him, but they said they didn't have the evidence. They knew what they were doing, be certain of that!' She ended by exhorting Robert to 'flee to the hills lest you be consumed'. Her arthritic fingers clawed the air in what might have been meant as a blessing before she retreated, wheezing, to her doorway.

It was not until late in the afternoon of Christmas Eve that Robert saw Mrs Atterby again. He poised himself to evade her, but her attention was concentrated upon the application to her front door of some late decoration, and his backward glance at the end of the lane found her still groping at her task as the darkness of the valley overflowed its sides and seeped into the sky.

The moon that rose on Christmas night brought stillness to the air. Tim had lain wide-eyed in his bed for hours, awaiting the time when he could be sure that Robert, with whom he shared the room, was asleep, so as to take up his vigil at the window. His brother's derision had not swayed him from his purpose; he was determined that if he did not attain a conclusive sighting of the nocturnal benefactor of infant legend that Christmas it would be through no lack of will on his part. Soon after midnight he crept to the window, which overlooked the lane from the upper floor of the house. Softly he opened the curtains to the deep night. The world was empty, and shadows gaped everywhere like glimpses of the abyss.

After he had watched for half an hour or so, Tim perceived that one of these shadows was moving slowly towards the house and, as it passed through a pool of moonlight, he saw that it was a dark-cloaked figure trudging soundlessly up the lane. With a barely controlled sense of elation Tim noted the heavy sack that it dragged behind it over the cobblestones. At first he thought that the object of his now fervent scrutiny would pass by his home as it had the others in the terrace, but as it drew level with his window, it paused and raised its cowled head. Tim prepared to withdraw from view, for his parents had warned him of the effect that the discovery of spectators was said to have upon the good Saint's seasonal generosity. He delayed for another few seconds when he noticed that this personage had not yet turned its gaze upon the house. Instead, it continued to face straight ahead, the angle of its hood suggesting that it was listening for something, or perhaps sniffing the air. After another moment or so had passed, however, it began to turn around, and Tim retreated hastily to his bed.

There remained but one obstacle to the satisfaction of Tim's curiosity. He had begged his father to leave the front door unbolted that night, but had met with intransigent refusal and an assurance that locks were no hindrance to the visitor he expected. This was proven when, less than a minute later, he felt the rush of frigid air that signalled the opening of the door. Almost simultaneously, his straining ears detected the sound of a heavy tread upon the bottom step of the staircase. The sound ascended slowly but unfalteringly, counterpointed by the soft bumping of the sack as it was pulled up behind. There was a further accompaniment that Tim's imagination, which was at that time generating all manner of fascinating images, failed to account for in any way, although a moment's consideration might have suggested that it was the product of the damage which was being done to the wooden bannisters by the intruder's progress.

Similar damage was sustained by the panelling of the bedroom door during the brief period of fumbling that preceded the admission into Tim's room of something he could distinguish in outline only; his first irrational impression was not so much that someone had come in as that a part of his bedroom wall by the door had been removed instantaneously, leaving in its place a hole into nowhere. The creaking of floorboards that marked the shadow's advance to a point some three feet inside the room enabled Tim to discard this disconcerting notion quickly and turn to the question of the procedure the visitant would follow in accomplishing his purpose. This even yet remained a matter for conjecture, for he now stood utterly motionless, an indeterminate bulk in the darkness. As Tim stared in an effort to penetrate the seamless black of the figure's robes, so as to obtain some sign of its intent, the first cold drops of fear began to trickle through the warmth of his excitement. The perfect stillness with which the figure held its pose, its bowed head still concealed beneath the hood, seemed unnatural, although Tim could not quite grasp why. He knew only that he could not bear to look upon that disquieting spectacle for long, and was parting his lips to call to his brother, when the dark head lifted at last.

Tim's next conscious memory was of the awakening of Robert and his parents by his screams, by which time the stranger had quit their home. That the boy had suffered a nightmare was a theory swiftly disposed of when the gouged and splintered condition of the woodwork, where inexplicably powerful hands had clutched it exploratively, was noticed. There was also the lingering odour, a fleshy reek that reminded Robert of the butcher's shop on a hot afternoon. But Tim could tell them little of what had transpired, or of the source of the horror that was subsequently to invest his every sight or remembrance of an unlit room, a hooded figure, or a sack that bulged with an anonymous burden. That which had answered his unvoiced invitation had granted him only the briefest communion before passing on to the fulfilment of its mission elsewhere. But in dreams to come, the dark bud of that moment would unfold, and in a world composed of shadow and crooked moon-washed lanes he would alternately run from or kneel before some ancient creature of the void, whose eyes glowed like hot cinders in the smoky pit where its face should have been, lit by the furnace of its eternal hunger.

The Reverend Piper's corpse was found in his church on Boxing Day. Of the myriad rumours that swarmed about this discovery, one of the more fanciful suggested that the intricate patterns that he had carved into his own flesh with a paper-knife were characters in an unknown language. What was eventually established was that he had bled to death from these wounds shortly before sunset on Christmas Eve. It was probably only this fact that caused the villagers to hesitate in attributing to the insane Vicar the kidnap of six children, all under the age of two, from their homes in the village between nightfall on the 24th of December and daybreak on the 25th. The largest police operation that the district had ever seen failed to trace the babies' bodies, much less any clue as to the whereabouts or motive of the perpetrator, the signs of whose passage through his victims' homes were as baffling as they were abundant.

The case was still 'under investigation' on the first anniversary of the tragedy, but by then the villagers had given up hope of its being solved by the authorities. Perhaps the red painted crosses that began to appear that next December on the doors of the village, doubtless following the example of Mrs Atterby, were a commemorative gesture. The new Vicar, at least, was happy to regard them as such, and to tolerate what he sometimes described to himself as an undercurrent of superstition, which happily did not seem to impede the rebirth of orthodox religious observance following his arrival in the parish. An upsurge of faith was, he knew, to be expected after a calamity of the type that had stricken these simple people, and he regarded himself as rather privileged to be in many ways the focus of their reawakened piety. Of course, there was the decidedly unpleasant business of his predecessor's history to be lived with; fortunately, the Church authorities had been most thorough in their removal of the deceased's effects, including the antique mirror in which it was said the madman had contrived to view his bizarre self-immolation. Even the vicarage's stock of books—'library' would be far too generous a term—had been rigorously weeded of any suspected to have been added during the previous eighteen months. The newly reappointed housekeeper, an efficient if overly talkative soul, was of the opinion that these items 'ought to have been buried with him', and for all that his successor cared they could have been; but the old woman had concluded with a sigh that 'they won't want to get rid of them, though; mayhap they'll find further use for them yet', and he supposed that this was fair enough also.

THE NIGHT BEFORE
CHRISTMAS
by Roger Johnson

Roger Johnson (b. 1947) is renowned
for his horror tales in the classic tradition of the
English ghost story. Most of them are set in his
native Essex. He is also a devoted admirer of the
Sherlock Holmes stories, and edits an invaluable
newsletter (*The District Messenger*) for
the Sherlock Holmes Society. 'The Night Before
Christmas' was specially written for this anthology.

'**G**od, how I hate Christmas!'
Hilary Falkner crushed out her cigarette and scowled.
This early in the evening the bar was almost empty. I
looked from her contemptuous expression to the harmless and discreet
Christmas tree that the landlord had placed near the fireplace. As she
continued, the thought occurred to me that Hilary Falkner wouldn't
be my choice for a companion on the last train home. Why on earth
had George Cobbett invited her along? Not out of pity, surely.

But the old man's face was quite expressionless as he watched her,
and listened to her complainings.

'All this fraudulent decoration! I mean, the garishness of it . . .
And always you have to spend Christmas Day with the bloody family!
And, dear God, the children! "I want this, I want that . . ." "What's
Father Christmas going to bring me this time? . . ." '

'Ah,' said George. 'Now we're coming to it. Father Christmas, eh?
Isn't he behind it all? That fat, jolly generous old spirit?'

Hilary's face relaxed suddenly, and she gave us a brief vulpine smile. In that instant I saw that, for all her sixty years and the initial impression of misanthropy, she was actually a very good-looking woman. She rubbed her chin with a rather masculine gesture. Then she sighed, and looked at George with calm eyes.

'You're right, of course,' she said. 'Though I'm blessed if I know how you knew. You're an artful old brute, George. Oh well, since we're all comfortable, I don't see any reason not to tell you. After all, the season's appropriate.' She shivered slightly.

I'll tell you (she said) about the worst Christmas I ever spent. And—damn you, George!—yes, it does have to do with Father Christmas. Not one that you'd wish to meet, believe me. 'A right jolly old elf?' Brrr!

When I was a child, my closest friend was a girl called Diana Calthrop. Diana and I were pretty much brought up together, because our families lived side by side, and our two birthdays fell within a fortnight of each other. She was a perfectly ordinary child, stolidly lower-middle-class, not unintelligent and not unattractive. What I'm trying to impress on you is that there was nothing at all unusual about her. Almost nothing. You see, she suffered from a recurring nightmare—and 'suffered' isn't too strong a word.

This dream—vision, or what you will—afflicted her perhaps three or four times a year, and for a day or so afterwards she would be in a truly pitiful state. It started, I think, some time before her third birthday. At least, it was then that she was, for the first time, able to be reasonably coherent about it. Her parents thought she was ill, and sent for the doctor. Those were the days when you could actually send for the doctor. He came, and he examined her—she shocked and silent all the while—and he could find nothing wrong. Nothing that he could put his finger on. He prescribed some sort of sedative, and sure enough, within a couple of days Diana was as right as could be.

Then it happened again, and since the cure had been so efficient the first time the doctor was summoned again, with the same result. The next time, she told me her parents began to suspect that she was shamming, especially as she seemed to recover quite satisfactorily without medical attention. But there was a next time, and a next, and it became pretty clear, even to the unimaginative Calthrops, that something really was wrong. But, as the doctor had said, it was nothing you could put your finger on. Still although the attacks (the right word, I think) occurred with erratic frequency, Diana always recovered within a few days. The worst after-effect was a sort of nervous melancholy.

Even then, you know, I wasn't sure that that was a good thing. It seems that every detail of the dream was forgotten within seconds of her waking, so that she had nothing tangible to tell her parents or the doctor—or to tell me, which, in the circumstances, she was rather more likely to do. All she could say was that she'd had 'that dream' again, and we would know what that meant. For me, it meant that there'd be an empty desk beside me at school, and that I mustn't call at the house next door and ask if Diana could come out to play. In time, as children do, I grew used to the situation, and so, I suppose, did she—to a degree, at least. But it wasn't a healthy situation. She was left with nothing to discuss, and nothing to exorcise.

Not healthy, and not pleasant, but the human child is a resilient creature. Somehow, Diana adjusted to these attacks. She came to expect them, and she knew just what effect they'd have on her and on her parents. Occasionally, she could even laugh about them, but it was a disconcerting and nervous kind of laughter.

She was still afraid, you see.

The climax—the first climax—came at the Christmas just after our fourteenth birthdays. Diana was growing up more quickly than I was. In the physical sense, at any rate. You could have taken her for a young woman of eighteen, whereas I was very much into the pigtails and puppy-fat stage. She was good-looking, too, with a sweet little heart-shaped face, framed by really glossy auburn hair. And her eyes were huge and clear. It was only the eyes, I think, that told you how young she really was.

Well, a small group of us had been invited away to spend Christmas at the house of a friend—not a very close friend—whose people were rather better off than ours were. There were the usual sort of tears from our mothers and warnings from our fathers, but I've a strong suspicion that they were all pretty glad to be shot of us. My own views on the family Christmas aren't by any means original.

The house was at Woodham Priors, not very far from Maldon. At the age of fourteen, and with the prospect of a lavish Christmas ahead, I didn't take very much notice of the building. It seemed very old, and was both glamorous and luxurious to us provincial girls. The bedrooms seemed enormous, and you can perhaps imagine the novelty of having a basin with running water actually in one's own room. If there was anything primitive about the arrangements, we either overlooked it or put it down to rustic charm.

The hall, where we ate and in fact spent much of our time, really was vast. The one wooden table would have been far too big for Diana's house or mine, but it left plenty of room here. I remember being just a little disappointed that there were no swords or shields or suits of armour; instead the walls bore only a dozen or so landscape paintings. Rather dull, I thought, but they couldn't detract from the magnificence of the room.

We arrived on the morning of the twenty-third. Some came by car, but Diana and I and a couple of others were collected from Witham station by our host's chauffeur. There were no fun and games on that first day; as we were told, suchlike frivolity belonged properly to Christmas Day itself. Still, there was a treat promised for Christmas Eve, and that was only a day away. In the meantime, we were put—in the most charming way—to earning our fun by helping to prepare the house. We hung decorations, gathered holly and mistletoe, brought home the Yule log, decked the great tree . . . I'd never enjoyed myself so much at Christmas.

The treat came after dinner on the following day, or rather, towards the end of the meal. We'd just started on our cocoa when there came a heavy knocking at the big front door. Our hostess said nothing as she got up to open it, but we could see that she was barely suppressing a grin of pure delight. The door was opened, and from behind it a resonant voice said:

'Open the door and let us in!
We hope your favours we shall win.
Whether we rise or whether we fall,
We'll do our best to please you all!'

One of the girls (I think she'd spent her childhood in Dorset) clapped her hands together and said, 'Why, it's the Mummers! I didn't know you had them here.'

We watched, fascinated, as a bulky figure stalked into the room, still chanting:

'A room, a room, a gallant room,
And give us room to rhyme!

We'll show you bold activity
Upon this Christmas time.'

From where we sat, Diana and I could see only one side of this extraordinary creature. He seemed to be completely enveloped in a vast dark green robe or gown, with a hood which shaded his face from us.

'Who is he?' Diana whispered, but I could only shrug and watch, as behind their leader there marched in a quite bizarre little troupe. First a tall man, very stern, dressed in old-fashioned military uniform and carrying a sword. He was followed directly by a slightly shorter man, whose uniform was black instead of red and who also carried a sword. Then came a little fellow wearing a countryman's smock and a battered hat. Behind him was thin man in frock coat and top hat, carrying a Gladstone bag. Finally came another small man in some sort of tunic and cap of red, holding, of all things, a soup-ladle in his hand. They were very grave, and they looked straight ahead of them as they entered, but we could see their faces clearly. The only face hidden from us was the leader's.

He walked slowly and deliberately to the centre of the hall, still chanting. There he halted, facing our host and hostess, pushed back his hood and bowed to them. The others grouped themselves on either side of him, three to the left and two to the right. The two men with the swords faced each other. As the big man straightened himself, I could see the back of a bald, pink head, rising from a fleecy mass of white hair. Then he turned to face us all.

His face was quite the jolliest thing I'd seen on that jolly day. The fat cheeks glowed red from the cold, the grey eyes twinkled like stars, the mouth held a half-smile, and the beard and moustache fully matched the woolly whiteness of the hair. They weren't false, either: there was a distinct yellow tinge to the hairs around the mouth, which told you that this old fellow was a cigar smoker. He began to speak again:

'In comes I, Old Father Christmas,
Welcome or welcome not.
I hope Old Father—'

There was a sudden, shocking scream from beside me. The deep, confident voice faltered and stopped, and all faces turned to Diana.

But Diana was no longer in her chair. As we looked, she slid like a rag doll to the floor. She was completely unconscious as our host carried her upstairs to the bedroom that the two of us shared. He made no fuss when I slipped away from the table to follow him, but allowed me to help in laying Diana comfortably on her bed. Below us, from an infinite distance, I could hear voices raised in declamation. The Mummers hadn't allowed this interruption to put them off for long.

'The poor kid's had a shock of some kind,' my host said, 'but I'm blessed if I can think what.' He turned to me. 'Did you notice anything that might have caused her to faint like this?'

He was a sensible man, and compassionate. I liked him for that, but I couldn't help him. I told him all I'd seen, and suggested feebly that my friend's distress must have been brought on by the sight of Old Father Christmas. He had already reached that conclusion, of course, but the idea still seemed pretty wild.

After a moment, he shrugged his shoulders and said, 'Well, we'll find out in time, I suppose. Meanwhile, there's the more urgent question of what to do with your friend. In other circumstances I'd be inclined to let her be and recover consciousness naturally, but— well—you've seen her face. You don't think, any more than I do, that this young woman is enjoying a peaceful sleep.'

It was true. The expression on Diana's pretty face wasn't at all a comfortable one.

The long and the short of it was that she had to be brought round, and this our host achieved in the gentlest way possible, by bathing her face with *eau de Cologne*. I was prepared, if necessary, to hold *sal volatile* under her nose, but it didn't come to that. Diana's eyelids fluttered briefly, and then her eyes suddenly opened wide. She took no more than a second to realise the situation. Her first words were, 'Whatever must you think of me?'

My quick embrace was enough, I think, to show how I felt. At that moment I must have looked a good deal less calm than my friend did. Our host kept his composure, but there was a distinctly quizzical look on his face. He peered intently at Diana, and then said, 'Don't worry about the rest of us. You did cause a bit of a disturbance, I'm afraid, but it can hardly be called a sensation. Do you mind talking about it? Only I'm rather curious to know what's behind it all. Something upset you pretty severely, and your friend and I (by the way, I'm afraid I don't know your name. Hilary? And you're Diana. Well, I'm glad to meet you both, though it's a rather odd meeting. I'm Richard. What was I saying? Oh, yes—) Hilary and I had reached the rather unlikely conclusion that your fit was brought on by the sight of Old Father Christmas.'

Diana swallowed hard and nodded. For the moment she said nothing.

'Just so,' he went on. 'Well, you'll agree that it does seem rather odd. Quite apart from the very unfrightening nature of the character, I'd have said that Uncle William was about the most amiable person I've ever met—and, what's more, he looks it. So, what's the story, eh? Do you know of something nasty about the old boy?'

Diana managed a very creditable smile. 'No,' she said firmly. 'I've never seen the old man before, and I know nothing about him. Probably he does look as nice as you say, but I'm afraid he put me in mind of something rather awful, so it wasn't your uncle I saw but— look here, do you really want to hear about it?'

Richard told her that he certainly did. I just nodded. I had a sudden notion of the truth, and I couldn't trust myself to speak.

Diana was very much more composed now, and looked quite like her old self. It was plain that she'd quite won over our host. She sat gracefully on the bed, with her legs curled under her, looking like a golden kitten. I perched myself on the other bed, while Richard sat in the one easy chair. Having politely asked permission, he lit a small cigar, using the metal waste-paper bin as an ashtray.

'Hilary knows as much of this as anyone,' said Diana. 'As much as I did myself until this evening. I know that sounds cryptic, but it will be explained, honestly. You see, ever since I can remember, I've suffered from nightmares, or rather, from a single nightmare that came again and again, several times during the year. Always it would leave me weak, nervous and frightened. And perhaps the worst part of it was that I couldn't afterwards remember a thing about the dream, except that it had terrified the wits out of me. I couldn't get rid of it, you see, because I didn't know what it was I wanted to get rid of. Do you see what I mean?'

He saw exactly, but, wisely, he said nothing.

'Well, now I know. In all that awful dreaming I've been haunted— menaced—threatened—by a man. A huge, bloated, grotesquely fat man, with a vast bald head and a long beard. The beard is thick and white, or light grey. And he looks at me with his little evil eyes, and there's a sort of dreadful confident humour in them—and he smiles. Always he smiles. He never says anything, but I know what he's telling me: "You're mine, all mine—and oh, what fun I'm going to have with you!" He picks me up, as if I was a doll, and he leers fatly at me, while his fingers are squeezing and caressing . . .' She broke off and shuddered, but she didn't cry, though I was sure I would have done.

'Nasty,' said Richard, at length. 'Very nasty. And though I'd hesitate to call Uncle William at all grotesque, it's plain now why the sight of him should have brought the dream back to you. You'll admit, I think, that the old boy looks just like the Ghost of Christmas Present. The dream, now: you say it's been with you since your childhood?'

'Yes, I told you. Ever since I can remember.'

'Odd that it should persist so. Can you remember anything else about the man? Has he changed at all over the years?'

'No. No, I don't think so. Though I have, of course.'

'Ah, he's followed you as you've grown up, eh? Well, I suppose that's to be expected, though I'm no psychologist. It does sound reasonable. Now, just one more question: do you connect the man in the dream with anyone you've seen or met?'

'No, not at all. Not even in a picture, otherwise I'd surely have remembered before. And really you know—' (She smiled charmingly at him.) '—your Uncle William doesn't look very much like the man in the dream. It's all—what's the word I want?—superficial. Besides—'

'Well?'

'Well, it's just that I'm not at all sure that the man in the dream is alive.'

There's not much more to tell about that Christmas. The three of us, I think, remained pretty thoughtful for a while, but it became clear that in remembering and recounting her strange dream Diana had at last managed to exorcise her bogey-man. She was soon her old self again, only more so, if you see what I mean. Bright, sweet and very happy. I was more than glad to fall in with her mood. We said very little to the others, and in any case they had more seasonal matters on their minds. Only Richard, who seemed to be a naturally reflective person, remained less than hysterically cheerful.

The holiday came to an end, as holidays must. I noticed that our host was particularly careful and particularly grown up in his goodbyes to Diana and me. On the one subject, at least, he seemed to regard us as equals, which I found very gratifying. It was something very unusual, in any case, to be on Christian name terms with the father of a school-friend. Diana's mood was still blessedly, quietly happy, but as he shook my hand Richard said discreetly, 'Keep an eye on that young woman. If she doesn't tell her people about the dream, then it's not up to you to do so. They sound like nice, ordinary folk, and I somehow think they're better off not knowing. You're a sensible lass, though. Just keep your eyes and ears open, and if anything happens that you don't like — anything connected with the dream, I mean — drop me a line.'

But nothing did happen, and for three years our only contact with him was a brief note on the Christmas cards that his daughter gave us. There was no repetition of the dream during all that time. Diana's parents suppressed their relief at first, but when six months had gone by and there were no disturbances their quiet pleasure was almost painfully evident. I continued to watch and listen, though Diana herself seemed quite unaware of it. It was almost as if the nightmare had never been, until at length she was even able to talk lightly about 'that funny dream' that she used to have.

Then came another Christmas, the one just after we turned eighteen. By now, of course, we'd both left school. Diana had got herself a good post as a private secretary, and I was training to be a teacher. Our circumstances at that age weren't especially desirable financially, so when we received a polite and friendly invitation to spend Christmas over at Woodham Priors we were both very pleased. The only qualms were over what our parents might say, but there proved to be no difficulty there. My mother, at any rate, had been hiding some slight disappointment that we'd not been invited back to stay with the girl she thought of as 'our rich friend', so she was quite as happy about it all as Diana and I were.

On the twenty-fourth of December we were met at the door of the house by Richard and his wife and daughter. The daughter — we hadn't seen her for something over a year — was like a stranger to us, though of course we all made the right social noises. Her mother was polite, pleasant and a touch absent-minded, but her father, Richard, didn't seem to have changed at all: he was as sympathetic and perceptive as ever.

Eventually the two women went off to see to something or other in the kitchen, and Richard said, 'I'm really very glad that you could come.'

Diana's smile just avoided being impudent as she asked: 'And was there a particular reason for asking us?'

His own smile, in answer, was very engaging. 'You mean, other than the fact that we rather like you? Yes, there was a reason. Two reasons. Firstly, I had an idle curiosity to find out what sort of young women you'd become. You've both turned out pretty well, you'll be pleased to hear.'

I caught a glance of amused naughtiness from Diana, and we curtsied in unison—but instead of laughing, Richard turned the joke back on us by gravely kissing our hands. Then we all laughed.

Richard's face became suddenly thoughtful, though, and he said, 'There was a second reason, you'll remember, for inviting you. The fact is that there's someone I'd like you to meet.'

There was a brief pause, and I said, 'Oh?', enquiringly.

'Yes. Someone you've both seen but haven't actually been introduced to. It's—well, it's my wife's uncle. Uncle William.'

I felt suddenly nervous, wondering if this was a wise move. The picture came into my mind of my friend's face, tortured and haunted, as it had been the one time she'd seen Uncle William. But it was soon dispelled by Diana's delighted exclamation, 'Oh, how marvellous! He helped me banish my nightmare, and I'd so love to meet him and thank him.'

I realised that Richard had been as delicately nervous as myself. His face, almost imperceptibly, relaxed, and he said, 'That's splendid. Now, I must tell you that the old fellow knows about your dream—which is more, by the bye, than my wife and daughter do. I thought it only fair to give him the story behind your rather dramatic behaviour when you were last here. You'll appreciate that he was just a little taken aback. He's not used to having young women faint at the sight of him.'

Uncle William was waiting for us in the smoking-room, though he wasn't actually smoking. There was a half-finished cigar in the ashtray, and his comfortable, bulky figure was fast asleep in the big armchair beside it. I fancy Richard was ready to wake him, but it wasn't necessary. As soon as the door clicked to behind us, the old man jerked, or rather bubbled, into consciousness.

'Bless me!' he said. And then, when he'd fished a pair of horn-rimmed glasses out of his breast-pocket and perched them rather dubiously on his small, round nose, 'Well, this is nice! The young feller warned me he was bringing the two gels here to see me, but I was expecting little things, you know. I didn't think they'd be such well set-up young wenches. Bless me!'

It was obvious why he'd been chosen to take the part of Father Christmas. His face and bald head glowed pinkly above the fleecy whiteness of his beard. His eyes, surrounded by a network of cheerful wrinkles, sparkled merrily. His belly shook in happy sympathy as he chuckled. Altogether, he was a man you couldn't help loving.

He made a move to stand up, but was politely and firmly pushed back by Richard. While the three of us got ourselves seated, Uncle William busied himself in relighting his cigar.

'Now,' he said, 'one of you's the nymph who had the bad dreams. Am I right?'

'You're right,' said Diana. 'I'm the—the nymph.'

He peered anxiously at her. 'Young Richard says you told him that the bogey-man in your nightmares looked a bit like me.'

'A bit.' She smiled, charmingly. 'But not very much. It's just that the man in the dream was—forgive me—fat and old, with a long white beard and a bald head. But he was huge; horribly, disgustingly obese, whereas you—'

He tapped his broad chest with a thick forefinger. 'Me?' he said, complacently. 'I'm fat. I know it, and I'm happy with it. But heaven help anyone who calls me obese! So he didn't look a lot like me, apart from certain obvious superficialities, eh? Well, that's a relief. I'd hate to think I'd caused distress to a nice looking wench like you.'

'You did, though,' I said, boldly. 'But it turned out for the best, because seeing you brought all the dream to the front of Diana's mind, so that she could see it and recognise it for what it was. It must have been a dreadful shock at the time, but since then she hasn't been troubled by it at all.'

'Shock therapy, eh? Well, I'm glad it all came out well.' For some reason he sounded just a little dubious.

Diana smiled happily. 'It certainly did, and I'm very grateful to you.' She darted a quick, mischievous glance at me, and then suddenly got up out of her chair, went over to the old man and kissed him on the top of his bald head. By the time the look of delighted surprise on his plump face had subsided into mere cheerful complacency, she was sitting demurely in her chair again. Richard was grinning broadly. I suspect I was, too.

Presently, I ventured a question: 'Uncle William—may we call you that?—why was it we didn't see you on Christmas Day that time?'

He waved a big hand dismissively. 'Ah, well, d'you see, it's because I wasn't here.'

'Not here? But—'

'No. It's quite simple. I was down here from my home in Worcester-shire, staying with my married daughter in Maldon, and I'd only called in here for the jollifications on Christmas Eve. When my son-in-law suggested reviving the old Mummers' play for the occasion, since there was to be a party of young gels here, I was pleased to join in. I've often been called on to play Father Christmas, but it was nice to have something more meaty than just saying "Ho ho ho!" and "Have you been a good little boy?" Anyway, as I say, I'd only popped over to Woodham Priors for those few hours. After that, it was back to Maldon, so that I could fight my way into the red gown and fill up the stockings for my grandchildren. We were kept pretty busy for the next couple of days, and then on the twenty-seventh I had to get off home. That's all there is to it. The past three years, the family's come over to Worcestershire to spend Christmas with me. This is the first time I've been here since you gave our little Mummers' play such an unexpected reception.'

Richard said, 'A while back, I gave the old man a full account of that little episode, including your description, Diana, of the nasty figure in your dream. It was then that he invited himself down here for this Christmas holiday.'

Uncle William scowled, but not very convincingly, and said, 'You know damned well that I've got an open invitation to stay here. Or maybe it's just my niece who likes to have me along? Ha! Very well then.' He turned his eyes back to Diana and me, and again that note of uncertainty crept into his voice. 'I had a reason for coming, d'you see, and between us Richard and I decided that it would be a good notion if you two young wenches were invited as well. The women of the house liked the idea, as I'd thought they would, so here we all are. I wanted to meet you both, of course, but there was more to it than that.

'Your description, my lass, of the incubus that haunted you since childhood put me in mind of something. The fact is, that an ancestor of mine fits that description pretty damn' closely. All right, I know: there must be quite a fair number of grossly fat old men about, even when you've discounted the ones who are clean-shaven or who have a full head of hair. However, they aren't all wicked old men, are they? And my great-uncle was that in spades. To put the cap on it all, he actually lived in this house. In fact, he had it built.'

'The house,' Richard explained, 'belongs to my wife. As the only child, she inherited it from her parents. It'll go to our daughter when she dies. I'm only here on sufferance.' He gave a short contented laugh.

'But it looks so old!' I said. 'Of course, we haven't had time to look at it properly today, but when we were here before I quite thought it must be Elizabethan.'

'Sorry to disappoint you. It was actually put up in about 1820. Of course, it was deliberately designed to look much older . . .'

'This wicked great-uncle,' said Diana. 'What was his name, and what did he do that was so wicked?'

'His name was Marcus Ridler,' said Uncle William. 'That's straight-forward enough. He was born in 1756. Yes, it shakes you a bit to think of that, eh? But his brother, my grandfather, who inherited when old Marcus died, was nearly forty years younger. To be strictly accurate, of course, they were half-brothers. Marcus died in 1839. Or rather, he disappeared then. The circumstances seem to be very vague, and frankly very muddy. There's no doubt that he'd got himself a really bad name in the area, and folks weren't too eagerly inclined to pry into the manner of his disappearance. Various reasons, no doubt. I rather fancy that they knew who was responsible and were inclined to praise and not condemn. The best way of praising, in the circumstances, was just to keep their mouths shut. Don't go asking me who might have done away with the old man, though, because I haven't any notion. It might have been any of several people. He'd made a powerful lot of enemies.'

'How, though?' I asked. 'What did he do?'

'Ha! Well, now we come to it. You'll notice I've been skirting around the subject rather. The fact is that it's pretty indelicate. I'm not especially worried about his being a relation of mine, because, after all, it was a long time ago, and he may have got his bad blood from his mother, so that it wouldn't have come down in our side of the family. I hope that's so. At any rate, we've all lived pretty blameless lives since his time.

'Basically, he was a satyr. I don't mean he had horns and hoofs, though they'd have been appropriate. Marcus Ridler was a lecher and a sadist. In fact, he read and approved of the Marquis de Sade's theses, and it seems clear enough from the accounts that survive that he did his best to put the madman's theories into practice. Everything about him, as far as I can tell, was perverted. He turned love into lust, authority into tyranny. His learning took him along paths of sheer vileness. And he rejoiced in inflicting pain. I'll spare you what I found written in one of my grandfather's letters about the things Marcus did to his mistress's pet spaniel. That's bad enough, but it wasn't only animals.

'Well, if Marcus was the bogey-man who tormented you, my dear, then I can only assume that at some time you must have heard of him, or seen a picture. At any rate, there's just one way I can think of to make sure whether it was Marcus Ridler who haunted you for all those years. Richard, my boy, I'm too old, too fat and too lazy to go dashing about the place, so will you be good enough to go up to my room and bring down my black dispatch-case? Thank you.'

Neither Diana nor I could bring ourselves to speak while our host was gone from the room, but I had a pretty strong notion of what was in that dispatch-case. Richard must have said something to his wife and daughter—though how he managed it without telling them anything explicit about Diana's nightmares was beyond me. At any rate, throughout the time we were closeted with Uncle William, we saw no sign of them.

Richard was back none too soon, carrying the dispatch-case. He handed it without a word to Uncle William, who unlocked it but didn't for the moment raise the lid.

'You'll have guessed,' he said, with more seriousness in his voice than I'd yet heard, 'that I've found a picture of Marcus Ridler. I knew there was one—in fact I'd seen it when I was a child, before I'd been told anything about him. I was too young and too trusting then to see beyond the humorous look on his fat old face, and my parents, bless 'em, would tell me only that he was the great-uncle who had built the big house. It was much later that I found out about his foul life and his doubtful end. I'd done my best over the years to put him out of my mind, but then Richard told me what you'd told him, and that brought it all flooding back. I was particularly struck, d'you see, by the coincidence: I mean, that it was in Marcus's own house that you'd remembered all the detail of your incubus. And since it was the sight of me that had sparked off that remembrance, well, I thought I owed it to us all to try and get to the heart of the matter. Now, my dear, would you rather you didn't see the picture?'

Diana's reply was emphatic: 'I want to see it. I want to know! You must understand that.'

He said, 'Just so,' and he opened the case and took out a small item wrapped in cotton-wool, which he peeled off to uncover a miniature in a gilt frame. He gazed at it for several seconds, shielding it from our eyes, before passing it across to Diana.

For a long, horrible moment Diana looked silently at the picture. Her face was white, and I could see a tic working at the left side of her mouth, but she said nothing. She'll scream, I thought. If she doesn't, I will! But she didn't scream, and she didn't faint. At last she closed her eyes and swallowed hard. Then she nodded.

'Yes,' she said. 'That's the man.'

Uncle William expelled a long breath, and harrumphed. 'Extraordinary!' he said. 'I hardly dared think it was, you know. One builds these fantastic explanations, not really believing . . .' He lapsed into silence while he lit a fresh cigar.

Diana's colour returned quickly to her cheeks, but her hand was shaking as she passed the picture to me. 'There,' she said. 'That's my bogey-man.'

The portrait looked like a cruel caricature of old Uncle William. The sitter was dressed in clothes of the early nineteenth century, and his bloated face leered at the viewer with a dreadful mock-benevolence.

'A nasty thing,' I said, with restraint, as I handed it to Richard.

Uncle William looked gloomily at us both for a short while, as if debating what to say. At last he decided. 'I'm sorry, my dear. Truly I am. I seem to be fated to distress you.'

'Cruel to be kind,' said Diana, smiling rather shakily. 'No, you're an old dear, and you've acted very sensibly. I won't deny that it's just a bit upsetting, but I'm glad to have seen the thing. God knows how that horrible face got itself into my dreams, but at least I know now that it was a real face, and a real person. Besides, you know, I've been quite free of the nightmare for four years now.'

The old man echoed her smile, but Richard remained grave. 'I can't help wondering,' he said, 'just how Marcus Ridler did find his way into your dream. You're quite sure that you'd never heard of him or seen his picture?'

'Quite sure. I was terribly young, remember, when I first had the dream, and if I'd seen anything as horrid as that then surely my parents must have seen it too. They'd have said something.'

'Um. Perhaps—but they knew as little as you did what it was that made your nights such a torture.' He shrugged his shoulders. 'Well, we'll just have to give it up as a mystery. It's all over now, and we've got a merry Christmas to look forward to. I'll call the womenfolk in and we'll break open a bottle. A good idea, I think. Let's drink to a happy reunion.'

Merry? Yes, I suppose we were, though the word suggests a touch of, well, rowdiness, which certainly wasn't present then. There were few belly-laughs, but lots of smiles and contented chuckles from old Uncle William. We were happy, which is better than being merry. It was the last time that I was truly happy at Christmas.

We went to bed—at least, the female members of the party did—not long after midnight, because we'd all agreed to attend the morning service at the parish church. Diana and I had separate rooms this time, but we sat up in my bedroom for quite a while chatting, before Diana said, 'Goodnight, dear, and have sweet dreams. I know I shall. The bad nights are gone now, and there are only the good times to look forward to.' She kissed me and left for her own room. Shortly afterwards I heard the two men talking in low voices and moving with exaggerated quietness along the corridor. Then I fell asleep.

I was awoken soon after six by a figure whose pale, drawn face I scarcely recognised as Richard's. 'Did you hear anything in the night?' he asked abruptly.

'No, I don't—I don't think so. I sleep pretty soundly. What's wrong? Richard, what is it?'

He came into the room and sat for a moment on the bed, taking one of my hands between his own. 'It's Diana,' he said, and I could see that he was forcing himself to be calm. 'She's gone from her room. Dear God, I wish I hadn't asked you to come here!' He peered anxiously at me. 'She doesn't walk in her sleep, does she? If it were only that . . . But I'm afraid, you see—I'm so afraid!'

'What? What are you afraid of?'

'I'm afraid that she's been taken.'

I shooed him out of the room while I hurried into my clothes. Then I went straight to Diana's room, where the four of them were. Our hostess was sitting in the easy chair, just looking dumbly at the floor, while her daughter knelt beside her, holding her hands. Richard and Uncle William stood over the bed; they were talking, and their voices sounded low and desperate. As soon as they saw me they stopped. Silently, the old man took my hand and gestured towards the bed.

The bedlinen seemed to have been roughly thrown or pulled off.

Diana's frock and stockings were strewn across the floor, and to me that was the most sinister touch, because I knew her to be the neatest person with her clothes.

'My wife was woken by some disturbance,' said Richard. 'It took some while before she thought that it might be coming from Diana's room or yours. When she came into the corridor she found the door of this room partly open. She looked in, and found things as you see them. I came as soon as she called me. By that time the other two were awake. I left the women with Uncle William and went to make a thorough search of the house. I looked into your room first of all, but you were clearly alone. There was no sign of Diana elsewhere, though, so I took the liberty of waking you on my way back.'

All sorts of mad and horrible pictures were before my mind's eye. My poor, sweet Diana! 'We must look again,' I said. 'This time I'll come with you.' I glanced at the two women, with their white faces and their inward-looking eyes, at Uncle William, who now suddenly looked very old. His plump features seemed to have fallen in; it was a terrible thing to see. These were good people, but right now they were quite useless. Only Richard and I could do what had to be done.

Until dawn came, we could search the house. That was all we could do, and we did it thoroughly. There was no sign of anything amiss— nothing that couldn't be put down to last night's merry-making. And there was nothing to be seen of Diana. The implications were terrifying.

Whe we got back upstairs, we found that Richard's wife had gone back to bed; her daughter had had the good sense to give her a sedative. Uncle William sat alone, an uncomprehending ruin of a man. We left him and went down to the hall, where the bright decorations seemed to me like a cruel joke.

At first light, we left the house and scouted the grounds. It wasn't long before Richard found traces of disturbance. It had rained at some time during the night, and in the mud of the stable-yard there were foot-prints that shouldn't have been there—large, deep prints. What they suggested so frightened me that I clung tightly to Richard's hand as we followed the trail. It was broken and erratic, and at one point there was horrible evidence of something being dragged along the ground, but it led inexorably to the stable block.

What we found there gave rise to a great deal of wild speculation in the area. Fortunately, perhaps, it never made the national press. As it was, dear old Uncle William was taken with a severe heart-attack from which he never fully recovered. He lingered for some months, but he was no more than an echo of his true self. The effect on me was less drastic, but more lasting.

Inside one of the stalls, the immense stone blocks that formed the floor had been flung aside and broken, while the thick-packed earth beneath was disturbed to a depth of about ten feet. The police, when they came, found the digging surprisingly easy. It wasn't long before they came upon the body of my poor friend. That, I suppose, was inevitable. What shocked them, but left Richard and me with only a sort of sick feeling of suspicions confirmed, was the other body.

It was, to be exact, the skeleton of an elderly man. The flesh was entirely gone, but there were fragments of clothing left, metal and bone. The skull had been crushed by a blow from something hard and heavy, and the bones of the legs and arms had been broken, probably before death. That was bad enough, but it was the injuries done to my poor friend's body that truly appalled me. They matched his in every respect. And his hands, dry, broken and bony, clasped hers possessively.

Hilary's hands were shaking so much that she couldn't hold her match steady to apply the flame to her cigarette. With bad grace, she accepted a light from me, and inhaled deeply. Her features relaxed as she expelled the smoke, and she looked at us with that unexpected sudden smile that quite altered the character of her face.

'Since that time,' she said, 'I've been the one to suffer nightmares.'

George peered at her with unusual sympathy. 'I expect,' he said gently, 'that the expression on your friend's dead face would be difficult to forget.'

She closed her eyes and drew at her cigarette again. 'You're right, of course,' she said. 'But it isn't that which haunts my nights. I see Diana, lying peacefully in her bed on Christmas Eve, waiting for Father Christmas, "that fat, jolly, generous old spirit"—and he comes to her, you see. He comes! And he's obscenely, grotesquely fat, and he leers down at her with lust in his wicked little eyes. He stretches out his huge hands . . .'

Hilary shuddered. 'Merry Christmas, everybody!' she said, and her smile was pure acid.

ON WINGS OF SONG

by *David G. Rowlands*

David G. Rowlands (b. 1943),
a biochemist by profession, is one of England's
most talented writers of horror and ghost stories.
He has had many excellent and original tales
published over the past twenty years, and is a
regular contributor to the *Holly Bough*, a Christmas
magazine published by the *Cork Examiner*.
'On Wings of Song' is a previously unpublished
Christmas tale, specially written for this anthology.

And lo, upon the ear comes light
That warning siren of the night . . .

I t was a hot June evening, humid and sticky, and I was sitting with my friend Patterson in the little summer house cum shed close by a wooden landing stage, where his garden banked the river. Midges were rising and dancing from the grass, and our companionable silence from within a protective fug of tobacco smoke was broken by the high-pitched whine of a mosquito. To my surprise Patterson looked uneasy, then startled, finally flapping with his paper at the offending insect.

'You don't need to worry,' I remarked jocularly, 'that's *Culex* and it seldom bites humans. *Anopheles* and *Theobaldia* are the ones to look out for: they do take man's blood, and they come silently: typical predatory females.'

Patterson smiled slightly and rather apologetically. 'Yes, I know that, but the keening of a mosquito in the dark has the most unpleasant associations for me.'

'Maybe you'd better tell me about it,' I suggested, 'and exorcise those associations.'

Patterson was silent awhile, his eyes fixed on the clouds of insects over the sluggishly-flowing water outside.

'Perhaps I will,' he said at last, 'but it requires some effort in setting the scene, for it happened one Christmas, when I was only a lad.'

'Sounds good,' I encouraged him. 'A nice Christmassy tale—very English and old country house stuff. But surely not mosquitos at Christmas? They go wherever it is the flies go . . ..'

'You won't take that flippant tone when you've heard the story, my friend,' he retorted, 'but anyway, you shall judge for yourself.'

We settled back in our chairs, and he began his tale as the light outside began to fail.

'You will remember the "Toytown" stories of Hulme-Beaman, I expect?' (I nodded) '—and the justly acclaimed adaptations for radio "Childrens Hour" narrated by "Uncle Mac", who was also Larry-the-Lamb; the wonderful fruity tones of Felix Felton, the Mayor, Ernest Jay, and others?' (I nodded again.) 'Then you'll also remember the original storybooks and the Toytown Theatre Royal, which supported a company of marionettes and presented regular plays. The most popular among these was "The Miller and his Men" with its dramatic concluding scenes of the explosion—so beloved of Montague Summers—plenty of red and green fire burned, and much penny gunpowder ignited.

'Despite its dated origins, this play was a favourite with my school-friend Christopher Wilson and I. Our Toy Theatre was not so grand as the Theatre Royal, for the actors were very much in the mould of what the Rev Summers called the *juvenilia dramatica*, cut from paper; and as well as the few printed cut-outs we could afford (and certainly not the Puffin Books "High Toby" at 3/6d!)—shades of the old "penny plain and two pence coloured" era, we adapted and abridged the plays for ourselves; designed the sets, drew and cut-out the characters, colouring them with "Junorite" inks. Ah, that brings it back; I can smell those inks now! Chris wrote most of the dialogue, and I wrote the music for the piano, or adapted (i.e. plagiarised) it from sheet music.

[298]

'I must echo the Rev Summers again, and make it clear that we took our productions seriously. They were prepared for the winter-time and during the four years our interest had developed, it had become a family custom to view our latest effort after tea on Christmas day.

'The previous year had been rather special. Chris's father, an excellent amateur carpenter, had taken our home-made cardboard edifice and stage (based on that at Windsor), and had converted it into the solidity of wood, with battery lighting, working curtains and even a safety screen of asbestos. My mother had made the curtains . . . all kept secret until the surprise was sprung. We were over the moon! Happily, we had a production worthy of the occasion with an abridged version of "Toad of Toad Hall", taking the characters from Shepard's much-loved illustrations, though my older sister, Moira, had quite a struggle with the key changes of the marvellous Fraser-Simpson music. It went down well, everyone joining in the choruses such as "A Walloping we will go" and "When the Toad came home"; nor will I forget the quiet charm of Chris's sister Jill singing the "Wind in the Willows" theme. What matters to my story, was that after this high-spot, we felt we were going to be hard pressed to better the achievement next year.

'Chris and I debated likely themes during the succeeding year, tossing ideas about, but being more engrossed in paddling our canoe, bug hunting, cycling and generally enjoying our respite from formal education in the spring and summer holidays.

'We were out on our bikes one day; zooming gleefully downhill, I remember, after a steep climb. Chris was leading, and he shouted back to me—his words gaining enthusiasm from the rush of air that carried them.

' "Here, what about doing a creepy thriller? Like *Dracula*?"

' "Huh, we don't know the story properly," I objected.

'However, Chris persisted with the idea and gradually I accepted it.

'The book was indeed present on Mr Wilson's shelves, but was not "permitted" reading. Naturally, because of this lukewarm veto, we had dipped into its pages; but had found it pretty boring. Recently however an enterprising publisher had latched on to the fact that whereas children would often not read the "classic" books supposed to be good for them, they would readily absorb them in strip cartoon form. So "Classics Illustrated" had appeared on the bookstalls, rather steeply priced for the late 1940s at one shilling, but with clever adaptations of the storylines and—important in avoiding parental censure

—well drawn characters. Most of the titles sold were from Scott, Dickens and Shakespeare, but lurking among the Alcott, Hodgson Burnett, Austen and Eliot, were *Treasure Island, Dr Jekyll & Mr Hyde, Frankenstein* and—yes, *Dracula*. This last we duly obtained and studied, though not without some financial difficulty. (The theatre has not changed!) The abridgement was good, and the pictorial format suggested some gripping scenes, and need for some ingenuity in creating effects of moonlight, wolves and bats flying. At least it was the right time of year for studying bat-flight at dusk.

'Indeed, we asked our local GP, Dr Edmonds, where to look for bats at rest (he was a noted local naturalist) and spent some time climbing around among the dangerous rotting timbers of the long-disused water mill nearby. We gained a lot of insect bites from the vicinity of the stagnant millpond, one of which gave me a skin infection and a sore ankle for a week, while Chris got a bad sore throat.

'While we were in agreement that bats made for a macabre effect, and had devised some shadowy lighting effects, ingeniously using heatwaves from a lit candle to give simulation of wavery movement to a silhouetted backdrop, Chris was not satisfied at representing The Count himself in bat form. Being an informed young naturalist, he wanted something that really did take blood at night in England, and since Stoker (or the mumbo-jumbo of vampire legend) allowed the undead to project themselves as flies or moths, he felt it was reasonable to depict The Count as a giant mosquito. This worked quite well for the flight scenes, but we had to assume some tucking away of extraneous legs and antennae when grounded and walking upright. Nevertheless, as a cardboard character it worked quite well. For as Chris scathingly remarked, the folklore is often pretty silly anyhow and when he retired to his coffin at day-break, floating in blood, the insect's waxy body would not become stained; since in the comic book pictures, the Count's invariable formal dress was spotless! I did point out that only *female* mosquitos sucked blood (males being vegetarian!) but was over-ruled. The sexual aspects of Stoker's yarn were definitely underplayed in the comic book version.

'Providing music was my headache. We had seen Disney's "Skeleton Dance" at a News Theatre (animated by Ub Iwerks, who later re-did it in colour for Columbia as "Skeleton Frolic") and I studied the sheet music in hope of inspiration. We listened to orchestrations of "Faust" and "Night on A Bare Mountain" on our wind-up gramophone; but in the end I was thrown back on my own resources (not helped by my sore ankle) in working out eerie chord sequences on the piano. My sister was not impressed with the MSS score she had to play.

'Chris had set up some splendidly macabre scenes, mostly back-lit and in silhouette and, as an original touch, where he had The Count floating in the air, or flying about his nefarious deeds in mosquito form, he was accompanied by an appropriate keening whine. True, it sounded more like an American Police Patrolman's motorbike siren than the furious expenditure of energy by *Culex*, but it was very effective as it skirled above the hushed chords of the piano, particularly when the mosquito-Count homed in on Lucy's bed in the darkened room. The sudden stopping of the whining note was ominously suggestive.

'During our rehearsals in the last few days up to Christmas though, I became aware that Chris had become unusually restless and irritable — downright snappy with the girls and abusive to me when we quarrelled over the staging or the repeating of some scene. However he was the Director/Producer and I put up with as much as I could, before exploding on Christmas Eve:

' "Look here, Chris! This is getting stupid. It's a play; we're supposed to enjoy it! If you keep on the way you are, we shall lose the girls' help with the music and dialogue; then we shall be sunk. It'd be a pity to have to do "Waterloo" again, on our own!"

' "Sorry, Pete," he muttered contritely. "You're right. I'll apologise to the girls. I feel so lousy . . . I hope I can hold out."

'He had perspiration standing out on his forehead. I felt his brow.
' "Crumbs, you idiot! You're feverish. You ought to be in bed."

' "After tomorrow," he said, "I'm taking Aspirin, that'll keep it at bay." And seemingly it did.

'It was our family custom to go round to the Wilsons for Xmas day (they returned the visit on New Year's Eve). Chris seemed a little het-up, but not off his food, and not unduly feverish. After tea, we settled down to the Toy Theatre presentation of "Dracula". Our mothers in particular were not too pleased at our choice of theme (always a closely-guarded secret), but it all went down well in the end, during the two 20 minute Acts. The dramatic sets and scenes were applauded, and the effects too; though it rankled slightly that no-one commented on the music (except adversely—Moira!).

'In the interval Chris confessed that he was feeling pretty ill again, but wanting to finish the performance before going to bed. I volunteered to do the clearing-up.

'Once it was all over, and the curtain down for the last time, Chris went off to bed. While packing away the boxes, I could hear his mother scolding him while taking his temperature, and dosing him with "Influenza Mixture".

'Back home again, I had a bit of supper (the inevitable lunch-time left-overs) and went to bed, eager to get down to reading one of a couple of the *Sanders of the River* books I had been given as a present. I read about Bosambo and the Ochori for a while, chuckled "O, Ko", to myself, then put out the light, crossing to the window and drawing back the curtain. It was most unseasonable. We had, as yet, no snow. The weather was rather mild and blustery-wet; not the stuff of jolly red faces, Ho-ho-ho, wassail and snowballing at all. I got back into bed, wondering how Chris was faring.

'Going to bed on a full stomach is never a good thing, and after the excitements of the day and the success of "Dracula", it was perhaps inevitable that I should dream.

'The part I remembered afterward was a darkened room in which I could hear the nagging whine of a mosquito flying around: quiet at first, but growing louder as the darned thing came closer. My eyes grew accustomed to the dark and I recognised Chris's room, and himself asleep in bed. He was tossing and turning, and muttering. All the while the mosquito buzz grew louder and a huge black shape with transparent wings settled lengthwise on the sleeping boy. The buzzing stopped. By this time I was shouting "Wake up, Chris! Wake up!", as the dream escalated rapidly into nightmare. The huge creature had sunk its proboscis into the boy's neck and part-turned huge bulbous eyes that glinted redly in my direction. I had seized Chris's canoe paddle and was about to try and drive off the intruder, when I woke up!

' "Phew," I thought. I was in a perfect bath of sweat, my pyjamas clinging uncomfortably to my body and my heart pounding with the horrid vividness of the dream. Normally when one awakes from a nightmare, the sense of fright remains, but the details fade; this just didn't happen. In my mind's eye I could still see the whole grisly tableau. I put on my light and looked at my wristwatch beside the bed . . . 1.30 am.

'With the ability to make snap decisions that comes so easily at eleven years of age, I pulled on some socks, tucking my pyjamas into them; then flannels and a jumper; finishing up with plimsoles. Quietly I opened my window. (Chris and I oiled hinges and catches regularly as we often used this mode of egress). It was an easy reach to the apple tree and down to the back garden. I dodged out of the gate—not without a wary look-about for red eyes!—and along the road to the Wilsons.

'It required a combination of ivy and downpipe to reach Chris's window ledge. I flashed my pocket torch through the latticed panes . . . his bed was empty, clothes turned about, and he . . . he was crawling away down the corridor. The toplight was open and I fished out the length of stout wire ending in a hook that we hung behind the rainwater spout. That dealt with the latch; the window swung open and I dropped silently inside. My light showed the boy crawling at the bend in the landing, making for his sister's room. I hissed out "Chris! What's the matter?" and at the turn of the corridor he looked back, his face distorted in pain. Now I was rather fond of Jill and didn't want him frightening her, so I lunged after him and we rolled down the three steps to his parents' landing. He was extremely hot, and wet with the sweat of fever; the flying torch also revealed red blotches on his neck and face. Our crash into the bedroom door roused the household.

'The immediate reaction was predictable for, as I said, it was not unknown for the pair of us to make illegal exits at night. However they quickly saw how ill the boy was.

'Poor Dr Edmonds was summoned from his bed and I hung about until he arrived; then an ambulance was ordered, and poor old Chris—accompanied by his mother—was rushed off to the Infirmary. "Encephalitis," his worried father said, "Inflammation of the brain." I was firmly packed off home: hopefully to get indoors the way I'd come, without disturbing anyone. This I managed, of course, but found it impossible to get back to sleep.

'So I sat up reading my Sanders and sucking a bullseye from a tin that Jill had given me. In the Ochori "pidgin" I read the words the sickness mongo . . . and "sleeping sickness" . . . fever, mosquitos.

'Coincidence, no doubt . . . but it linked up uncannily with my dream, and something had been wrong then, after all! I crept downstairs to find the Medical Dictionary, a venerable tome from the days when virology was a new science. Ah, there it was: "Encephalitis, commonly called inflammation of the brain", had many causes but—yes, that caused by viral infection of which the Mansonia mosquitos were vectors, was called African or Japanese Sleeping

[303]

sickness; the "singing" *Culex* mosquito was also a vector.

'I let myself out of the house again, and into the drizzly early dawn. What a Christmas, I thought! This is one I shall never forget.

'Dr Edmond's Surgery lamp was still glowing red and, as always, the Waiting Room door was open. A message that he had been called out and please to wait, or leave a message, was chalked on the wallboard.

'I sat there, tired and dispirited, thumbing listlessly through the *Picture Post* and *Illustrated* and *Punch*, until I heard his big Austin car in the drive. I ran out to meet him.

' "What's this? Still about, Peter?" he cried, "You are a bad lad."

' "How's Chris?" I blurted out.

'He shook his head wearily, "Very poorly, I'm afraid".

' "Has he got sleeping sickness?" I cried.

' "Here in England? Good heavens no! What on earth put that ide . . . a." His words ran down to a halt, and he looked sharply at me.

' "By George, Peter. Out of the mouths of babes and sucklings, eh? Supposing you are right; if it *is* a virus, then I've given him the wrong things—the drugs will not help him." He stopped, seeing my apprehension, and continued more briskly. "But there, he's a strong lad with a lot of reserves. He'll make it. Come in, now, and we'll have some hot tea, eh?"

'We sat in the kitchen, drinking tea and eating chocolate biscuits out of a tin.

' "What on earth made you think of sleeping sickness?", he asked. "It is certainly a form of encephalitis, but not the one I was thinking of."

'I told him about my dream, expecting him to laugh at it . . . but he didn't.

' "Well," he said, "I don't believe in your dream, but your notion of the mosquito as a vampire and spreader of disease is quite right, of course. But he could only get it from *Mansonia*, and it's not common over here. Why the only place I can think of is . . ."

' "The mill pond," I supplied, "where we went looking for bats."

' "Good Lord, yes," he said. "Well, I must phone the Infirmary. If your notion is right, he'll need constant watching. Cheer up." He clapped me on the shoulders. "He's a healthy youngster. He'll make it."

'It was a miserable Boxing Day for us all; and New Year.

'Because Dr Edmonds's confidence proved to be wrong. For a while Chris did hold his own, then—gradually—he began to sink, getting weaker and paler and bloodless. They gave him a transfusion at the end, but it did no good, and he died within three weeks, never leaving the Infirmary. It shattered me for months, and the effect on our two families was immense.

'Later that year, in the summer, Dr Edmonds took me for a walk. I was off to boarding school, and ostensibly the notion was to sound me out on the "Facts of Life"; but in truth, we talked of the fact of death, and of Chris. We walked by the Old Mill. The pond had been drained by the Public Health Authority months earlier, and the building itself fenced off and wired up.

' "When we did the *post mortem* on Chris," said the Doctor, "we found what at first we thought was a growth in his intestine; but it was a large hookworm, that had fastened there and had been draining his blood. The eggs of these things are carried by *Mansonia* as well as the viral encephalitis. I discussed it with Ross, and we worked out the incubation period for eggs in the bloodstream to be about four months. Just the time you boys were looking around here. How right your vampire notion proved to be! Not just the original bite and infection —for by the way, like the vampire of legend, *Mansonia* will return to the same source for blood meals until replete and ready to lay its own eggs; but in the parasite that grew within poor old Chris, feeding on his blood." He sighed, "I remember seeing the film 'Nosferatu' years ago, and the vampire there was presented as a purveyor of disease and pestilence as well as a lamprey of the life force. It was a chance in a million, but it was me who told you where to study the bat roosts for your play. I shall carry that knowledge for the rest of my life." '

It was dark now in the summer house, as Patterson rose to his feet.

'And so shall I,' he said. 'Now you know why I hate mosquitos and why Christmas has melancholy associations. Come on, let's get back to the house.'

THE SANTA

by Jessica Amanda Salmonson

Jessica Amanda Salmonson (b. 1950)
is one of the busiest writers in the new generation of
American horror writers, with many novels, short
stories and anthologies to her credit. These include
*The Swordswoman, Ou Lu Khen and the Beautiful
Madwoman, Tales By Moonlight,* and a definitive
edition of Fitzjames O'Brien's horror stories.

Michele lay clutching Clowny, her mush-faced cloth dolly in motley and jester's cap.

Her eyes shone with worry.

Mother looked into the room, face bright with happiness. What was mother's secret? Michele didn't know.

'You go to sleep now, honey,' said mother, hand hovering by the light switch. 'You don't want Santa to miss our house because you were wide awake, do you?'

'Uh-uh,' said Michele, though the truth was, she was afraid of the Santa. Anyone who could come down chimneys like that was scary.

Mother turned off the light.

'Kiss-kiss,' said mother, sounding far, far away.

Then she closed the door.

It was dark in the room, so dark. Snowflakes danced and whirled outside the window, capturing the light from the porch. Wind whistled underneath the eaves: Oooo. Woo-oooo. Michele drew the covers up around her chin, then Clowny's. Her big wide eyes looked all around but her head didn't move. 'It's okay, Clowny,' she whispered soothingly. 'You don't have to be afraid. I'll take care of you.'

Clowny smiled.

There was a scraping at the window and Michele gulped down a cry. She looked at the shining snowflakes against the frosty glass. 'Who— who's there?' said her sweet, piping, frightened voice. 'Santa?'

For a moment the snowflakes formed into the visage of a white-bearded man with fur-fringed red cap and bloodshot eyes.

Oooo. Woo-oooo.

The house became still within. The line of light at the bottom crack of her bedroom door disappeared. Mommy and daddy had gone to bed. For a while Michele could hear them whispering. Their whispering was strange and far off and full of some inconceivable conspiracy that must have involved Michele. Were they going to do something to her? What did they have planned?

After what felt like a long time, she threw the covers back. She was wearing a yellow nighty, yellow as her hair. She and Clowny crept toward the door. She reached upward, turned the knob, looked into the hall.

Green and red and yellow shadows blinked and moved and blended.

There was no one in the hall.

Her pink and naked feet trod softly through the corridor. Mommy's and daddy's bedroom door was slightly ajar. She heard daddy's snoring. She crept more stealthily and came into the living room.

The Christmas tree lights made the oriental carpet look like a living, moving serpent's skin. The blinking made strange, changing shapes upon the ceiling. Underneath the tree were plenty of boxes prettily wrapped. 'See that, Clowny?' she said. 'See that?'

Her foot stepped into something wet. She pulled her foot away and looked at the huge footprint on the oak floor between the carpets. There was another footprint, and another, leading from the fireplace to the tree and back again to the fireplace. Michele drew back into a shadow by the davenport. She said, 'I think he's gone now, Clowny. It's going to be all right.'

She crept toward the fireplace, holding her breath. She bent forward and craned her neck to look up into the dark cavity of the chimney.

She heard a faint crackling sound. A hard flake of soot dropped like a stone into the back of the fireplace, whispering through old ashes.

A scratch at the door made her whirl around, staring, shivering. The front door was panelled with little windows. She thought she saw the big black boot of an enormous man running away from the porch.

The falling snow obscured everything, though the porch light tried to light the driveway and the yard.

She stood beside the gaudy, aromatic tree looking at the boxes. Somehow the boxes were suggestive of horrible secrets. What was sealed in them? What waited underneath the seductive wrappers? She and Clowny approached the door and looked out through a panel of glass. 'See that, Clowny? See that? There's nothing to be afraid of. The Santa's nice.'

Out on the snow-covered lawn, so faint a silhouette it might have been the trick of a sensitive imagination, the enormous man in red and white and black costume was running back and forth, hopping, rolling in the snow, standing on his hands and doing amazing cartwheels.

Despite herself, Michele giggled.

The big bearded man stopped. He looked toward the house. From somewhere he materialized a large, limp bag. His finger invited Michele outside to play. The eaves were hallooing: woo-ooo-waaarm-innn-the-baaag.

'Do you want to, Clowny?' she asked, looking at the sweet, mushed, smiling face, then through the glass again. 'I don't know if we should. But do you want to?'

Now the fat Santa was running around in a circle, around and around, holding the floppy bag above his head, filling it with wind and snow.

Michele laughed. She reached for the door's lock, then the handle. She and Clowny stepped onto the snowy stoop. Behind her, the door closed quietly. She turned back and tried to get it open, for it was very cold outside. But the door was locked.

Ooo-wooo.

She looked upward at the eaves.

Something was still out there on the lawn, invisible on account of the whirling blizzard. It was the Santa. Full of doubt and hope and a sense of strangeness, Michele went barefoot through the snow, looking for the Santa. From the middle of the yard, she looked back, and saw the sparking, glittering Christmas tree aflame. The window curtains were burning.

She looked upward at the wooing roof and saw something round and eerie leaping from chimney to gable to dormer, then straight up.

In the early dawn the firemen quested glumly through the ashes. Michele they found by accident, stumbling over her body underneath the snow. Her blue legs and blue arms stuck out from her yellow nightdress. Her eyes were frozen open and her face was pressed close to a ragged clownish doll.

Had the Santa tried to save her or had he burned the house? Ah! We'll never know. We'll never know.

ACKNOWLEDGEMENTS

The Publisher has made every effort to contact the Copyright holders, but wishes to apologise to those he has been unable to trace. Grateful acknowledgement is made for permission to reprint the following:

'Back for Christmas' by John Collier. Reprinted by permission to Peters Fraser & Dunlop Group Limited.

'A Christmas Story' by 'Sarban'. Reprinted by permission of William Heinemann Limited.

'The Waits' by L.P. Hartley. Reprinted by permission of Hamish Hamilton Limited.

'Florinda' by Shamus Frazer. Copyright © Estate of Shamus Frazer, reproduced by permission of Mrs Joan N. Frazer.

'The Hanging Tree' by R. Chetwynd-Hayes. Reprinted by permission of Thorsons Publishing Group Limited.

'The Grotto' by Alexander Welch. Copyright © Alexander Welch by kind permission.

'Just Before Dawn' by Eugene Johnson. Copyright © Eugene Johnson by kind permission.

'The Buggane' by Peter Tremayne. Copyright © Peter Tremayne by kind permission.

'The Uninvited' by John Glasby. Copyright © John Glasby by kind permission.

'A Present for Christmas' by A.J. Merak. Copyright © A.J. Merak by kind permission.

'The Deliverer' by Simon MacCulloch. Copyright © Simon MacCulloch by kind permission.

ACKNOWLEDGEMENTS

'The Night Before Christmas' by Roger Johnson. Copyright © Roger
Johnson by kind permission.

'On Wings of Song' by David G. Rowlands. Copyright © David G.
Rowlands by kind permission.

'The Santa' by Jessica Amanda Salmonson. Reprinted from W. Paul Ganley's
Weirdbook 23/24 copyright 1988 by Jessica Amanda Salmonson.